Ø 103

D1631560

75

Tel. 50181

CITY OF LEICESTER POLYTECHNIC

TECHNOLOGY LIBRARY

Please
stam
re

BIOCHEMICAL ASPECTS OF ANTIMETABOLITES AND OF DRUG HYDROXYLATION

Fifth FEBS Meeting

Volume 15

GAMMA GLOBULINS Structure and Biosynthesis

Volume 16

BIOCHEMICAL ASPECTS OF ANTIMETABOLITES AND OF DRUG HYDROXYLATION

Volume 17

MITOCHONDRIA Structure and Function

Volume 18

ENZYMES AND ISOENZYMES Structure, Properties and Function

FEDERATION OF EUROPEAN BIOCHEMICAL SOCIETIES
FIFTH MEETING, PRAGUE, JULY 1968

BIOCHEMICAL ASPECTS OF ANTIMETABOLITES AND OF DRUG HYDROXYLATION

Volume 16

Edited by

D. SHUGAR

*Department of Biophysics, University of Warsaw;
and Institute of Biochemistry and Biophysics
Academy of Sciences, Warsaw, Poland*

 1969

ACADEMIC PRESS · London and New York

ACADEMIC PRESS INC. (LONDON) LTD.
Berkeley Square House
Berkeley Square
London, W1X 6BA

U.S. Edition published by
ACADEMIC PRESS INC.
111 Fifth Avenue
New York, New York 10003

Copyright © 1969 by the Federation of European Biochemical Societies

LEICESTER POLYTECHNIC
LIBRARY

3/3/82

615.28

FED

577.12 : 615.28

CITY OF LEICESTER POLYTECHNIC LIBRARY

Library of Congress Catalog Card Number: 70-106795

Printed in Great Britain by
Spottiswoode, Ballantyne and Co. Ltd
London and Colchester

This volume contains the Proceedings of two Symposia held at the Fifth Annual Meeting of the Federation of European Biochemical Societies, Prague, July 1968. Papers 1-6 comprise the Symposium entitled "The Application of Antimetabolites in Biochemical Investigations" (organised by K. Slavik, J. Škoda and A. Wacker); Papers 7-23 comprise the Symposium entitled "Hydroxylation of Drugs in Living Organisms" (organised by R. T. Williams and J. Wagner).

Editorial note. A major portion of the editorial work of this volume was carried out while the editor was Visiting Scientist at the Department of Biochemistry, Faculty of Medicine, University of Laval, Quebec, Canada, with the support of the Medical Research Council of Canada.

Contents

THIOPURINES AS INHIBITORS OF THE IMMUNE RESPONSE. By
G. Hitchings and G. B. Elion   1

ALLOPURINOL, AN INHIBITOR OF XANTHINE OXIDASE; PHYSIO-
LOGICAL AND BIOCHEMICAL STUDIES. By G. H. Hitchings .   11

THE ROLE OF PHARMACOLOGICALLY ACTIVE NUCLEOSIDE
DERIVATIVES IN RNA TRANSLATION. By J. Škoda . . .   23

BIOCHEMICAL BASIS OF RESISTANCE TO FOLIC ACID
ANTAGONISTS. By M. T. Hakala   31

MECHANISM OF REDUCTION OF FOLATE AND DIHYDROFOLATE.
By S. F. Zakrzewski   49

THE APPLICATION OF ANTIFOLICS TO THE STUDY OF FOLATE
INTERCONVERTING ENZYMES OF DIFFEREŇT ORIGIN. By
K. Slavík, V. Slavíková, K. Motyčka and E. Hermanová . .   65

HYDROXYLATION OF DRUGS IN THE ORGANISM. By R. T. Williams   81

GENERAL BIOLOGICAL ASPECTS OF N-HYDROXYLATION. By
H. Uehleke   97

MECHANISMS OF OXIDATION BY ENZYMES IN THE ENDOPLASMIC
RETICULUM. By J. R. Gillette   109

THE INDUCTION OF HYDROXYLATING ENZYMES BY DRUGS. By
H. Remmer   125

METABOLIC INTERACTIONS OF DRUGS AND STEROID
HORMONES IN RAT LIVER MICROSOMES. By S. Orrenius and
B. P. Lisboa   143

THE ACTION OF AROMATIC N-HYDROXYLATED COMPOUNDS ON
METABOLISM OF RED BLOOD CELLS. By J. Wagner . . .   161

THE CARCINOGENIC ACTION OF OXIDATION PRODUCTS OF
AROMATIC COMPOUNDS. By E. Boyland   183

THE METABOLISM OF CARCINOGENIC NITROSAMINES AND THE
METABOLIC FATE OF THEIR ALKYL GROUPS. By P. N. Magee   205

CORRELATION OF N- AND C-OXYGENATION OF AROMATIC
AMINES WITH CONDITIONS WHICH INCREASE THE CARCINO-
GENICITY OF THESE COMPOUNDS. By E. Arrhenius   . . .   209

THE ROLE OF HYDROXYLATION PRODUCTS IN HYPER-
SENSITIVITY TO SALICYLATES AND AMIDOPYRINE. By M.
Ledvina   227

HYDROXYLATION OF 4-HYDROXYPHENYLPYRUVATE IN
RELATION TO THE FORMATION OF 3,4-DIHYDROXYPHENYL-
ALANINE. By K. F. Gey   233

THE FORMATION OF HYDROXY DERIVATIVES OF CINCHOPHEN
IN MAN AND RAT. By Z. Šípal and A. Jindra   239

MODEL INVESTIGATIONS ON THE FUNCTION OF TETRAHYDRO-
PTERIDINES AS COFACTORS IN BIOLOGICAL HYDROXYL-
ATIONS. By L. Jaenicke and A. Wahlefeld   249

HYDROXYLATION AND SUBSTRATE BINDING OF CYCLOHEXANE
BY LIVER MICROSOMES. By V. Ullrich, J. Schädelin and Hj.
Staudinger   261

DIRECT HYDROGEN TRANSFER FROM SUBSTRATE TO ENZYME
IN HYDROXYLATIONS CATALYSED BY XANTHINE OXIDASE.
By R. C. Bray, P. F. Knowles and F. M. Pick   267

LIPID PEROXIDE FORMATION AND DRUG HYDROXYLATION BY
MICROSOMES. By E. D. Wills   273

CONCLUDING REMARKS. By S. Orrenius   279

AUTHOR INDEX   283

FEBS Symposium, Volume 16, 1969, pp. 1-10

Thiopurines as Inhibitors of the Immune Response

G. H. HITCHINGS and G. B. ELION

Wellcome Research Laboratories,
Burroughs Wellcome & Co. (U.S.A.) Inc.,
Tuckahoe, New York, U.S.A.

Transplantation and immunosuppression have become household concepts within the last year, primarily because of the publicity accompanying heart transplants. To an outsider, the field of transplantation appears to have developed with explosive suddenness. Appearances are close to the truth. The first tentative experiments in human renal homotransplantation were taking place as recently as 1961-2, when nearly the whole of the transplant world could be seated around one table. At the First Transplantation Congress in Paris in June 1967, there were 1500 members. This reflects a sustained exponential growth rate, which, according to my rough calculations, corresponds to a doubling time of 6 or 7 months. Meanwhile human renal allotransplantation has progressed in status from a tentative surgical experiment almost to the point of a therapeutic procedure where current success rates (transplant functioning well at the end of a year) in expert hands are of the order of 95% [1]. Nevertheless it is abundantly clear that, for both transplantation and autoimmune disease, there is ample room for improvement in one's ability to control and modify immunological responses. It is clear, too, that drugs, and particularly antimetabolites, not only have practical applications but are useful in unravelling some of the complexities of immune reactions. It is reasonable to suppose that further progress towards the practical ends will come in large measure from a deeper penetration into the biochemical events of the immune reaction, and more precise definitions of drug action.

I shall speak in the main about two closely related drugs, 6-mercaptopurine and azathioprine ("Imuran"). There is some objective justification for this selection, apart from my personal interest in these agents. Mercaptopurine was the drug used for much of the early work on drug-induced immune tolerance, and azathioprine is a constant feature of almost all the regimens used in organ transplantation [2-5] and is being explored widely in the therapy of autoimmune disease [6-8].

Mercaptopurine arose from a program of study of antimetabolites in relation to nucleic acid biosynthesis [9, 10]. The objective was to create analogues of the nucleic acid bases that would produce specific biochemical lesions. Mercapto-purine was successful in the sense that it is a specific antagonist of hypoxan-thine. But its synthesis, and the discovery of its antileukemic effects, had preceded the working out of the biosynthetic pathways leading to purine-containing metabolites [11-13]. It then became apparent that hypoxanthine, in the form of its ribonucleotide, inosinic acid, is not only the first biosynthetic purine, but the core of all purine metabolism. Mercaptopurine imitates it faithfully. It competes with hypoxanthine phosphoribosyltransferase, and is converted to thioinosinic acid. Thioinosinate, in turn, is an inhibitor of succinoadenylate synthetase and lyase, and thus inhibits the formation of adenylate from inosinate. Thioinosinate is also an inhibitor of inosinate dehydro-genase, interfering with the conversion of inosinate to xanthylate and thence to guanylate. But it also apparently can be a substrate for these enzymes since, in at least one system, administered mercaptopurine was identified in DNA in the form of thioguanine. This implies the formation of thioxanthylate, thioguany-late, and a long sequence of further reactions. Thioguanylic acid is a known inhibitor of inosinate dehydrogenase and ATP:GMP phosphotransferase [14]. Both thioinosinate and thioguanylate are feed-back inhibitors of purine biosyn-thesis, but this property is even more pronounced in a further metabolite of thioinosinic acid, 6-methylthiopurine ribonucleotide, the product of an S-methy-lation that occurs in vivo [15, 16].

None of the biochemical work comes to grips with the main point, the drug's selective effects, and at present a multitude of sites involving nucleotides and nucleic acids have to be considered in relation to its biological actions.

Azathioprine was designed as a carrier or "masked" form of mercaptopurine [17, 18]. It evolved from studies of substituted mercaptopurines, and was conceived as having the right balance of stability and lability to permit the delivery of mercaptopurine to target sites with improved efficiency. It was found in the laboratory to be cleaved readily by all sorts of sulfhydryl reagents [17]. This reaction is highly polarized. When carried out with ^{35}S-labelled azathio-prine, the sulfur atom is found exclusively with the purine moiety [13]. Biological investigations suggested that it is somewhat superior to mercapto-purine in a number, but not all, of the immunological systems in which comparisons have been made, and it is generally regarded as preferable for organ transplantation and autoimmune disease.

Studies of the metabolism of the drug provide a basis for such a distinction. In vivo a significant amount of methylnitrothioimidazole was formed, and, unexpectedly, when the metabolism was studied with ^{35}S material, some of the labelled atom was found in association with the imidazole moiety [19]. It is now clear that amines, in addition to sulfhydryl compounds, can participate in the nucleophilic attack on the imidazole moiety that liberates mercaptopurine [20]. The metabolic products, other than mercaptopurine, do not in themselves seem to be immunosuppressive. But it is conceivable that depletion of important sulfhydryl or amine groups could occur in the process of cleavage.

One can make a rather sharp distinction between the antimetabolites and agencies like irradiation, certain radiomimetic drugs, thoracic duct drainage, and so on, which appear to act through reduction of the total mass of lymphoid tissue. The latter can depress the immune response at any stage. They have their greatest effects on a primary response when given before it [21, 22]. The actions of antimetabolites, on the other hand, are much more discriminative. The most sensitive points in their actions are events that are recognizable as involving critical steps in the sequence of the developing response. I hope to devote the bulk of this lecture to the illustration of these.

An immune response necessarily begins with recognition of a substance or cell as somehow foreign; in other words, distinct from self. For the production of circulating antibodies, there is probably a processing of the antigen, possibly a transfer of the product from macrophage to lymphocyte, proliferation and differentiation of responding cells ending in plasma cells capable of synthesizing large amounts of more or less specific antibodies. The antibody is released, combines with and removes antigen, often with serum complement forming part of the complex. Cell-borne immunity is probably the more important response with respect to homograft rejection, and possibly some categories of auto-immune disease. It is still uncertain to what extent the processes involved in the production of sensitized lymphocytes parallel those for antibody-producing cells. Certainly the ultimate differentiated cells are quite distinct, but it seems possible that the repository of immunological memory, the small lymphocyte, is the progenitor of both types.

The afferent path of the immune response, recognition, is still imperfectly understood, but considerable enlightenment has been brought to bear on the problem of distinction between self and non-self [23]. When foreign cells and antigens are introduced before an animal becomes immunologically competent, they are not recognized as foreign even though later the animal becomes capable of responding to other, often closely related, stimuli. This state of immune tolerance is maintained as long as the antigen is present. When antigens are present in excess of the capacity of the cell to respond, the immune mechanisms appear to be blocked. Tolerance thus bears a strong resemblance to "immune paralysis", a state of unresponsiveness earlier known to be achievable with large doses of strong antigens [24], and more recently by prolonged administration of minute, sub-stimulatory doses of antigen [25].

Drug-induced immune tolerance is another aspect of the same phenomenon. It is specific for the antigen, and strikingly dependent on the dose and timing of both drug and antigen. These principles can be illustrated by reference to the original experiments of Schwartz and Dameshek [26, 27]. The antibody response in rabbits to bovine serum albumin could be strikingly modified by the administration of mercaptopurine. Treatment before the administration of antigen had no effect, or a slightly stimulating effect. This was in obvious contrast to x-irradiation and radiomimetic drugs where pretreatment reduces the subsequent response. Treatment with mercaptopurine during the phase of antibody production was ineffective, again a point of difference from irradiation and from inhibitors of protein synthesis. However, where treatment was instituted at the time when the antigen was given, there was complete suppression of the response. Moreover, when these animals were given a challenging dose of antigen a few weeks later, they were immunologically tolerant to the antigen.

In his first experiments, Schwartz [28] had found that mercaptopurine had little or no effect on a secondary response if the primary response had been allowed to proceed normally. But La Plante et al. [29] were able to demonstrate that, with large doses of both antigen and drug, the secondary response could be suppressed, and again, many of the animals became tolerant of the antigen.

The importance of both drug and antigen to immunosuppression is further illustrated by experiments from our laboratory [30]. In these experiments both drug and antigen were varied to produce 9 combinations and appropriate controls. Immunosuppression increased as expected with increasing dosage of drug, but it was observed that with higher doses of antigen there was much greater suppression than with lower doses.

It is clear, then, that antigen contributes to immunosuppression. The similarity to immunological paralysis may be brought out further by reference to experiments of Brooke and Schwartz. Schwartz [31] showed that the production of unresponsiveness of rabbits to bovine serum albumin with mercaptopurine treatment very markedly depended on the dose of antigen employed, and was pronounced only with high doses of antigen. Brooke [32] employed a pneumococcal polysaccharide in mice, an antigen that is capable of inducing immune paralysis unaided, when given in doses somewhat higher than those employed in this study. Treatment with mercaptopurine, however, allowed unresponsiveness to be produced at the lower doses of antigen. Thus, the effect of the drug was to increase the sensitivity of the animal to the immune-paralyzing effects of antigen.

Schwartz [27] also had shown that drug-induced immune tolerance was specific for the antigen use. Rabbits made tolerant to human serum albumin were still capable of responding to bovine gamma globulin when both antigens were given simultaneously. A number of authors have illustrated this specificity, but perhaps one of the nicer experiments is that of Frisch, for it both illustrates specificity and casts further light on drug timing. Frisch [33] had found that the most sensitive period to single doses of thioguanine was 48 hours after antigen, and that when the drug was given before the 12th hour or after the 72nd hour it was ineffective. He gave human erythrocytes to mice, and 48 hours later gave thioguanine and sheep erythrocytes. Four days later, the mice were making antibodies to the sheep erythrocytes, but the response to the human erythrocytes had been suppressed.

The antimetabolites also have permitted further discrimination among phases and types of immune reactions. With many antigens, the first antibody formed after stimulation is of the macroglobulin IgM, 19S type. Ordinarily this is replaced after some days or weeks by 7S antibody, IgG. Several workers have shown that low doses of mercaptopurine can selectively inhibit the formation of 7S antibody, and that under these circumstances 19S antibody persists [34, 35]. In animals with persistent 19S antibody, the injection of 7S antibody results in a prompt cessation of 19S antibody production [34, 36, 37]. There thus seems to be some kind of feed-back control of 7S antibody on 19S antibody production.

A point of major interest is the association of 7S antibody production with immunological memory. When 7S antibody production is blocked, so is memory, and a second encounter with antigen gives rise to a primary response, not a secondary response.

In a somewhat similar way, it has been possible for several authors to show that the drugs can produce selective effects on cell-borne immunity as compared with circulating antibody responses. For example, Spiegelberg and Miescher [38] induced thyroiditis in guinea pigs by the injection of thyroglobulin in adjuvant into the foot pad. Treatment with mercaptopurine, using various regimens, gave substantial suppression of thyroiditis and significant suppression of delayed hypersensitivity reactions with only minor effects on the circulating antibody response. Delayed hypersensitivity and cell-borne tissue attack are the reactions most pertinent to graft rejection. One would like to think that their suppression reflects a blockade in the formation of sensitized lymphocytes. An element of uncertainty arises in that these drugs can be shown to have direct effects in cell-cell interactions.

Thus Wilson [39] found that azathioprine could prevent the destruction of target cells by sensitized lymphoid cells at concentrations which were not cytotoxic to the lymphoid cells. The inference can therefore be drawn that blockade of immune reactions does not necessarily involve cell destruction.

Perhaps it has become apparent that there is a high degree of inconclusiveness with respect to interpretations of the cellular and biochemical events of the immune response. In many instances dichotomies can be proposed and each of the alternatives would have the same operational result.

In the first place, there are two main types of theory of the immune response—theories that remind one of centuries-old theological arguments about predestination and free will. Each has a variety of forms, but basically the clonal selection hypothesis proposes that the body contains thousands of clones of cells, each committed to respond to the stimulus of one antigen by the production of one appropriate antibody [40]. Instructional theory supposes that in some way the antigen serves as a template, or stimulates the production of a template, that causes the synthesis of an antibody with the right configuration to combine with the antigen [41].

There are elements in the immune response supporting both interpretations. That recognition is predetermined seems highly probable. Immunological tolerance can be produced to a single antigen, leaving the remainder of the immunological machinery completely intact. From the point of stimulation to the completion of the primary immune response, there is no operational distinction that would exclude either clonal selection or instructional theory. But when the primary response is over, one has a sensitized lymphocyte, ready to respond to a second stimulus with a more rapid and qualitatively different type of response.

Neither clonal selection nor instructional theory provides adequate mechanistic theory. Clonal selection in its original form assumed relatively enormous rates of mutation in the differentiating lymphocyte at the DNA level [40, 42]. Modifications have postulated a potential for variation at other subcellular levels [43], but all the concepts are unsupported by direct evidence. The early conceptions of template theory are not adaptable to present knowledge of the transcription and translation of the genetic code. Presently there are only the vaguest hints as to how an instructional process might be accomplished—hints that repressor proteins are involved in the switch mechanisms which turn on and off the transcription of messengers, and that foreign substances like streptomycin and neomycin can produce reproducible misreading in translation at the ribosomal level [44].

The primary, and most sensitive, target for drugs and antigens is the inductive phase of the immune response. This phase is time dependent, and relatively independent of cell numbers. This point was established beautifully by Šterzl and his collaborators [45, 46]. These authors stimulated cells with antigen *in vitro*, transferred the cells to appropriate recipients, and showed that the time of appearance of antibodies, and the effects of mercaptopurine, were relatively independent of the number of cells transferred over a 10-fold range.

What then does occur during induction? Šterzl has emphasized DNA synthesis on the basis of the effects of antimetabolites and other substances after transfer. Recent unpublished data concerning the effects of drugs during the *in vitro* phase seem to support this concept. But there is room for much more manipulation of the *in vitro* phase of the transfer experiment than has been carried out to date. The cellular and biochemical evidence would not be inconsistent with the view that, under the stimulus of antigen, a lymphoblastic transformation occurs and that responding cells are thrown into the S-phase of the cell cycle. Both biochemical and cytobiological studies are hindered by the fact that responding cells make up only a small proportion of the total numbers.

Until recently, it has not been possible to observe the whole response *in vitro*. One could stimulate *in vitro*, or one could observe antibody production *in vitro*, but in order to complete the induction period, cells stimulated *in vitro* seemed to require special conditions of nurture found only *in vivo*. Even Fishman and Adler [47-49], who had had limited success with antibody production *in vitro*, had gone back to reimplantation in animals of lymphocytes in millipore chambers. But the recent success of Mishell and Dutton [50, 51] may open new possibilities for direct observation. Fishman's studies support the view that antigen must be processed. In his system macrophages are exposed to antigen, and then lymphocytes are exposed to extracts of the macrophage, incubated in chambers *in vivo*, and become antibody producers. He could distinguish two kinds of signal in the macrophage extract, a short-lived early signal that was blocked by short exposure of the macrophage to actinomycin, and a longer-lived signal that was blocked by longer exposure to actinomycin. Both signals appeared to be sensitive to ribonuclease. There are various problems, both quantitative and qualitative, with this system, which remain to be resolved.

The quantitative aspects of the primary response are instructive. There is no general agreement on the importance of cell division in the primary response. This is in contrast to the secondary response, where rapid division of antibody-producing cells or their immediate precursors is a generally acknowledged and well-supported feature [52]. This view needs only to be tempered somewhat by the suggestion that recruitment, as well as multiplication, contributes to the pool of antibody-producing cells.

It is clear, however, that, quantitatively, the response is dependent on the amount of antigen, or to the persistence of antigen, since persistence is dose-dependent. In any case, it may be that antigen is required not only to initiate cellular differentiation, but also to complete it. Several authors have put forward the interpretation that the receptive X-cell differentiates to a Y-cell which multiplies, and is transformed to a Z-cell, the end, antibody-producing cell. Šterzl [46, 53] has shown that when the primary response is maximally stimulated, a subsequent secondary response is depressed. In his view, antigen enters a second time to cause the differentiation of Y to Z; in his terms it may produce an "exhaustive differentiation".

Other authors view a direct passage, from X to Z, as possible, and subject to the influence of antigen. Any interpretation must also take into account the memory cell, probably a long-lived small lymphocyte, awaiting a second antigenic stimulus to produce a secondary response. Since the secondary response gives rise to a distinct antibody it may be necessary to postulate Y' and Z' cells to carry it out.

Finally, I should like to consider once more the possible interpretations of immune tolerance and immunosuppression. Here again, there is a dichotomy of interpretation. One view would be that responsive cells enter a phase of rapid cell multiplication. The drugs presently known to be active are mainly drawn from the category of antileukemic drugs which are cytotoxic to rapidly dividing cells. It is postulated that the responsive clone is thereby eliminated, and a state of unresponsiveness ensues. A possible telling argument against the multiplication-rate idea might be that the secondary response involves more rapid multiplication than the primary, but is the more difficult to control. Somewhat modified, this interpretation might read that initial stimulation gives rise to a lymphoblastic transformation, and that drugs like 6-mercaptopurine have selective cytotoxic effects on lymphoblasts.

The other possible interpretation is that the drugs somehow inhibit cellular differentiation (or specifically DNA synthesis). This reduces the competence of the cell to respond, and makes it easier for antigen to block the response. Either interpretation would account for the specificity of the tolerance. But the cell destruction interpretation is less able to accommodate one additional fact. Sensitization accompanies tolerance. Tolerance seems to persist only as long as antigen is present. There is a need for further direct evidence on this point, but indirect evidence supports it. The duration of neonatal tolerance depends on the initial dose of antigen, and can be extended by additional doses. When previously tolerant animals respond, they do so with a typical secondary response. Direct support of a similar sequence in drug-induced tolerance has not been put forward, but it is possible to read this interpretation into Schwartz's results. The later the animals were challenged, the smaller the percentage that remained unresponsive [31].

On the whole, the similarities between antigen-induced and drug-induced tolerance support the idea that it is antigen that is the controlling element—that somehow the drug makes it easier for antigen to jam the machinery. This leaves one with two mysteries and very few clues as to the mechanism by which either drug or antigen might act.

In conclusion, I have tried to point out some of the features of the immune response that might be amenable to study by biochemical as well as cellular investigations. The challenges are great, but the possibility for exciting and rewarding insights is even greater.

REFERENCES

1. Starzl, T. E., Groth, C. G., Terasaki, P. I., Putnam, C. W., Brettschneider, L. and Marchioro, T. L., *Surgery Gynec. Obstet.* **126** (1968) 1023.
2. Murray, J. E., Barnes, B. A. and Atkinson, J., *Transplantation* **5** (1967) 752.
3. Hume, D. M., Lee, H. M., Williams, G. M., White, H. J., Ferré, J., Wolf, J. S., Prout, G. R. Jr., Slapak, M., O'Brien, J., Kilpatrick, S. J., Kauffman, H. M. Jr. and Cleveland, R. J., *Ann. Surg.* **164** (1966) 352.

4. Calne, R. Y., "Renal Transplantation", 2nd Ed., Edward Arnold, London 1967.
5. Starzl, T. E., Marchioro, T. L., Iwasaki, Y. and Kashiwagi, N., *in* "Immunity, Cancer, and Chemotherapy: Basic Relationships on the Cellular Level" (edited by E. Mihich), Academic Press, New York 1967, p. 351.
6. Fifth International Symposium on Immunopathology, Punta Ala (Italy) 1967, Grune and Stratton, New York 1968, pp. 359-417.
7. Adams, D. A., Gordon, A. and Maxwell, M. H., *J. Am. med. Ass.* **199** (1967) 459.
8. Mackay, I. R., *Quart. Jl. Med.* **37**, No. 147 (1968) 379.
9. Hitchings, G. H., Elion, G. B., Falco, E. A., Russell, P. B., Sherwood, M. B. and Vander Werff, H., *J. biol. Chem.* **183** (1950) 1.
10. Hitchings, G. H., *in* "Chemotherapy of Cancer" (edited by P. A. Plattner), Elsevier, Amsterdam 1964, p. 77.
11. Elion, G. B. and Hitchings, G. H., *Adv. Chemotherapy* **2** (1965) 91.
12. Hitchings, G. H. and Elion, G. B., *in* "Cancer Chemotherapy, Basic and Clinical Applications", 15th Hahnemann Symposium, Grune and Stratton, New York 1967, p. 26.
13. Elion, G. B., *Fedn Proc. Fedn Am. Socs exp. Biol.* **26** (1967) 898.
14. Miech, R. P., Parks, R. E. Jr., Anderson, J. H. Jr. and Sartorelli, A. C., *Biochem. Pharmac.* **16** (1967) 2222.
15. Bennett, L. L., Brockman, R. W., Schnebli, H. P., Chumley, S., Dixon, G. J., Schabel, F. M., Dulmadge, E. A., Skipper, H. E., Montgomery, J. A. and Thomas, H. J., *Nature, Lond.* **205** (1965) 1276.
16. Caldwell, I. C., Henderson, J. F. and Paterson, A. R. P., *Can. J. Biochem.* **44** (1966) 229.
17. Elion, G. B., Callahan, S., Bieber, S., Hitchings, G. H. and Rundles, R. W., *Cancer Chemother. Rep.* **14** (1961) 93.
18. Elion, G. B., Callahan, S. W., Rundles, R. W. and Hitchings, G. H., *Cancer Res.* **23** (1963) 1207.
19. Elion, G. B. in Ref. 6, p. 400.
20. Elion, G. B., unpublished observations.
21. Hitchings, G. H. and Elion, G. B., *Pharmac. Rev.* **15** (1963) 365.
22. Berenbaum, M. C., *in* "Immunity, Cancer, and Chemotherapy: Basic Relationships on the Cellular Level" (edited by E. Mihich), Academic Press, New York 1967, p. 217.
23. Medawar, P. B., *in* "Ciba Foundation Symposium on Cellular Aspects of Immunity" (edited by G. E. W. Wolstenholme and M. O'Connor), Little, Brown and Co., Boston 1959, p. 140.
24. Felton, L. D., *J. Immun.* **61** (1949) 107.
25. Mitchison, N. A., *Proc. R. Soc.* **161** (1964) 275.
26. Schwartz, R. S., Stack, J. and Dameshek, W., *Proc. Soc. exp. Biol. Med.* **99** (1958) 164.
27. Schwartz, R. S., and Dameshek, W., *Nature, Lond.* **183** (1959) 1682.
28. Schwartz, R. S., Eisner, A. and Dameshek, W., *J. clin. Invest.* **38** (1959) 1394.
29. LaPlante, E. S., Condie, R. M. and Good, R. A., *J. Lab. clin. Med.* **59** (1962) 542.
30. Nathan, H. C., Bieber, S., Elion, G. B. and Hitchings, G. H., *Proc. Soc. exp. Biol. Med.* **107** (1961) 796.

31. Schwartz, R. S. and Dameshek, W., *J. Immun.* **90** (1963) 703.
32. Brooke, M. S., *Transplantation* **4** (1966) 1.
33. Frisch, A. W. and Davies, G. H., *Proc. Soc. exp. Biol. Med.* **110** (1962) 444.
34. Sahiar, K. and Schwartz, R. S., *Science, N.Y.* **145** (1964) 395.
35. Borel, Y., Fauconnet, M. and Miescher, P. A., *J. exp. Med.* **122** (1965) 263.
36. Uhr, J. W., *Science, N.Y.* **145** (1964) 457.
37. Finkelstein, M. S. and Uhr, J. W., *Science, N.Y.* **146** (1964) 67.
38. Spiegelberg, H. L. and Miescher, P. A., *J. exp. Med.* **118** (1963) 869.
39. Wilson, D. B., *J. exp. Med.* **122** (1965) 167.
40. Burnet, M., "The Clonal Selection Theory of Acquired Immunity", Vanderbilt Univ. Press, Nashville 1959.
41. Pauling, L., *J. Am. chem. Soc.* **62** (1940) 2643.
42. Lederberg, J., *Science, N.Y.* **129** (1959) 1649.
43. Finch, L. R., *Nature, Lond.* **201** (1964) 1288.
44. Gorini, L., in "Immunity, Cancer, and Chemotherapy: Basic Relationships on the Cellular Level" (edited by E. Mihich), Academic Press, New York 1967, p. 167.
45. Jarošková, L., Městecký, J. and Šterzl, J., *Folia microbiol., Praha* **11** (1966) 102.
46. Šterzl, J., in "Immunity, Cancer, and Chemotherapy: Basic Relationships on the Cellular Level" (edited by E. Mihich), Academic Press, New York 1967, p. 71.
47. Fishman, M., *J. exp. Med.* **114** (1961) 837.
48. Fishman, M. and Adler, F. L., *J. exp. Med.* **117** (1963) 595.
49. Fishman, M. and Adler, F. L., in "Immunity, Cancer, and Chemotherapy: Basic Relationships on the Cellular Level" (edited by E. Mihich), Academic Press, New York 1967, p. 177.
50. Mishell, R. I. and Dutton, R. W., *Science, N.Y.* **153** (1966) 1004.
51. Mishell, R. I. and Dutton, R. W., *J. exp. Med.* **126** (1967) 423.
52. Nossal, G. J. V. and Mäkelä, O., *J. exp. Med.* **115** (1962) 209.
53. Šterzl, J., *Nature, Lond.* **209** (1966) 416.

FEBS Symposium, Volume 16, 1969, pp. 11-22

Allopurinol, an Inhibitor of Xanthine Oxidase;

Physiological and Biochemical Studies

G. H. HITCHINGS

Wellcome Research Laboratories,
Burroughs Wellcome & Co. (U.S.A.) Inc.,
Tuckahoe, New York, U.S.A.

Allopurinol is noteworthy as an example of the new breed of therapeutic agents, those that arise by design and have known mechanisms of action. This drug is an off-shoot of a program [1-3] of purposeful exploration of enzymes and metabolic pathways in the field of nucleic acid biosynthesis and metabolism. It was the thesis of this program that the identification and characterization of cell receptors, through the study of antimetabolites, could lead to the discovery of biochemical diversities among organisms that would be exploitable in chemo-therapy, and to an understanding of metabolic idiosyncrasies that would lead to rational therapy.

At the time this program began, the anabolic enzymes of purine and pyrimidine biosynthesis were still unknown, and cultures of *Lactobacillus casei* were used as a convenient means of detecting such enzymes. However, xanthine oxidase and guanase were known and were used to explore structure:activity relationships at the free purine level [4-6]. In each case the experiment could be designed to test the analog for activity both as a substrate and as an inhibitor. Some years later we were able to reach back into this file of antimetabolites and data, to pick out and develop a drug for the control of hyperuricemia.

Drug development must always be tentative in its beginnings, until foresee-able obstacles have been overcome and potential problems solved. More often than not, unforeseen and often unforeseeable problems arise, and the project must be abandoned or greatly modified. The development of allopurinol was quite exceptional in that many of the possible limitations to its use were found, in fact, not to be real, and several of the unexpected findings have contributed to

11

its success.* In the course of these studies, several interesting aspects of human renal physiology and biochemistry have been clarified.

It is nearly 100 years since Garrod [7] was able to associate gout with hyperuricemia and to suggest that hyperuricemia might arise either from overproduction of uric acid or depressed excretion. It is still unclear whether depressed clearance is a cause or an effect, but it has been established that many hyperuricemics are over-producers of uric acid.

The first therapy for gout consisted of colchicine, and it and the newer anti-inflammatory agents, butazolidine and indomethacin, are used to reduce the inflammation and pain of an acute attack. Uricosuric drugs provided a major advance; they control serum urate, and, therefore, the deposition of solid urate deposits (tophi) in many patients. They tend to increase the renal load of urate, however, and thus increase the hazard of renal urate stone formation.

A more logical approach to the problems of hyperuricemia, it seemed to us, would be to inhibit uric acid production. It had been found, not surprisingly, that it is not feasible to reduce purine biosynthesis at an early stage without the appearance of general toxicity [8, 9]. Inhibition of urate formation at the last step, through inhibition of xanthine oxidase, was not precluded by any known facts. Rather, it appeared through studies of xanthinuric subjects that a congenital absence of xanthine oxidase is not incompatible with reasonably good health [10, 11]. Nevertheless, the properties of the proposed inhibitor, the effects of inhibition of the enzyme, and the physiological properties of the precursors of uric acid, hypoxanthine and xanthine, had to be examined with care.

Allopurinol, 4-hydroxypyrazolo(3,4-d)pyrimidine was chosen for exploration on several grounds: (1) It was a strong inhibitor of xanthine oxidase *in vitro* (2) It was also a substrate for the enzyme forming a product which also was an inhibitor, and (3) It did not seem to be involved in anabolic reactions as witnessed by its failure to inhibit *L. casei,* and its inactivity in other biological systems, e.g. trials against transplantable tumors.

A convenient and unambiguous way of testing its activity *in vivo* was to observe its action on an exogenously supplied substrate, 6-mercaptopurine.

---

* Among the possible limitations were: (1) The possibility that accumulation of xanthine would induce xanthine oxidase synthesis, since induction of the enzyme by xanthine had been reported. Serum xanthine levels are not, in fact, very much increased when allopurinol is used but, in any case, no detectable induction of xanthine oxidase occurs during therapy. (2) A possible involvement of xanthine oxidase in iron metabolism has been reported and this gave rise to the suggestion that this parameter might be affected by allopurinol therapy. The preponderance of evidence is on the side of no significant effect. (3) The possible involvement of xanthine and hypoxanthine in tumor growth also had been put forward. In a well designed trial, allopurinol was found not to influence the growth rate of a rat hepatoma which had been selected on theoretical grounds as a suitably sensitive tissue. These and other possible complications of allopurinol therapy have been discussed in more detail previously [7a].

When 6-mercaptopurine is administered to animals or man it undergoes complex degradative reactions which include oxidation of the purine ring and sulfur atom, and S-methylation, but the most prominent reaction is the xanthine oxidase-catalyzed oxidation of the purine ring in the 2- and 8-positions to form 6-thiouric acid [12, 13]. Both in the mouse and in man it could be shown that this reaction could be inhibited by the administration of moderate doses of allopurinol [14, 15]. At the same time the potency of 6-mercaptopurine was increased 3- or 4-fold, corresponding to the sparing of the drug from metabolic destruction.

Similarly, short-term trials of allopurinol in man demonstrated that serum and urinary urates were depressed, and that hypoxanthine and xanthine began to appear in the urine [16], although in less than equivalent amounts, a point that will be examined in some detail later in this paper.

The chronic toxicity of allopurinol is still somewhat ambiguous. Initially the somewhat anomalous observation was made that the tolerated dose of allopurinol increased with increasing size of the species tested—quite the opposite of the constant dose per unit of body surface rule. Examination showed that the limiting factor, in each case, was the precipitation of xanthine in the kidney. As a result, the intrinsic toxicology of allopurinol *per se* is still unknown. Certainly, in single doses, relatively enormous amounts are well tolerated.

The resolution of the size-dose relationship came with the recognition that total purine end product per unit of body weight diminishes as the size of the animal increases. This parameter bears some relation to body surface, but this correlation is not absolute since, for example, the purine end product excreted by a 10 kg dog approximates that of a 70 kg man. Water flux also varies from species to species. The net result is that under conditions of a moderately high inhibition of xanthine oxidase (e.g. decrease in purine end product by 50%) the urinary xanthine would exceed the saturating level by several-fold in the mouse, rat and dog, but human urine would be only one-half to two-thirds saturated [7a] and human renal xanthine stones have not arisen as a side effect of allopurinol therapy.

The therapeutic effects of allopurinol depend in a variable degree on the properties of its metabolite, oxipurinol. The conversion of allopurinol to oxipurinol is extremely slow *in vitro,* but takes place rapidly *in vivo* [17]. Allopurinol, therefore, is cleared by the circulation by two processes, renal and metabolic. Its renal clearance appears to be essentially at the glomerular filtration rate [17, 18]. Oxipurinol, on the other hand, is cleared at a low rate by the human kidney. This is in striking contrast to the behavior of other purines and purine analogs, and to the treatment of this substance by the kidneys of lower species. In these respects it resembles uric acid rather than hypoxanthine, xanthine, 6-mercaptopurine and other analogs. This resemblance extends to its substrate activity for pyrimidine nucleoside phosphorylase [19].

Oxipurinol and uric acid are the only two purines so far found to give rise to 3-ribosyl derivatives, *in vivo*.

Examination of tissue distribution revealed that both allopurinol and oxipurinol are equally distributed in body water with no significant concentration in any tissue. Neither exhibits a significant binding to plasma proteins. It seemed probable, therefore, that oxipurinol was, like uric acid, being reabsorbed in the human renal tubule. A preliminary test of this assumption was to test the effects of uricosuric drugs on oxipurinol clearance, and the clearance did indeed rise under the influence of benemid [17]. The behavior of oxipurinol as a uric acid-like substance has been confirmed by detailed studies in mongrel and Dalmatian dogs and human subjects [20]. In man the clearance approximates three times the uric acid clearance, and the plasma levels of oxipurinol can be predicted from knowledge of the uric acid clearance of the patient, and the dosage of allopurinol [20].

Assessment of the relative contributions of allopurinol and oxipurinol to the therapeutic activity of allopurinol is difficult. Allopurinol is the stronger inhibitor of xanthine oxidase *in vitro* by a factor of 10. Both substances may exhibit competitive kinetics with xanthine as substrate. But each may also exhibit pseudoirreversible inactivation of the enzyme. Allopurinol inactivates the enzyme in the absence of substrate, while oxipurinol inactivates the enzyme in the presence of substrate. In both instances activity can be restored by prolonged dialysis [17].

The biological half-life of allopurinol depends on the level of xanthine oxidase inhibition. At high doses where xanthine oxidase is strongly inhibited, conversion to oxipurinol is slow, and the drug is cleared primarily by renal excretion. Similarly, in patients on continued therapy in whom oxipurinol has accumulated, the persistence of allopurinol is longer than after single doses of the drug. This effect is more prominent among patients with poor renal function (urate clearance) and high levels of oxipurinol, than among patients with good renal function and low levels of oxipurinol. Adding to the complications is the fact that patients with poor urate clearances are likely to have substantial urate deposits that contribute to serum urates. Low urate clearance and dissolution of tophaceous deposits both contribute to the maintenance of high serum urate values in the face of adequate xanthine oxidase inhibition and tempt the unwary clinician in the direction of overtreatment of such patients. A further complication is the unresponsiveness of patients with poor urate clearances to uricosuric drugs. In these patients oxipurinol clearance is often increased more than urate clearance, and the effect of adding a uricosuric drug to a regimen of oxipurinol depends on the balance of the two clearance effects. A reduction in xanthine oxidase inhibition may be the more prominent and, in this case, a rise, rather than a fall, in serum urate may result [20]. The proper method of monitoring the effects of allopurinol and oxipurinol would be the measurement of urinary hypoxanthine and xanthine, but present methods are too cumbersome for routine use.

Inhibition of urate formation would be expected to result in the accumulation of the precursors of the inhibited reaction, hypoxanthine and xanthine. These substances do, in fact, occur in increased amounts in the urine when allopurinol is given, but the rise in serum oxypurines is small. Figure 1 presents the data for 4 patients. It will be seen that a sizeable reduction of serum urate value occurred in each patient when allopurinol was given, but that only a small fraction of this (one-tenth or less) was replaced by serum oxypurines.

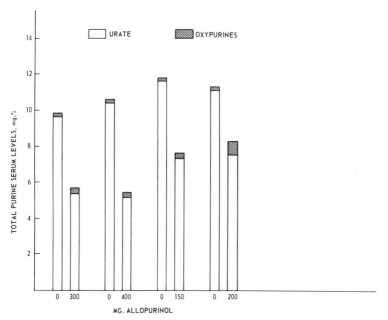

Figure 1. Serum levels of uric acid and oxypurines in four patients before and after therapy with daily doses of allopurinol, 150 to 400 mg per day.

A major factor limiting the rise in serum oxypurines is the high renal clearance of these substances. Earlier attempts to measure the renal clearance of hypoxanthine and xanthine were handicapped by the inaccuracies attendant on estimations of these materials at low concentrations. Infusions in allopurinol-treated patients, however, gave relatively constant blood levels and accurate clearance rates, and these were found to lie in the region of glomerular filtration rate values [21]. The net effect of allopurinol therapy, therefore, is to produce a clearance of total purine end product that lies somewhere between that of urate and that of the oxypurines—a clearance rate which rises as the degree of xanthine oxidase inhibition increases.

A second, more subtle, factor limiting the rise of serum and tissue oxypurines is the decreased purine turnover that occurs when allopurinol is given. This was a totally unexpected benefit of therapy.

The median decrease in total purine end product is about 35% and may be as great as 65%. It seems to be proportional, in a general way, to the degree of oversecretion that the patient exhibits initially [7a].

There was not complete agreement in the beginning that this effect was real, and indeed it does not seem to be universal. Some, but not all, of the exceptional cases have been explained.

At this point it is necessary to recall some earlier information on urate formation. When isotopically labelled glycine is given, a significant proportion of it appears in the uric acid. The excretion of labelled uric acid is biphasic; part appears promptly, the remainder is excreted over many days. In the hyperexcretor the proportion appearing in the early fractions is much augmented, and the decline is rapid [22]. In terms of specific metabolites, the initial rapidly-formed urate would arise from newly synthesized inosinic acid, while that formed later would come from the further anabolites of inosinate, adenylate, guanylate, their derivatives, and eventually nucleic acid [23].

The existence of a direct course, "shunt pathway", from glycine to uric acid, suggests that normally inosinate (and possibly xanthylate) are synthesized at rates that maintain pool sizes in excess of those used for anabolism to adenylate, guanylate, etc., and that free purines arise from these and are catabolized to uric acid.

Two explanations have been put forward for the inhibition of purine biosynthesis by allopurinol. Wyngaarden suggested that allopurinol might be converted to its ribonucleotide, which would act, by pseudofeedback inhibition, to inhibit the phosphoribosylpyrophosphate amidotransferase that catalyzes the first step in purine biosynthesis. Wyngaarden supported this view by obtaining small amounts of allopurinol ribonucleotide by enzymatic synthesis and showing that this substance is, indeed, an inhibitor of the enzyme [24].

It is possible by standard feedback techniques to demonstrate that purine biosynthesis is inhibited when allopurinol is administered. The results of some experiments are set forth in Table 1. In these experiments [^{14}C]glycine was given to animals bearing Ehrlich ascites tumor, after treatment with diaza-oxonorleucine (DON). The control cells accumulate formylglycine amide ribonucleotide (FGAR) as a result of the inhibition of its conversion to formylglycine amidine ribonucleotide (FGAM). The administration of a substance that inhibits FGAR formation diminishes this accumulation, and is therefore identified as an inhibitor of an earlier step in purine biosynthesis (Fig. 2). The data of Table 1 show that allopurinol and its metabolite, oxipurinol, qualify as feedback inhibitors by this test [24a]. However, one essential step is missing. Neither allopurinol, nor oxipurinol, appears to be converted, *in vivo,* to its ribonu-

Table 1. Ehrlich ascites feedback inhibition, %*.

Inhibitor	Dose in mg/kg		
	5·5	16	50
6-MP		(48)	91
HPP	42	40	58
DHPP		33	50
Hx	$(10)_{7.5}$		11
Xa			21
Ad	$(50)_{7.5}$		
Hx + HPP(50)			69
Xa + HPP(50)			46

* Inhibition of FGAR accumulation 1 hour after [^{14}C] glycine in DON-treated animals.

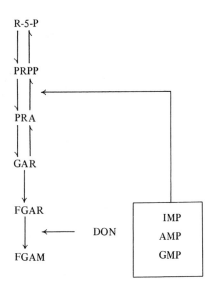

Figure 2. Early steps in purine biosynthesis, inhibition by diaza-oxonorleucine (DON) and feedback inhibition by ribonucleotides (see text).

cleotide. This is shown by the data of Table 2. In these experiments the radioactive compounds were given to mice bearing Ehrlich ascites tumor, and the harvested cells were examined for the presence of nucleotides in the acid solubles. Under these circumstances the amino analog of allopurinol is converted to its ribonucleotide to the extent of nearly 5% of the dose administered, but the 1·8% of the dose of allopurinol found in the acid solubles could be accounted for as oxipurinol (1·5% of the dose) or unchanged allopurinol (0·3% of the dose) [24a]. The view that allopurinol does not affect purine biosynthesis directly is also supported by its failure to influence the purine turnover in a xanthinuric patient [25].

Table 2. Nucleotide formation *in vivo* Ehrlich ascites, 1 hour.

Precursor	% of dose in acid-soluble	Identity
[^{14}C] hypoxanthine (pretreated with allopurinol)	31	1% AMP+GMP 30% higher tides
[^{14}C] allopurinol	1·8	1·5% as DHPP 0·3% as HPP
4-aminopyrazolo-pyrimidine	$> 4·7$	4·7% as APPRP

Hypoxanthine, when given alone, is a poor precursor of nucleic acid purines [23, 26]. However, when allopurinol is also given, it becomes an excellent precursor [26]. Similarly, xanthine given alone is hardly incorporated at all, but when allopurinol is also administered, it also shows a significant incorporation into nucleic acid purines [27].

The explanation of the apparent feedback inhibition exhibited by allopurinol, therefore, appears to lie in the reutilization of hypoxanthine and xanthine that occurs when their catabolism is prevented by the inhibition of xanthine oxidase. In this view, hypoxanthine and xanthine are in equilibrium with their respective ribonucleotides. Increases in their levels would be reflected in a tendency towards increases in the ribonucleotide pools, but this would be counterbalanced by feedback inhibition of the natural ribonucleotides on the first step of purine biosynthesis.

In the last year, considerable progress has been made towards an understanding of the metabolic events in patients in whom this regulatory mechanism seems not to be operative. The extreme is found in patients with Lesch-Nyhan syndrome [28]. Such patients have gross overproduction of purines [29]. When given allopurinol, uric acid is replaced stoichiometrically by hypoxanthine and xanthine [30-32]. Moreover, purine turnover is not inhibited by the usual feedback inhibitors [30, 33, 34].

These patients have been found to have an almost complete absence of hypoxanthine:guanine phosphoribosyltransferase [32, 34-36] (inosinate pyrophosphorylase). Xanthine also seems to be a substrate for this enzyme [36]. The failure of these patients to reutilize hypoxanthine and xanthine, therefore, is explained on the basis of a lack of the enzyme requisite to their anabolism. As a corollary, the lack of controls would be attributed to the failure of the normal nucleotide pools to reach levels adequate for inhibition of the amidotransferase.

If, indeed, the lack of inosinate pyrophosphorylase is the only or the major defect in this genetic abnormality, there are some interesting implications for purine biochemistry. One would have to assume that breakdown of inosinate (and xanthylate) normally proceeds at a very rapid rate, and that most of the free purine is salvaged by the action of pyrophosphorylases. If salvage prevails, the reason for the rapid catabolism of exogenously supplied hypoxanthine and xanthine is not immediately apparent. One possible explanation lies in the tissue distribution of xanthine oxidase, which is largely in liver and kidney. In other tissues with very low xanthine oxidase concentrations the phosphoribosyltransferase reactions may predominate [37].

Ironically, the solution of the Lesch-Nyhan puzzle fails to distinguish between the two possible mechanisms mentioned above, by which allopurinol might control purine biosynthesis, for either would require hypoxanthine:guanine phosphoribosyltransferase. But in addition to the direct search for allopurinol ribonucleotide, one may bring enzyme kinetics to bear on the problem. The binding constant for allopurinol with this enzyme is approximately 10^{-3} while that for hypoxanthine (and that of mercaptopurine) is about 5×10^{-6} [38]. To be an effective competitor of hypoxanthine for this enzyme, therefore, allopurinol would have to reach concentrations several hundred-fold higher than that of hypoxanthine. In fact, the concentration ratio *in vivo* would rarely reach levels as much as 5-fold (assuming allopurinol 5 μg/ml, hypoxanthine 1 μg/ml).

Finally, the contrast between the biochemical effects and therapeutic applications of two analogs of hypoxanthine may be brought out by comparative enzyme kinetics. Mercaptopurine is bound to both inosinate pyrophosphorylase and xanthine oxidase with enzyme:substrate dissociation constants that are closely comparable. It is an effective competitor of hypoxanthine for anabolic reactions and its ribonucleotide participates in a multitude of anabolic reactions analogous to those of inosinate [39]. Allopurinol, on the other hand, is bound 20-fold more tightly to xanthine oxidase, and 200-fold less tightly to inosinate pyrophosphorylase than is hypoxanthine. Its actions, therefore, are exclusively directed towards its effects on xanthine oxidase.

The basic cause of gouty hyperexcretion and overproduction remains a mystery. Nevertheless one feels that the explanation must lie in a faulty regulatory mechanism for purine biosynthesis. Since most patients respond to therapy with allopurinol by reduction in total synthesis and the activity of the "shunt" pathway, the phosphoribosylpyrophosphate amidotransferase, the normal control point, would appear to be responsive to normal control mechanisms. If so, the fault would lie in a failure of the controlling ribonucleotides, adenylate and/or guanylate, to be maintained at adequate levels. Since both are required for maximum feedback inhibition, a slight defect in the formation of either might account for elevated synthesis *de novo*. A further possibility might lie in excessive activity of xanthine oxidase since inadequate salvage might result either from a defective salvage enzyme, as in Lesch-Nyhan syndrome, or from an excessively rapid catabolism of salvageable purine base. Whatever the final answer may be, the field of research seems to have been narrowed significantly by recent investigations involving the use of metabolic inhibitors.

SUMMARY

(1) Allopurinol, an analog of hypoxanthine, is an effective inhibitor of xanthine oxidase *in vivo*. It is a substrate, as well as an inhibitor, of the enzyme, and the product, oxipurinol, is also an inhibitor.

(2) Oxipurinol behaves as a uric acid analog in the human kidney, with clearance values 2-3 times the individual urate clearances. As a consequence of its retention, the range of fluctuations in xanthine oxidase inhibition, during therapy, is minimized.

(3) Renal clearances of hypoxanthine and xanthine are high. Patients treated with allopurinol excrete a mixture of hypoxanthine, xanthine and uric acid, and the resultant clearance of purine end product is higher than that of urate alone. The solubility of total purine end product is also increased above that of urate by division among the three constituents.

(4) Therapy with allopurinol results in a decrease in total purine end product in most patients, probably as a result of reutilization of hypoxanthine and xanthine when these are protected from catabolic destruction.

(5) The physiological, biochemical and therapeutic properties of allopurinol and mercaptopurine are consistent with their binding constants and substrate activities for hypoxanthine:guanine phosphoribosyltransferase, and xanthine oxidase, respectively.

REFERENCES

1. Hitchings, G. H., Elion, G. B., Falco, E. A., Russell, P. B., Sherwood, M. B. and Vander Werff, H., *J. biol. Chem.* **183** (1950) 1.
2. Hitchings, G. H., Elion, G. B., Falco, E. A., Russell, P. B. and Vander Werff, H., *Ann. N. Y. Acad. Sci.* **52** (1950) 1318.

3. Hitchings, G. H., *in* "Chemotherapy of Cancer" (edited by P. A. Plattner), Elsevier, Amsterdam 1964, p. 77.
4. Hitchings, G. H. and Falco, E. A., *Proc. natn. Acad. Sci. U.S.A.* **30** (1944) 294.
5. Lorz, D. C. and Hitchings, G. H., *Fedn Proc. Fedn Am. Socs exp. Biol.* **9** (1950) 197.
6. Lorz, D. C. and Hitchings, G. H., *Abstr. Am. chem. Soc.* (1956) 30c.
7. Garrod, A. B., "The Nature and Treatment of Gout and Rheumatic Gout", 2nd Ed., Walton and Maberly, London 1863, p. 326.
7a. Hitchings, G. H., *Ann. rheum. Dis.* **25** (1966) 601.
8. Zuckerman, R., Drell, W. and Levin, M. H., *9th Int. Congr. Rheum.* Toronto, **2** (1957) 204.
9. Grayzel, A. I., Seegmiller, J. E. and Love, E., *J. clin. Invest.* **39** (1960) 447.
10. Engelman, K., Watts, R. W. E., Klinenberg, J. R., Sjoerdsma, A. and Seegmiller, J. E., *Am. J. Med.* **37** (1964) 839.
11. Watts, R. W. E., Engelman, K., Klinenberg, J. R., Seegmiller, J. E. and Sjoerdsma, A., *Nature, Lond.* **201** (1964) 395.
12. Hamilton, L. and Elion, G. B., *Ann. N.Y. Acad. Sci.* **60** (1954) 304.
13. Elion, G. B., Mueller, S. and Hitchings, G. H., *J. Am. chem. Soc.* **81** (1959) 3042.
14. Elion, G. B., Callahan, S., Nathan, H. C., Bieber, S., Rundles, R. W. and Hitchings, G. H., *Biochem. Pharmac.* **12** (1963) 85.
15. Elion, G. B., Callahan, S., Rundles, R. W. and Hitchings, G. H., *Cancer Res.* **23** (1963) 1207.
16. Hitchings, G. H., *Cancer Res.* **23** (1963) 1218.
17. Elion, G. B., *Ann. rheum. Dis.* **25** (1966) 608.
18. Elion, G. B., Kovensky, A., Hitchings, G. H., Metz, E. and Rundles, R. W., *Biochem. Pharmac.* **15** (1966) 863.
19. Krenitsky, T. A., Elion, G. B., Strelitz, R. A. and Hitchings, G. H., *J. biol. Chem.* **242** (1967) 2675.
20. Elion, G. B., Yü, T. F., Gutman, A. B. and Hitchings, G. H., *Am. J. Med.* **45** (1968) 68-77.
21. Klinenberg, J. R., Goldfinger, S. E. and Seegmiller, J. E., *Ann. intern. Med.* **62** (1965) 639.
22. Benedict, J. D., Roche, M., Yü, T. F., Bien, E. J., Gutman, A. B. and Stetten, D., *Metabolism* **1** (1952) 3.
23. Wyngaarden, J. B., Seegmiller, J. E., Laster, L. and Blair, A. E., *Metabolism* **8** (1959) 455.
24. Wyngaarden, J. B., *Arthritis Rheum.* **8** (1965) 883.
24a. Elion, G. B., unpublished observations.
25. Seegmiller, J. E. and Frazier, P. D., *Ann. rheum. Dis.* **25** (1966) 668
26. Pomales, R., Bieber, S., Friedman, R. and Hitchings, G. H., *Biochim. biophys. Acta* **72** (1963) 119.
27. Pomales, R., Elion, G. B. and Hitchings, G. H., *Biochim. biophys. Acta* **95** (1965) 505.
28. Lesch, M. and Nyhan, W. L., *Am. J. Med.* **36** (1964) 561.
29. Nyhan, W. L., *Arthritis Rheum.* **8** (1965) 659.
30. Sorensen, L. B. and Benke, P. J., *Nature, Lond.* **213** (1967) 1122.
31. Rosenbloom, F. M., Kelley, W. N., Miller, J. M. and Seegmiller, J. E., *Arthritis Rheum.* **10** (1967) 307.

32. Rosenbloom, F. M., Kelley, W. N., Miller, J. M., Henderson, J. F. and Seegmiller, J. E., *J. Am. med. Ass.* **202** (1967) 175.
33. Nyhan, W. L., Sweetman, L., Carpenter, D. G., Carter, C. H. and Hoefnagel, D., *J. Pediat.* **72** (1968) 111.
34. Seegmiller, J. E., Rosenbloom, F. M. and Kelley, W. N., *Science, N.Y.* **155** (1967) 1682.
35. Kelley, W. N., Rosenbloom, F. M., Miller, J. M. and Seegmiller, J. E., *New Engl. J. Med.* **278** (1968) 287.
36. Kelley, W. N., Rosenbloom, F. M., Henderson, J. F. and Seegmiller, J. E., *Biochem. biophys. Res. Commun.* **28** (1967) 340.
37. Rosenbloom, F. M., Henderson, J. F., Caldwell, I. C., Kelley, W. N. and Seegmiller, J. E., *J. biol. Chem.* **243** (1968) 1166.
38. Krenitsky, T. A., unpublished observations.
39. Hitchings, G. H. and Elion, G. B., *in* "Cancer Chemotherapy" (edited by I. Brodsky and S. B. Kahn), Grune and Stratton, New York 1967, p. 26.

FEBS Symposium, Volume 16, 1969, pp. 23-30

The Role of Pharmacologically Active Nucleoside Derivatives in RNA Translation

J. ŠKODA

*Institute of Organic Chemistry and Biochemistry,
Czechoslovak Academy of Sciences, Prague, Czechoslovakia*

Most of the antimetabolites of nucleic acid components undergo anabolic changes in sensitive biological systems; one of the rare exceptions to this rule is that some purine analogues inhibit xanthine oxidase without any change in the molecule.

A very important role in the anabolic pathway of anomalous bases belongs to the nucleosides. Ribosylation or deoxyribosylation of these bases, which increases the solubility in aqueous media, leads in many cases to an increase in their inhibitory effects, and often increases their selective toxicity.

The anomalous nucleosides may undergo enzymic phosphorylation and the nucleoside 5'-monophosphates formed may interfere with the enzymes of nucleic acid metabolism. Most of the known antimetabolites of the precursors of nucleic acids act through this mechanism.

Some of the anomalous nucleosides are, however, phosphorylated to a higher degree, and the nucleoside-5'-triphosphates or deoxyribonucleoside 5'-triphosphates could be either inhibitors or substrates of RNA polymerase or DNA polymerase. Thus, the antimetabolite interferes with the formation and function of the biopolymers at the highest position in the hierarchy of the conservation and transfer of genetic information.

The consequence of these biochemical events, translated into practical application of these compounds as drugs, is the possibility of the induction of teratogenetic, mutagenetic and cancerogenetic changes.

As is known, the study of the mutagenetic and cancerogenetic effects of drugs in animals is complicated, very time-consuming and expensive. In addition, it is necessary to take into account the possible inter-species differences in the reaction to the drug, which may result in a false assessment of their "absolute safety" when applied to man.

Let me first draw your attention to 6-azauridine and its triacetylderivative— azaribine. 6-Azauridine has pronounced antiviral and antifertility properties, and was successfully applied to the control of psoriasis and to the treatment of the

23

skin cancer *mycosis fungoides* [1]. Nevertheless, in spite of the positive results of the clinical tests with 6-azauridine, this compound is not widely used because it is not possible to eliminate the infinitesimal incorporation of the analogue into the informational macromolecules.

Recent advances in molecular biology have made possible an understanding of the mechanism by which anomalous bases and their derivatives can bring about the above mentioned potentially dangerous effects. We now know that these effects are produced by the incorporation of the anomalous components into nucleic acids and their subsequent disruption, by changed binding effects, of the transcription and translation processes. Since these phenomena can now be studied *in vitro* and the altered properties of the nucleic acids measured, we now have a basis for predicting the possible harmful effects of anomalous bases and their derivatives which one would like to test as drugs.

I would like to inform you briefly about some of our results obtained in close collaboration with Drs. V. Lisý and I. Rychlík from the Department of Molecular Biology, and Drs. J. Smrt, J. Beránek and A. Holý from the Department of Organic Synthesis of this Institute.

We initially attempted to prepare polyribonucleotides that would contain internucleotidically-bound 6-azauridylic acid. The enzymic synthesis of such polymers was not feasible because 6-azauridine $5'$-diphosphate proved to be an inhibitor of polynucleotide phosphorylase [2], while 6-azauridine $5'$-triphosphate inhibits RNA-synthetase [3].

In contrast to 6-azauridine $5'$-diphosphate, we found that 6-azacytidine $5'$-diphosphate is a substrate of polynucleotide phosphorylase prepared from the cells of *Micrococcus lysodeikticus* [4]. The copolymerisation of 6-azacytidine $5'$-diphosphate with uridine $5'$-diphosphate and cytidine $5'$-diphosphate gave high yields of polymers. We have previously demonstrated that the copolymer of cytidylic acid with 6-azacytidylic acid has a lower T_m value and a different melting profile than polycytidylic acid [4]. This finding indicates that the introduction of 6-azapyrimidine residues into the polyribonucleotide chain alters its secondary structure.

The anomalous copolymers, containing different amounts of the 6-azapyrimidine component, were studied as messenger RNA in the *in vitro* proteosynthetic system of *Escherichia coli* [5]. It follows from Fig. 1 that the incorporation of [^{14}C] phenylalanine into a polypeptide controlled by a copolymer of uridylic and 6-azacytidylic acids in the ratio 3:1 is very low. A copolymer containing only 10% of the anomalous nucleotide is still a poor messenger for the incorporation of phenylalanine (Fig. 2.). As we found subsequently, these copolymers had no messenger activity for any amino acid which includes uridylic or cytidylic acid in its codon, such as leucine, proline and serine.

Although the comparison of the coding abilities of our anomalous polyribonucleotides was made only with polyuridylic acid, it can be calculated that the

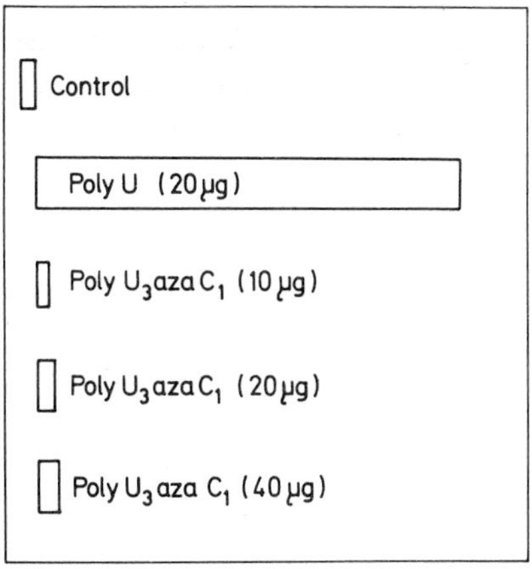

Control

Poly U (20 μg)

Poly U$_3$aza C$_1$ (10 μg)

Poly U$_3$aza C$_1$ (20 μg)

Poly U$_3$aza C$_1$ (40 μg)

Figure 1. Incorporation of [^{14}C] phenylalanine into polypeptides in the presence of poly U and poly U$_3$azaC$_1$.

Incubation mixture composition: 70μl of preincubated S-30 *Escherichia coli* fraction; 150μg sRNA (*E. coli*) in 20μl; 20μl of the following solution: 0·6M-KCl, 0·1M magnesium acetate, 1M Tris-acetate pH 7·8, 0·06M mercaptoethanol, 0·02M adenosine triphosphate and 0·002M guanosine triphosphate; 0·02μC [^{14}C]Phe-tRNA in 20μl; 20μl of amino acids mixture (0·02μmole of each, without phenylalanine); total volume 0·2 ml. Incubated 40 min at 35°C, precipitated and washed with 5% TCA and with ethyl alcohol, dissolved in formic acid and placed on the planchets for radioactivity measurement (2π flow counter).

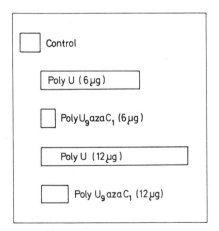

Figure 2. Incorporation of [^{14}C] phenylalanine into polypeptides in the presence of poly U and poly U$_9$azaC$_1$. Conditions as in Fig. 1.

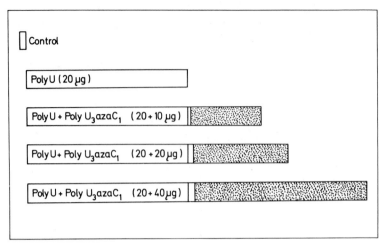

Figure 3. Stimulation of the messenger activity of poly U in the presence of poly U_3azaC_1. Conditions as in Fig. 1.

coding ability of poly UC should be much higher than that of the corresponding anomalous models. Thus it follows from our experiments that 6-azacytidylic acid cannot replace cytidylic or uridylic acids in the codon.

An interesting observation was made when we measured the messenger activity of poly U in the presence of the copolymer of uridylic and 6-azacytidylic acids [5]. The anomalous polyribonucleotide, which alone shows only very low messenger activity, significantly enhances the messenger activity of poly U for phenylalanine (Figs. 3 and 4).

In a further series of experiments [5], we studied the binding properties of trinucleoside diphosphates, containing 6-aza analogues in place of natural

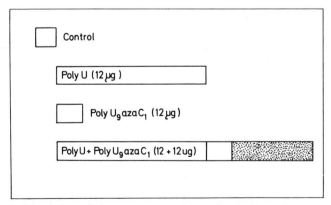

Figure 4. Stimulation of the messenger activity of poly U in the presence of poly U_9azaC_1. Conditions as in Fig. 1.

pyrimidines. In these binding experiments, the ability of a trinucleoside diphosphate to form a complex between the ribosomes and proper [^{14}C]amino-acyl-tRNA is measured. The complex formed is isolated from the incubation mixture by filtration and the radioactivity on the filter is a measure of the binding capacity of the oligonucleotide.

We prepared the triplets analogous to the trinucleoside diphosphates of GpUpU or GpUpC, which, as is well known, code for valine. The results of the binding experiments, not yet published, are shown in Fig. 5. It can be concluded from these findings that the replacement of any pyrimidine ribonucleoside in the

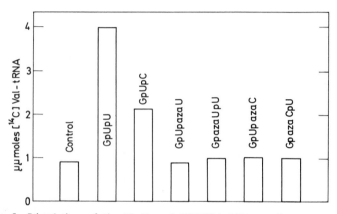

Figure 5. Stimulation of the binding of [^{14}C] Val-tRNA to ribosomes by GpUpU, GpUpC and their analogues containing 6-azapyrimidine ribonucleosides.

The incubation mixture contained 10^{-1}M Tris-HCl (pH 7·5). 5×10^{-2}M-KCl, 2×10^{-2}M magnesium acetate, 0·5 A_{260} unit of trinucleoside diphosphate, 2·5 A_{260} units of ribosomal suspension and $7·5 \times 10^{-3}\mu$C [^{14}C]Val-tRNA in 0·15 ml. Incubated 20 min at 25°C. Before filtration through membrane filter (0·3 – 0·5μm pore size) the samples were cooled and diluted. The radioactivity of the washed dry filters was measured in a flow proportional windowless counter.

valine codon by either 6-azauridine or 6-azacytidine always results in a non-functional unit that we call a "dead codon triplet".

It is interesting that the binding of [^{14}C]valyl-tRNA to ribosomes is negative even with triplets containing 6-azauridine or 6-azacytidine in the third position. This position corresponds, in the postulated valine anticodon, to inosine, which is assumed to be at position one. Inosine possesses maximum freedom in the Watson and Crick type of base pairing as it can pair with uridine and cytidine, as well as adenosine. The effect of 6-azapyrimidine derivatives thus comes into play even in the least specific position of the triplet. It should be emphasized here that IR spectrophotometry showed that residues of 6-azacytosine are able to form hydrogen bonds with guanine residues. The experiments carried out at the level of substituted bases, nucleosides and nucleotides cannot, therefore, be considered as critical for the behaviour of these antimetabolites in higher codon formations.

It is evident from our experiments that the incorporation of 6-azapyrimidines into nucleic acids would probably not cause errors in the transfer of genetic information, and as a consequence would not be dangerous to the organism, particularly as regards mutagenesis and cancerogenesis. This is so because, if such incorporation could take place, all the codons and anticodons would possess no coding and binding activity. .

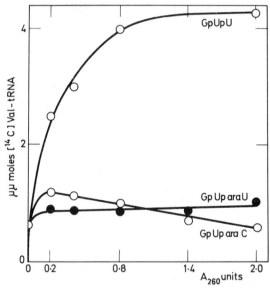

Figure 6. Stimulation of the binding of [^{14}C] Val-tRNA to the ribosomes with the aid of trinucleoside diphosphates containing arabinosides. For explanation see Fig. 5.

In further work [6] we investigated whether the binding properties of the triplet GpUpU would be influenced by the substitution of arabinose for the ribose residue. We found (Fig. 6) that triplets containing arabinose residues are practically incapable of stimulating binding.

To a certain extent, arabinose can be considered as an "analogue" of both ribose and deoxyribose. It is known that the replacement of the ribose moiety by a deoxyribose residue considerably reduces the binding capacity of the triplet ApApA. From a comparison of the binding capacity of the arabinosyl analogues—analogues with the binding ability of "deoxyribosyl"—it is evident that the shifting of the hydroxyl group from the position *cis* to that of *trans* at the 2'-position of the sugar residue has a much greater negative effect on binding than the full loss of the hydroxyl group.

The problem as to whether cytosine arabinoside is incorporated into nucleic acids has not yet been satisfactorily resolved. It is of considerable significance because cytosine arabinoside is of appreciable clinical importance as an antiviral and cancerostatic agent. As we have shown (Fig. 6), the triplets containing the arabinosyl moiety in the third position are almost incapable of stimulating binding. Similarly, as in the case of the 6-azapyrimidine nucleosides, we can predict that an eventual incorporation of cytosine arabinoside into nucleic acids would lead to the formation of a "dead code".

Let me now briefly summarize the results of other laboratories concerning the coding properties of oligo- and polyribonucleotides with anomalous components, which are of some practical importance.

Poly-5-fluorouridylic acid, as well as other 5-halogenated (or methylated) polyuridylic acids [7, 8] are effective "messengers" for the incorporation of phenylalanine into polypeptides. The halogenation can, however, change the qualitative character of the code: in addition to the incorporation of phenylalanine, poly-5-bromouridylic acid is also effective for the incorporation of leucine and isoleucine, and to a certain extent also of serine. 5-Fluorouracil behaves in the polymers only as uracil and not as cytosine or adenine.

The antibiotic tubercidin (7-deazaadenosine) can substitute for adenosine, but not for cytidine or guanosine in the triplet ApApA [9]. 8-Azaguanine can replace guanine, but not adenine. Nevertheless, the coding activity of polymers with 8-azaguanine is lower than that of the polyribonucleotides with guanine [10].

As far as I know, there is no knowledge about the coding properties of polyribonucleotides containing 2-thiouracil, despite the fact that this analogue is incorporated into the RNA of many biological systems.

Finally, I would like to point out that the artificial "dead codes", mentioned earlier, could serve as good models for the study of growth termination of a polypeptide chain in *in vitro* experiments.

REFERENCES

1. Škoda, J., *in* "Progress in Nucleic Acid Research", Vol. II (edited by J. N. Davidson, W. E. Cohn), Academic Press, New York 1964.
2. Škoda, J., Kára, J., Šormová, Z. and Šorm, F., *Biochim. biophys. Acta* 33 (1959) 579.
3. Goldberg, I. H. and Rabinowitz, M., *Biochim. biophys. Acta* 72 (1963) 116.
4. Škoda, J. and Šorm, F., *Biochim. biophys. Acta* 91 (1964) 352.
5. Lisý, V., Škoda, J., Rychlík, I., Smrt, J., Holý, A. and Šorm, F., *Colln Czech. chem. Commun.*, 33 (1968) 4111.

30 J. ŠKODA

6. Škoda, J., Lisý, V. and Smrt, J., not published.
7. Grunberg-Manago, M. and Michelson, A. M., *Biochim. biophys. Acta* **80** (1964) 593.
8. Grunberg-Manago, M. and Michelson, A. M., *Biochim. biophys. Acta* **87** (1964) 593.
9. Ikehara, M. and Ohtsuka, E., *Biochem. biophys. Res. Commun.* **21** (1965) 257.
10. Grünberger, D., Meissner, L., Holý, A. and Šorm, F., *Biochim. biophys. Acta* **119** (1966) 432.

FEBS Symposium, Volume 16, 1969, pp. 31-47

Biochemical Basis of Resistance to Folic Acid Antagonists*

M. T. HAKALA

Department of Experimental Therapeutics, Roswell Park Memorial Institute, Buffalo, New York, U.S.A.

Resistance to an antimetabolite is in most cases a relative and not an absolute entity, i.e. a cell which can tolerate a higher concentration of an inhibitor than another is the resistant one. The elements which can be involved in making the cells resistant include a slower uptake of the inhibitor, decreased affinity to the target site, increased availability of competing metabolites, increase in target enzyme, increase in turnover number or ability to destroy the inhibitor. Resistance to folic acid antagonists is often encountered in cancer chemotherapy *in vivo*. Leukemic cells, for example, might be either inherently resistant or can

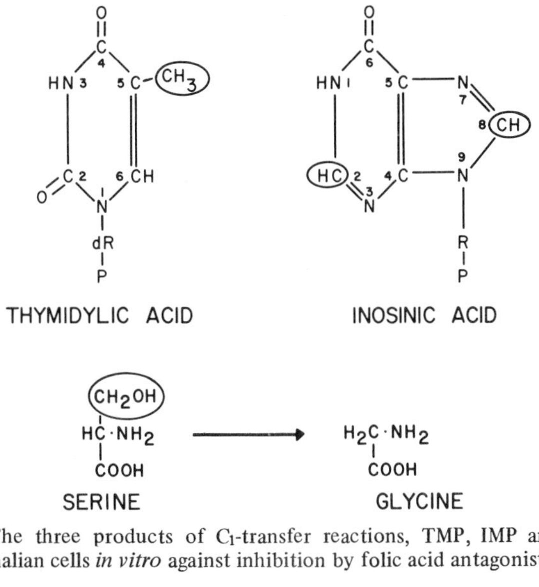

Figure 1. The three products of C_1-transfer reactions, TMP, IMP and glycine which protect mammalian cells *in vitro* against inhibition by folic acid antagonists.

* This work has been supported in part by a research grant CA-04175 from the National Cancer Institute of the United States Public Health Service.

become so after a certain course of treatments with amethopterin, the 4-amino-N^{10}-methyl analog of folate. The degree of resistance *in vivo* needs to be only 2—4-fold to make the drug useless due to toxicity to the host.

Folic acid analogs are inhibitors of dihydrofolate reductase (tetrahydrofolate dehydrogenase) and thereby prevent the conversion of folate and dihydrofolate to tetrahydrofolate. The latter is necessary as a coenzyme for C_1-unit transfers in numerous enzymatic reactions. The three products of these reactions which are most vital for the growth of mammalian cells *in vitro* are illustrated in Fig. 1. When glycine, thymidine and a purine are supplied in the medium the growth of mammalian cells is undisturbed even by saturation levels of amethopterin [1, 2], while omitting of any one of the three compounds results in cessation of growth. Indeed, in the presence of amethopterin and a purine, a nutritional requirement of mammalian cells for thymidine can be demonstrated, as is seen in Fig. 2. Similarly, a requirement for adenine appears in amethopterin-thymidine medium (Fig. 3). Thus, in the presence of thymidine, glycine and purine mammalian cells appear to be absolutely "resistant" to folate analogs. However, this "resistance" is not due to an inherent property of the cells but is due to circumstances; the elimination of the products from the medium restores the "lost" sensitivity of the cells.

To learn about the biochemical basis of the true resistance to folate analogs in mammalian cell systems, we developed some years ago resistant sublines of mouse Sarcoma 180 cells. This was done in monolayer cultures of these cells grown in Eagle's medium [3] which was supplemented with glycine and either thymidine (AT) or hypoxanthine (AH) by gradually increasing the concentration of amethopterin in the medium. The process required a few months and resulted in cell lines which are 67- (AH/67), 174- (AT/174) and 3000-fold (AT/3000) resistant to the drug [4, 5]. One of the processes involved in the development of resistance was clearly a selection (Table 1). Most of the parent cells were killed while only those cells survived which either were inherently resistant or had a capacity to become so. On the other hand, the loss of resistance in the absence of the drug was very slow with a half life of about 30-40 days [4].

Our task now was to find out what changes had occurred in S-180 cells when they became resistant to amethopterin. One of the early observations was that in the high-speed supernate of the resistant cells no free amethopterin was detected while large amounts of it were released after heating. Thus, somehow amethopterin was tightly bound to a constituent present in the cell supernate. The more resistant the cell was the larger was the amount of bound amethopterin. Amethopterin was eventually found to be tightly bound to dihydrofolate reductase, a fact which all along in these studies had been used as a means of quantitating the drug [4, 6]. The folate reductase content of the resistant cells was greatly increased (Table 2). While a major fraction of the enzyme within the cells acted as a trap for amethopterin, only 2-20% remained free to carry on its

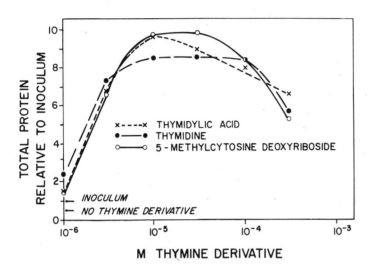

Figure 2. The ability of thymidine and derivatives thereof to support the growth of mammalian cells in Eagle's medium [3] supplemented with 10^{-6}M amethopterin, 3×10^{-4}M glycine and 3×10^{-5}M hypoxanthine [2].

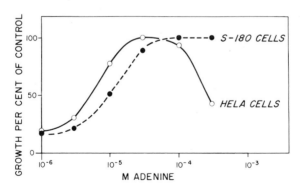

Figure 3. The ability of adenine to support the growth of S-180 and HeLa cells in Eagle's medium [3] supplemented with 10^{-6}M amethopterin, 3×10^{-5}M thymidine and glycine [2].

Table 1. One-step selection of amethopterin-resistant cell lines [5].

Starting cell line	Selective medium		Culture conditions		Comments
	Type	Amethopterin	Inoculum	Area	
		μM		cm^2	
S-180	AH	0·5	2×10^7	60	All dead in 10 to 11 days
S-180	AT	0·5	2×10^7	60	A few clones in 40 days
AT/174	AT	50	10^6	30	A few clones in 25 days

usual functions. The resistant sublines were found to be resistant not only to amethopterin but to other folate analogs as well (Table 3).

The fraction of amethopterin-bound enzyme inside the cells was found to be dependent on the extracellular concentration of the drug as is shown in Fig. 4 for AT/3000 cells. At 1 μM amethopterin in the medium only one-half of the total enzyme in these cells was in the form of enzyme-amethopterin complex [7]. Yet the dissociation constant of this complex is about 10^{-11}M [8]. Thus it is strikingly clear that an effective permeability barrier between the medium and the intracellular space causes a large concentration gradient in favor of the medium. It became therefore important to learn whether the uptake of folate analogs by the resistant cells was also altered. Figure 5 shows that there were no differences between the resistant and the sensitive cells in respect to the rate of amethopterin uptake. It was also clear that the rate of uptake was directly proportional to the extracellular concentration of the drug. In some other

Table 2. Folic acid reductase in S-180 cells grown in maintenance media [7].

S-180 Cell line	Amethopterin in medium M	Folic acid reductase	
		Total* μmoles/kg	Free % of Total
Sensitive			
Parent	0	0·38 ± 0·065	100
AH/S	0	0·6	100
Resistant			
AH/67	5×10^{-7}	17·3 ± 0·85	16·8 ± 3·2
AT/174	5×10^{-7}	25·8 ± 0·90	22·0 ± 3·3
AT/3000	5×10^{-5}	121 ± 11·5	2·6 ± 0·73

* Total is the sum of free and amethopterin-bound enzyme.

Table 3. Dihydrofolate reductase content of S-180 cells and their sensitivity to folate analogs*.

S-180 Subline	Folate reductase mμmoles/g packed cells	μM required for 50% inhibition of growth†		
		Amethopterin	Aminopterin	Dichloro-amethopterin
Sensitive				
Parent	0·38 ± 0·065	0·054 ± 0·0016	0·0064	
AH/S	0·6	0·076 ± 0·032	0·020	0·2
Resistant				
AH/67	17·3 ± 0·85	2·1	0·38	2·8
AT/174	25·8 ± 0·90	12·0	1·6	10·0
AT/3000	121·0 + 11·5	160	33·0	

* Part of this data has been published [5].
† Determined in Eagle's medium [3] containing 1 μM folic acid and supplemented with 10% of horse serum.

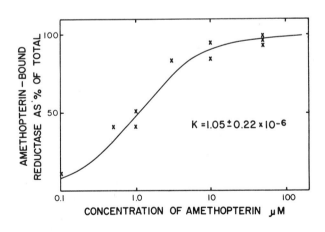

Figure 4. The fraction of intracellular dihydrofolate reductase bound by amethopterin in AT/3000 cells maintained at varied concentrations of amethopterin in the medium [7].

36   M. T. HAKALA

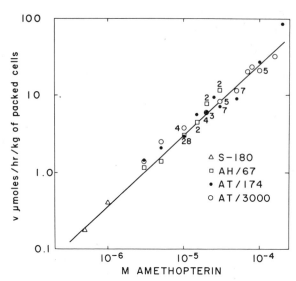

Figure 5. The rate of influx of amethopterin into sensitive and resistant sublines of S-180 cells at varied concentrations of amethopterin. [7].

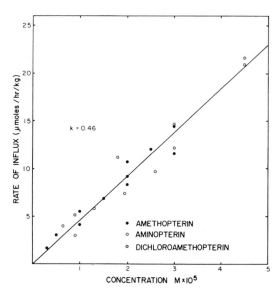

Figure 6. The rate of influx of different folic acid antagonists into AT/174 subline of S-180 cells at varied extracellular concentrations. Methodology as in Fig. 5.

instances of resistance to amethopterin (L-1210 and L-5178 cells), a decreased rate of uptake has been observed [9, 10]. Also, in contrast to S-180 cell system, the rate of uptake in L-1210 cells seems to be a saturable process [10]. The other folate analogs, aminopterin and dichloro-amethopterin were taken up by S-180 cells with a rate equal to amethopterin (Fig. 6). As was seen in Table 3 aminopterin is a much more potent inhibitor of all sublines of S-180 cells than either amethopterin or dichloroamethopterin. The reason for this difference is not immediately clear since each is a stoichiometric inhibitor of dihydrofolate reductase of these cells at pH 6·0 when folate is the substrate. The relative toxicity of these analogs *in vivo* appears similar to that in cell culture and has been shown to reflect the degree of enzymatic oxidation of these analogs [11]. There are other stoichiometric inhibitors of dihydrofolate reductase of these

Table 4. Stoichiometric inhibitors of dihydrofolate reductase as inhibitors of cell growth.

Compound*	M Required for 50% inhibition of growth of AH/S cells†
Folate Analogs	
1. Amethopterin	7×10^{-8}
2. Aminopterin	2×10^{-8}
3. Dichloroamethopterin	2×10^{-7}
Pyrido-Pyrimidine	
4. 2, 4-Diamino-5-methyl-6-sec-butyl-pyrido (2, 3-d) pyrimidine	5×10^{-8}
Pyrimidines	
5. 2, 4-Diamino-5-(3′, 4′-dichlorophenyl)-6-ethyl pyrimidine	$6 \cdot 5 \times 10^{-8}$
6. 2, 4-Diamino-5-(3′, 4′-dibromophenyl)-6-methyl pyrimidine	7×10^{-8}
7. 2, 4-Diamino-5-(3′, 4′-dichlorophenyl)-6-methyl pyrimidine	8×10^{-8}
S-Triazines	
8. 1-(3′-chloro-4′-methylphenyl)-4, 6-diamino-1, 2-dihydro-2-dimethyl-s-triazine · HCl	3×10^{-7}
9. 1-(3′, 4′-Dichlorophenyl)-4, 6-diamino-1, 2-dihydro-2-dimethyl-s-triazine · HCl	3×10^{-7}

* Compounds 4, 5, 6 and 8 were generously supplied by Dr. George Hitchings, Burroughs Wellcome and Co., Tuckahoe, N.Y., 7 is a CCNSC compound 19494, and 9 was kindly supplied by Dr. E. J. Modest, The Childrens Cancer Research Foundation, Boston, Massachusetts.
† AH/S cells, an amethopterin-sensitive subline of S-180 cells [5], were grown in the presence of the inhibitors for 6-7 days in Eagle's optimal medium [3] containing 1 μM folic acid and 10% of horse serum.

cells which differ from each other at the cellular level and are listed in Table 4, which shows that aminopterin and the pyrido-pyrimidine (4) are the most potent inhibitors while Cl_2-amethopterin and the S-triazines are least so. These differences in a cellular system might be caused by differences in enzymatic oxidation as was indicated for amethopterin and Cl_2-amethopterin [11, 12].

The folate analogs discussed above are not only stoichiometric, but also competitive, inhibitors of dihydrofolate reductase [8, 13]. Even folate in high excess at pH 6·0 can remove these stoichiometric inhibitors from the enzyme and in the presence of H_2-folate at higher pH the stoichiometry is completely

Table 5. Competitive relationship between folinic acid and folate analogs with respect to inhibition of growth*.

S-180 Subline	Ratio of molar concentrations when growth is inhibited by 50%†	
	Amethopterin/Folinic Acid	Aminopterin/Folinic Acid
Sensitive		
Parent	9·0 ± 0·076	0·8
AH/S		1·30 ± 0·025
Resistant		
AH/67	594 ± 26	20·9 ± 1·7
AT/174	1530 ± 180	110·3 ± 6·7

* The data concerning amethopterin has been published [4]. The S-180 sublines have been described in refs. 4 and 9.
† Cells were grown in folic acid-free Eagle's medium [3] supplemented with five different concentrations of folinic acid varied from 0·003 to 0·3 μM.

lost and taken over by a clearly competitive situation. However, a derivative of tetrahydrofolate, namely, 5-formyltetrahydrofolate (folinic acid) has no effect on the binding of amethopterin to the enzyme. Yet this compound in a cellular system effectively protects the cells against amethopterin as well as aminopterin in a clearly competitive manner (Table 5). In the presence of a certain concentration of folinic acid the resistant cells tolerate a much higher concentration of amethopterin than the sensitive cells. It is clear again that aminopterin, as in folic acid medium, is a more potent inhibitor than amethopterin, also in folinic acid medium. This competitive relationship concerning growth inhibition does not concern the uptake process. It is true that folinic acid can slow down the uptake of amethopterin (Table 6) but the effect is not a competitive one and the concentrations of folinic acid required to do so are higher by several orders of magnitude than those needed for growth. The finding of Burchall [14] that 10^{-5}M folinic acid protected the *E. coli* dihydrofolate reductase against inactivation by pronase equally well as 10^{-4}M folate, indicates that the possible binding of folinic acid to the mammalian enzyme needs re-investigation.

Table 6. Effect of folinic acid on the rate of amethopterin uptake by AT/174 cells.

Medium containing	Ratio of amethopterin/folinic acid	% Decrease in rate of uptake
5 μM Amethopterin		
50 μM Folinic Acid	0·1	25
10 μM Amethopterin		
50 μM Folinic Acid	0·2	58
100 μM Folinic Acid	0·1	69
200 μM Folinic Acid	0·05	55
20 μM Amethopterin		
50 μM Folinic Acid	0·4	27
100 μM Folinic Acid	0·2	51
200 μM Folinic Acid	0·1	49
50 μM Amethopterin		
50 μM Folinic Acid	1·0	0
100 μM Folinic Acid	0·5	4
200 μM Folinic Acid	0·25	1

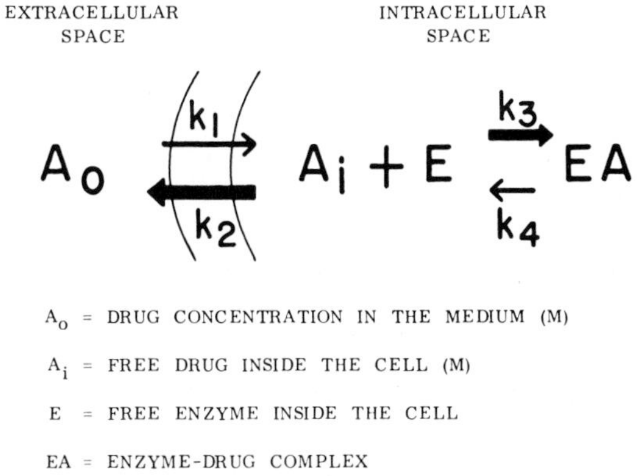

EXTRACELLULAR SPACE   INTRACELLULAR SPACE

$$A_o \underset{k_2}{\overset{k_1}{\rightleftharpoons}} A_i + E \underset{k_4}{\overset{k_3}{\rightleftharpoons}} EA$$

A_o = DRUG CONCENTRATION IN THE MEDIUM (M)

A_i = FREE DRUG INSIDE THE CELL (M)

E = FREE ENZYME INSIDE THE CELL

EA = ENZYME-DRUG COMPLEX

Figure 7. Schematic presentation of the overall process of cellular amethopterin uptake resulting in formation of dihydrofolate reductase-amethopterin complex.

The total cellular process of dihydrofolate reductase inhibition by amethopterin seems to involve at least four rate processes (Fig. 7). By far the fastest seems to be the formation of the EA-complex ($k_3 \sim 18 \times 10^7$/h), followed by efflux ($k_2 \sim 9$/h), influx ($k_2 \sim 0.3$/h), and lastly by the dissociation of EA-complex ($k_4 \sim 18 \times 10^{-4}$/h). Because of this situation the concentration of free amethopterin within the cells is always much below that in the medium [15]. The uptake of this drug, in general, is extremely slow when compared with most other drugs. To give a concrete example; it would require 12 hours to saturate dihydrofolate reductase even in the sensitive S-180 cells at 10^{-7}M amethopterin.

Table 7. Physical dimensions of various cell types.

Cell type	Diameter μ	Surface area μ^2	Volume μ^3	Surface/volume
Sarcoma-180	19	1134	3590	0.316
L-1210	9	254	382	0.665
Lymphocytes	9-12	254-452	382-904	0.665 − 0.50
Plasmocytes	14-20	615-1256	1440-4190	0.428 − 0.30
Monocytes	12-22	452-1520	904-5570	0.50 − 0.273
Megakaryocytes	100	31,400	523,000	0.06

When drug uptake is as slow as this, there are two factors which can greatly influence its selectivity of action. These are factors not usually considered, namely, the rate of cellular multiplication and the cell size. If the cell generation time is shorter than the time required for saturation of the target site the rapidly multiplying cell will escape the action of the drug while a slowly growing cell is inhibited. The other factor which becomes important is the cell size. Table 7 lists sizes of various cells and shows as an example that the cell surface per volume of L-1210 cells is more than twice as large as that of S-180 cells. This could well be the reason for the relative resistance of S-180 cells *in vivo* to amethopterin as compared with L-1210 cells.

So far the only difference between the amethopterin-sensitive and -resistant S-180 cells which we have discussed is the quantity of dihydrofolate reductase. Titration with amethopterin had revealed 300 times more enzyme in AT/3000 cells than in the sensitive parent cells. It was important to establish whether the enzyme in the sensitive and resistant cells differed qualitatively. No qualitative changes have been discovered as yet. The different parameters investigated are listed in Table 8. The kinetic characteristics, molecular size, electrophoretic mobility and relative reaction rates, when folate or dihydrofolate are substrates, are identical for both enzymes.

Table 8. Comparison of S-180 cells sensitive and resistant to amethopterin.

Growing cells *in vitro*	Resistant	Sensitive	Ref.
Requirement for Folate (1/2 Max. growth)	$1 \cdot 3 \times 10^{-7}M$	$1 \cdot 5 \times 10^{-7}M$	4
Requirement for Folinic Acid (1/2 Max. growth)	$1 \cdot 5 \times 10^{-9}M$	$1 \cdot 4 \times 10^{-9}M$	4
Uptake of folate analogs	slow	same	7

Chromosomal constitution			
Modal number		no correlation	5
Markers		no correlation	5

Dihydrofolate reductase			
K_m for Folate	$1 \cdot 1 \times 10^{-5}M$	$1 \cdot 1 \times 10^{-5}M$	4
Turnover number per min per amethopterin binding site	27	27	4
Relative rate of reduction of H_2-Folate (pH 7·0) and Folate (pH 6·0)	39	38	26
Electrophoretic mobility at pH 6·5 and 8·7	to anode	same	26,27
Molecular weight (Sephadex)	21,000	same	26,27

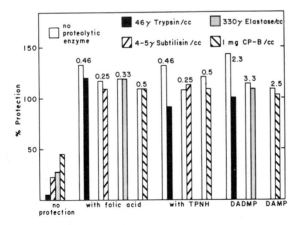

Figure 8. Protection of dihydrofolate reductase of AT/3000-subline of S-180 cells by substrate, coenzyme and diamino analogs of folate against inactivation by various proteolytic enzymes [16].

The dihydrofolate reductase of the resistant AT/3000 cells has been purified and studied further. This cell is so rich in the enzyme that 4-6% of the cell supernatant protein is dihydrofolate reductase. When the supernatant is passed only once through a Sephadex G-75 column the enzyme which is recovered is already 40% pure. The enzyme is inactivated by proteolytic enzymes such as trypsin, chymotrypsin, subtilisin, elastase and carboxypeptidase B, but not by carboxypeptidase A or by leucine aminopeptidase [16]. These inactivations can be prevented by substrates, coenzymes and substrate analogs as is seen in Fig. 8. Burchall has observed similar protection of *E. coli* dihydrofolate reductase against pronase [14]. Protection was also observed of S-180 enzyme against inactivation caused by metal chelators such as versene and *o*-phenanthroline as well as against inactivation caused by SH-reagents, iodoacetamide, *p*-chloromercuribenzoate and 5, 5'-dithiobis-(2-nitrobenzoic acid) (Ellman's reagent).

The inactivation by metal chelators suggested that dihydrofolate reductase might be a metalloenzyme, nothing unusual for a dehydrogenase, many of which are Zn-enzymes. Therefore, several enzyme preparations were purified on a Sephadex G-75 column in conditions strictly avoiding cationic contamination. The fractions were then analyzed for metal content using an atomic absorbtion spectrophotometer model 303 of Perkin-Elmer. Far less than one equivalent per amethopterin binding site was found of Zn, Co, Mn, Mo, Ni, Cu and Fe. Mg and Ca were inconsistently present in various fractions and were not specifically associated with dihydrofolate reductase. Thus, at the moment there is no analytical evidence to support the suggestion that dihydrofolate reductase would be a metallo-enzyme, even though it is inactivated by chelating agents. It has been pointed out by many investigators that the activity of this enzyme is greatly affected by ions in general [17-20]. We have also observed that the dihydrofolate reductase of S-180 cells is influenced by the ionic environment. When the substrate was folate and the reaction was carried at pH 6·0, it was found that histidine buffer promoted the highest activity followed by phosphate and the lowest activity was observed in tartrate buffer (Fig. 9). On the other hand, the extent of activation caused by Mg^{2+} was dependent not only on the buffer anion but also on pH (Figs. 9 and 10). Thus, at pH 5·0 much less Mg^{2+} was required for optimal activation than at pH 6·0. Even though the activity varied, there was no change in the number of amethopterin binding sites; the activation of the enzyme changed only the slope of the titration curve while the intercept at abscissa stayed the same [16]. The sensitivity of dihydrofolate reductase activity to variation in ionic environment indicates that the quantitation of the enzyme by titration with amethopterin is a far more reliable measure of purity than the so-called specific activity. The protection of dihydrofolate reductase against chelating agents by substrates, their analogs and by coenzymes suggests that the enzyme-protector complex might involve a cation.

The protection of dihydrofolate reductase against inactivation by SH-reagents

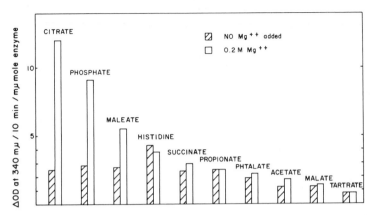

Figure 9. Effect of the type of buffer (Na-salt) at 0·1M and pH 6·0 on the rate of reduction of folate in the presence and absence of 0·2M MgCl$_2$. The activity was determined at 340 mμ as described elsewhere [21] and was related to the molar quantity of the enzyme. The latter was estimated by titrations with amethopterin as has been described [16].

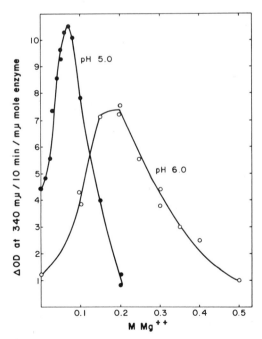

Figure 10. Effect of pH and of MgCl$_2$ concentration on the activation of dihydrofolate reductase in 0·1M citrate (Na-salt) using folate as the substrate. Methodology as in Fig. 9.

was used to determine the number of SH-groups essential for activity and amethopterin binding [21]. This was done on a 37% pure preparation of the enzyme, taking advantage of the fact that the number of enzyme molecules could be accurately determined by titration with amethopterin. The total SH-content of these preparations was fortunately low, a necessity for success in this type of analysis. Two SH-groups were found to be essential for folate reductase activity and for amethopterin binding (Fig. 11). The remaining

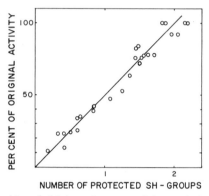

Figure 11. Relationship of folate reductase activity and the number of protected SH-groups as determined in 37% pure enzyme preparations of AT/3000 cells by titrations with Ellman's reagent in the presence of various protectors [21].

SH-groups most likely were part of the foreign protein. The task now remaining, as far as the dihydrofolate reductase of S-180 cells is concerned, is its complete purification, amino acid analysis and, hopefully, X-ray crystallography.

It was of interest to know whether other enzymes, especially the tetrahydro-folate-dependent ones, had changed when S-180 cells became resistant to amethopterin. The most significant finding was that in the resistant subline developed in the presence of thymidine (AT) the TMP-synthetase was quite low while two enzymes leading to purine synthesis were high (Table 9). On the other hand, in the resistant subline developed in the presence of hypoxanthine (AH), one enzyme leading to purine synthesis was low while TMP-synthetase was increased [22].

If the content of the target enzyme has anything to do with selectivity of inhibition, one would expect that the AT subline would show increased sensitivity to TMP-synthetase inhibitors. Moreover, a compound such as homo-folate [23], which requires an enzymatic reduction to tetrahydrohomofolate to become an inhibitor of TMP-synthetase, should be especially inhibitory to AT cells which are rich in dihydrofolate reductase and poor in TMP-synthetase. Two H_4-folate analogs, which in enzymatic assays have proven to be inhibitors of TMP-synthetase [24], were also tested. Table 10 lists the results and shows that

Table 9. Activities of tetrahydrofolate-dependent enzymes in sublines of S-180 cells [22].

Enzyme	Specific activity mμ moles/mg protein/h				
	Sensitive Cells		Resistant Cells		
	Parent AH/S	AH/67	AT/174	AT/3000	
erine hydroxymethyl transferase	40	–	39	39	–
,10-Methylenetetrahydrofolate dehydrogenase	117	–	40	261	–
,10-Methenyltetrahydrofolate cyclohydrolase	24	–	24	78	–
^{10}-Formyltetrahydrofolate synthetase	40	–	20	56	–
hymidylate synthetase (room temperature)	7·7	20	10	0·28	–
ihydrofolate reductase, μmoles/kg cells	0·38	0·6	17·3	25·8	121

Table 10. Sensitivity of sublines of S-180 cells to potential inhibitors of TMP synthetase.

Enzyme content	S-180 Subline			Ref.
	Sensitive	Resistant		
	AH/S	AT/174	AT/3000	
(1) Dihydrofolate reductase mμ moles/g cells	0·6	28·5	121	5
(2) TMP-synthetase mμ moles/mg prot/h at 37°C	28·5	0·43		28
50% Inhibition of growth M				
5-Fluorodeoxyuridine	$2 \cdot 2 \times 10^{-8}$	9×10^{-9}		28
Homofolate	7×10^{-6}	$6 \cdot 6 \times 10^{-6}$	$5 \cdot 1 \times 10^{-6}$	29
H_4-Amethopterin	$1 \cdot 9 \times 10^{-7}$	$1 \cdot 4 \times 10^{-5}$		
H_4-Cl_2-Amethopterin	5×10^{-7}	5×10^{-5}		

5-fluorodeoxyuridine and homofolate are slightly better in inhibiting AT cells than the sensitive subline. However, H_4-folate analogs behave more like folate antagonists, being less inhibitory for AT-cells. To explain these results one should know more about the cellular uptake of these compounds, their intracellular conversion to active forms and about their breakdown. Nahas and Friedkin [25], for example, discovered that in L-1210 cells H_2-homofolate was not converted to H_4-homofolate as it is in cell-free preparations.

CONCLUSION

The resistance to amethopterin in mammalian cells is one of the most thoroughly investigated cases of drug resistance. Not only is the target enzyme well studied but the cellular properties with respect to drug uptake, as well as the activities of tetrahydrofolate-dependent enzymes, are known. In the case of mouse Sarcoma-180 cells the cellular change associated with resistance is a clear-cut one. Only the quantity of dihydrofolate reductase has changed. The excess enzyme in resistant cells acts as a trap for amethopterin. The slow influx of amethopterin plays an important role in the resistance. In multiplying cell populations, which continuously form new cells containing new dihydrofolate reductase, the slow influx permits enough enzyme to remain free to carry on its normal functions. We have also pointed out here how, with a slowly penetrating drug such as amethopterin, the selectivity of action at the cellular level is greatly influenced by cell generation time and especially by the cell size.

REFERENCES

1. Hakala, M. T., *Science, N.Y.* **126** (1957) 255.
2. Hakala, M. T. and Taylor, E., *J. biol. Chem.* **234** (1959) 126.
3. Eagle, H., *Science, N.Y.* **122** (1955) 501 and **130** (1959) 432.
4. Hakala, M. T., Zakrzewski, S. F. and Nichol, C. A., *J. biol. Chem.* **236** (1961) 952.
5. Hakala, M. T. and Ishihara, T., *Cancer Res.* **22** (1962) 987.
6. Werkheiser, W. C., Zakrzewski, S. F. and Nichol, C. A., *J. Pharmac. exp. Ther.* **137** (1962) 162.
7. Hakala, M. T., *Biochim. biophys. Acta* **102** (1965) 198.
8. Wang, D. H. and Werkheiser, W. C., *Fedn Proc. Fedn Am. Socs exp. Biol.* **23** (1964) 324.
9. Fischer, G. A., *Biochem. Pharmac.* **11** (1962) 1233.
10. Sirotnak, F. M., Kurita, S. and Hutchison, D. J., *Cancer Res.* **28** (1968) 75.

11. Johns, D. G., Iannotti, A. T., Sartorelli, A. C. and Bertino, J. R., *Biochem. Pharmac.* **15** (1966) 555.
12. Ti Li Loo and Adamson, R. H., *Biochem. Pharmac.* **11** (1962) 170.
13. Nichol, C. A., *in* "Advances in Enzyme Regulation", Vol. 6 (edited by G. Weber), Pergamon Press, Oxford 1968, p. 305.
14. Burchall, J., *Molec. Pharmac.* **4** (1968) 238.
15. Hakala, M. T., *Biochim. biophys. Acta* **102** (1965) 210.
16. Hakala, M. T. and Suolinna, E.-M., *Molec. Pharmac.* **2** (1966) 465.
17. Bertino, J. R., *Biochim. biophys. Acta* **58** (1962) 377.
18. Kaufman, B. T., *Biochem. biophys. Res. Commun.* **10** (1963) 499.
19. Kaufman, B. T., *Proc. natn. Acad. Sci. U.S.A.* **56** (1966) 695.
20. Reyes, P. and Huennekens, F. M., *Biochemistry, N.Y.* **6** (1967) 3519.
21. Hakala, M. T., *Molec. Pharmac.* **4** (1968) 162.
22. Raunio, R. and Hakala, M. T., *Biochem. Pharmac.* **17** (1968) 1744.
23. Goodman, L., DeGraw, J., Kisliuk, R. L., Friedkin, M., Pastore, E. J., Crawford, E. J., Plante, L. T., Al-Nahas, A., Morningstar, Jr. J. F., Kwok, G., Wilson, L., Donovan, E. F. and Ratzan, J., *J. Am. chem. Soc.* **86** (1964) 308.
24. Slavik, K. and Zakrzewski, S. F., *Molec. Pharmac.* **3** (1967) 370.
25. Nahas, A. and Friedkin, M., *Fedn Proc. Fedn Am. Socs exp. Biol.* **27** (1968) 389.
26. Raunio, R. P. and Hakala, M. T., *Molec. Pharmac.* **3** (1967) 279.
27. Zakrzewski, S. F., Hakala, M. T. and Nichol, C. A., *Molec. Pharmac.* **2** (1966) 423.
28. Suolinna, E.-M., Slavik, K. and Hakala, M. T., *Fedn Proc. Fedn Am. Socs exp. Biol.* **26** (1967) 813.
29. Nichol, C. A. and Hakala, M. T., *Biochem. Pharmac.* **15** (1966) 1621.

FEBS Symposium, Volume 16, 1969, pp. 49-63

Mechanism of Reduction of Folate and Dihydrofolate

S. F. ZAKRZEWSKI

Department of Experimental Therapeutics,
Roswell Park Memorial Institute,
Buffalo, New York, U.S.A.

INTRODUCTION

The enzyme dihydrofolate reductase, which reduces H_2-folate* to H_4-folate has been isolated from different, normal, as well as malignant animal tissues [1-6], many species of bacteria [7-10] and recently some protozoa [11, 12]. As far as it has been investigated, all dihydrofolate reductases originating from animal tissues have in common the ability to utilize folate as substrate. With either substrate NADPH is the hydrogen donor, yet H_2-folate is reduced at a much higher rate than folate. In spite of this the study performed with dihydrofolate reductase from cultured cells of Sarcoma-180 indicated that the activation energy is 8·9 kcal higher for H_2-folate as substrate than for folate [1]. In other words, more energy is needed to reduce H_2-folate than folate. This is in accord with the chemical behaviour of these compounds. Dithionite reduction of folate to H_2-folate, for instance, proceeds fast at room temperature [13], whereas dithionite reduction of H_2-folate to H_4-folate requires prolonged heating at 75°C [14], indicating that even at this elevated temperature the rate of reduction is slow. In the case of the enzymatic reduction, higher positive entropy of activation is the driving force which causes H_2-folate to be reduced faster than folate [1].

A few years ago Pastore and Friedkin using mammalian enzyme demonstrated that during the dihydrofolate reductase reaction a direct transfer of hydrogen from the A side of NADPH to H_2-folate takes place [15]. Later the same finding

---

* Abbreviations: H_2-folate, 7-methyl-H_2-folate, H_4-folate, 7-methyl-H_4-folate; 7,8-dihydrofolate, 7-methyl-7,8-dihydrofolate, tetrahydrofolate and 7-methyl-tetrahydrofolate, respectively. $NADPH^3$-A and $NADPH^3$-B; nicotinamide-adenine-dinucleotide phosphate tritiated on A and B side, respectively.

K_m = Michaelis constant
V_{max} = Maximal reaction velocity
v = Initial reaction velocity
s = Substrate

49

was reported by Blakley and his co-workers [16]. The latter group worked with the reductase from *S. faecalis,* which varies from the animal enzyme in its inability to utilize folate as substrate. In neither case was the position of the hydrogen incorporation unequivocally established.

Three questions thus arose:

(1) How does the single enzyme reduce folate as well as H_2-folate, each substrate requiring addition of hydrogen in a different position?

(2) Does the reduction of folate to H_4-folate proceed through H_2-folate?

(3) Why do some bacterial reductases which otherwise resemble closely the animal enzymes lack the capability to reduce folate?

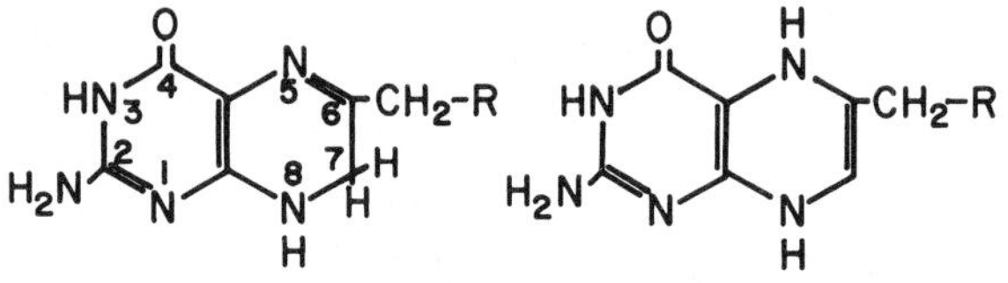

7,8—DIHYDROFOLATE   5,8—DIHYDROFOLATE
R=p—Aminobenzoate

Figure 1. Structural formulas of 7,8-dihydrofolate and 5,8-dihydrofolate.

Concerning points 1 and 2, an attractive hypothesis was conceived in our laboratory. It has been suggested that the enzymatic reduction of H_2-folate involves an intramolecular rearrangement to 5,8-H_2-folate, which is followed by the transfer of hydride ion from NADPH to position 7 of 5,8-H_2-folate (Fig. 1). Thus when folate is the substrate, the first step of the reduction would be the transfer of a hydride ion to position 7 of folate to form H_2-folate. Subsequently rearrangement would take place and another hydride ion from NADPH would be transferred again to position 7 to form H_4-folate. This hypothesis was based on the observation, which will be discussed later, that intramolecular rearrangement takes place during the dithionite reduction of H_2-folate. The preliminary studies of the enzymatic reduction also pointed to such rearrangement [17]. This, however, has been disproved by the results obtained by Pastore, who unequivocally demonstrated by NMR techniques that deuterium from NADPH was found in position 6 of folinic acid prepared by the enzymatic reduction of H_2-folate followed by formylation [18]. We have reinvestigated our earlier results with the use of more refined radioactive techniques and a model compound, 7-methyl-H_2-folate. The rearrangement occurring during the dithionite reduction could thus be confirmed; however the original concept, that rearrangement takes place during the enzymatic reduction, has been disproved. In the subsequent paragraphs our isotope studies of the mechanism of the chemical reduction of H_2-folate and enzymatic reduction of folate and H_2-folate will be presented. Also, some kinetic and thermodynamic studies designed to elucidate the mechanism of binding of NADPH to the reductase in the presence of folate and H_2-folate respectively, will be discussed.

Use of hydrogen isotopes for study of the mechanism of a reaction has the disadvantage of extremely strong isotope effects. This is especially true if incorporation or removal of tritium from a carbon atom which carries more than one hydrogen is being followed. In order to avoid this effect, which frequently hampered our earlier studies of the mechanism of reduction of H_2-folate, we decided to use a model compound 7-methyl-H_2-folate (Fig. 2). This

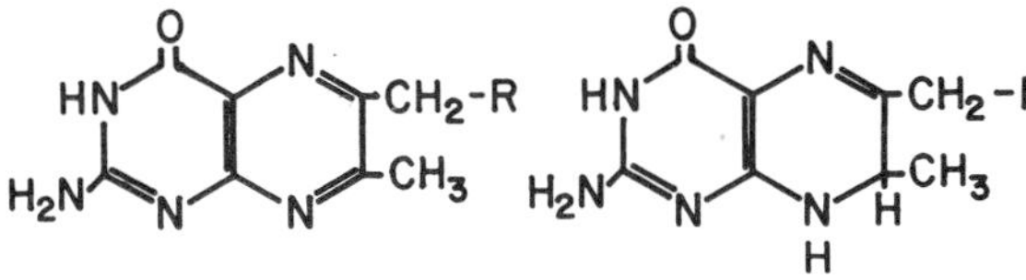

7-METHYLFOLATE   7-METHYL-
                                  7,8-DIHYDROFOLATE
R = p—Aminobenzoate

Figure 2. Structural formulas of 7-methylfolate and 7-methyldihydrofolate.

compound has only one hydrogen in position 7 and no hydrogen in position 6. Thus, the incorporation or removal of tritium in or from these positions could be easily studied.

All enzymatic studies described below were performed with a crude enzyme preparation from cultured cells of Sarcoma 180 strain AT/3000 [1].

Preparation of 7-methylfolate

7-Methylfolate was prepared according to a published procedure [19]. This compound closely resembles folate in its physical and chemical properties. It is a strong competitive inhibitor ($K_i = 1\cdot3 \times 10^{-6}$M) of dihydrofolate reductase; however, unlike folate it is not reduced by this enzyme [20].

Attempts to reduce 7-methylfolate to 7-methyl-H_2-folate with dithionite at room as well as at elevated temperature were unsuccessful. However, it could be reduced with zinc in alkaline solution [20]. The crude material was then purified by chromatography on DEAE cellulose. Purified 7-methyl-H_2-folate had an ultraviolet spectrum identical with that of H_2-folate and gave correct elemental analysis [20].

7-Methyl-H_2-folate as a substrate and inhibitor of dihydrofolate reductase

7-Methyl-H_2-folate is a substrate for dihydrofolate reductase and is reduced to 7-methyl-H_4-folate. Not only is this compound reduced at a slower rate than H_2-folate but also the kinetics of this reduction appear somewhat peculiar (Fig.

52   S. F. ZAKRZEWSKI

3). Two reaction rates are evident. The initial fast reaction is followed by a slow one. Assuming the molar extinction coefficient (ϵ_{340}) for this reaction to be the same as that for reduction of H_2-folate and extrapolating the slow and fast rates to a common intercept it could be estimated that 46% of the substrate was reduced at the faster rate. Since carbon 7 of 7-methyl-H_2-folate is asymmetric, it appears that each isomer is reduced at a different rate. The ratio of the fast rate

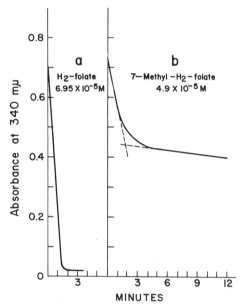

Figure 3. Change of absorbance versus time during the enzymatic reduction of: (a) H_2-folate; (b) 7-methyl-H_2-folate.

Each cuvette contains: 0·05M phosphate buffer pH 6, 1·22 x 10^{-4}M NADPH cell extract of S-180 (enzyme concentration a/b = 1/10), and H_2-folate and 7-methyl-H_2-folate as indicated in a total volume of 1 ml. The change in absorbance at 340 mμ was recorded with a Cary 14 spectrophotometer at room temperature.

to that of the slow one was estimated to be about 70. Since 7-methyl-H_2-folate has another asymmetric carbon in the L-glutamate portion of the molecule, an attempt has been made to separate the two stereoisomers (A—the more active and B—the less active) by chromatography on DEAE-cellulose acetate. The elution was carried out with a linear gradient consisting of 1% 2-mercapto-ethanol in the mixing flask and 2·0M ammonium acetate, containing 1% 2-mercaptoethanol in the reservoir. The ultraviolet absorption of the effluent was monitored and recorded with an automatic recording device (Uvicord). A single broad peak was obtained. This peak was divided into four segments (I-IV). The individual fractions in each segment were pooled and evaporated *in vacuo* until most of the ammonium acetate was removed. The content of 7-methyl-H_2-

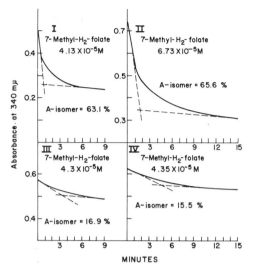

Figure 4. Change in absorbance versus time during the enzymatic reduction of different fractions of 7-methyl-H$_2$-folate. Conditions as in Fig. 3.

folate in each of the four fractions was determined spectrophotometrically and each fraction was assayed as substrate for dihydrofolate reductase. From the plots presented in Fig. 4 the proportion of the A-isomer in each fraction could be calculated. It can be seen that the A-isomer is enriched in fractions I and II, and the B-isomer is enriched in fractions III and IV. Fractions I-IV were also assayed as inhibitors of dihydrofolate reductase in the presence of H$_2$-folate as a substrate. As expected, they were competitive inhibitors (Fig. 5). The K_i values

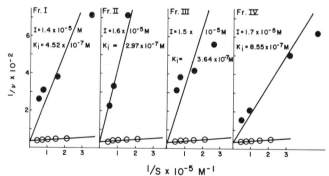

Figure 5. Inhibition of the reduction of H$_2$-folate by different fractions of 7-methyl-H$_2$-folate.

Each cuvette contains: 0·05M phosphate buffer pH 6, 1·15 x 10^{-4}M NADPH, cell extract of S-180 (amount which reduces 2·3 x 10^{-6}M H$_2$-folate per min), H$_2$-folate and 7-methyl-H$_2$-folate as indicated in a total volume of 1 ml. Otherwise the experiment was conducted as in Fig. 3.

were: 4·52, 2·97, 3·64 and 8·6 × 10⁻⁷M, respectively. The mean values are: for fractions I and II (enriched A-isomer) 3·8 x 10^{-7}M and for fractions III and IV (enriched B-isomer) 6·1 x 10^{-7}M. Thus it appears that both isomers have about the same affinity for the enzyme, yet they are reduced at considerably different rates. Table 1 shows comparisons of some kinetic constants for folate, H_2-folate, 7-methyl-folate and 7-methyl-H_2-folate.

Table 1. Comparison of some kinetic constants for folate, H_2-folate, 7-methylfolate and 7-methyl-H_2-folate.

Compound	K_m (M x 10^6)	Turnover number (min⁻¹) pH 6	pH 7	K_i (M x 10^6)
Folate	4·0	7·2	–	–
7-Methylfolate	not a substrate			1·33
H_2-Folate	6·1	226	–	–
7-Methyl-H_2-folate				
Isomer A	–	37*	4·6*	0·38
Isomer B	–	0·5*	–	0·61

* These values were estimated by comparing the rate of reduction with that of H_2-folate.
–These values were not determined.

Preparation of tritiated 7-methyl-H_2-folate

When zinc reduction of 7-methylfolate was carried out in the presence of tritiated water, highly radioactive 7-methyl-H_2-folate was isolated. Although this reaction involves hydrogenation of the 7,8-double bond, part of the tritium was incorporated in positions other than at carbon 7. Table 2 represents the results of experiments in which several preparations of tritiated 7-methyl-H_2-folate

Table 2. Incorporation of tritium into 7-methyl-H_2-folate.

Source of tritium, H_2O (³H)	Specific activity			Total tritium	
	7-Methyl-H_2-folate	7-Methyl-folate	Lost on oxidation	At C-7	Other positions
C/mole		C/mole		%	
0·9	0·294	0·164	0·130	44	56
0·9	0·010*	0·003	0·007	70	30
0·9	0·017*	0·006	0·011	65	35
0·225	0·074	0·054	0·020	27	73

* These samples were diluted with non-radioactive 7-methyl-H_2-folate before purification; thus, the yield of the tritium incorporation cannot be ascertained from these two samples.

were oxidized to 7-methylfolate. During this reaction tritium from position 7 should be entirely eliminated. Thus, tritium which was retained in 7-methylfolate must have been incorporated elsewhere. The distribution of tritium between carbon 7 and other positions seems to be, among other factors, dependent on the specific activity of tritiated water used in the reaction. At low specific activity a high percentage of tritium was incorporated outside carbon 7. It has been established by further degradation of 7-methylfolate that, of the remaining radioactivity, 66% was at C-9 and the rest in the 7-methyl group [20].

Mechanism of reduction of 7-methyl-H_2-folate to 7-methyl-H_4-folate
The tritiated 7-methyl-H_2-folate could be used to study the mechanism of reduction of this compound to its tetrahydro derivative. As has been mentioned before, 7-methyl-H_2-folate has only one hydrogen at carbon 7. Thus, when 7-methyl-H_2-folate tritiated at position 7 is reduced to 7-methyl-H_4-folate, all tritium should be removed from position 7 if the reduction is preceded by a rearrangement. No tritium, however, should be removed if the reduction proceeds through the direct addition of hydrogen to the 5,6-double bond. Tritiated 7-methyl-H_2-folate has been reduced by four different methods:
   (a) reduction with dithionite at 70°C;
   (b) reduction with borohydride at room temperature;
   (c) catalytic hydrogenation in water;
   (d) enzymatically.
In cases (a)-(c) the product of each reaction was purified by chromatography on DEAE cellulose acetate, using acetic acid containing 2-mercaptoethanol as eluant [21]. In case (d) the crude reaction mixture was purified on Sephadex G-25 to remove the bulk of the protein. The fractions containing low molecular weight material, essentially free of protein, were combined and purified on a DEAE-cellulose column as described for experiments (a)-(c). In each case 7-methyl-H_4-folate was obtained. The identity of 7-methyl-H_4-folate was established by comparing its properties with that of H_4-folate. Both compounds could be eluted from a DEAE-acetate column with acetic acid, had identical ultraviolet spectra, released diazotizable amine upon oxidation in acid and could be converted to the corresponding 5,10-methenyl-derivatives by formylation. It can be seen from the data presented in Table 3 that the reduction with dithionite (Exp. 1 and 2) led to the loss of tritium equivalent to that present at carbon 7. On the contrary, there was practically no loss of tritium during the catalytic hydrogenation and enzymatic reduction of 7-methyl-H_2-folate. The reduction with borohydride falls between these two extreme cases. Under this condition an equivalent of about 40-45% of tritium present at carbon 7 was removed. There is no direct proof in the case of the dithionite reduction that tritium was actually removed from position 7. It is, however, noteworthy to mention, that in each individual experiment the amount of tritium removed is proportional to

Table 3. Change in tritium content upon reduction of tritiated 7-methyl-H_2-folate to 7-methyl-H_4-folate.

Exp. No.	Type of reduction	7-Methyl-H_2-folate		Radioactivity lost upon reduction to 7-methyl-H_4-folate		
		Total specific activity	Specific activity at C-7	Specific activity	% of total	% of activity at C-7
		$C/mole \times 10^2$		$C/mole \times 10^2$		
1	$S_2O_4^=$	29·4	13·0	13·2	45	101
2	$S_2O_4^=$	7·4	2·0	2·2	30	110
3	H_2, PtO_2 in H_2O	1·7	1·1	0·1	6	9
4	BH_4^-	7·4	2·0	0·9	12	45
5	BH_4^-	1·0	0·7	0·3	30	43
6	Enzyme	2·8	0·8	0	0	0

that at C-7 rather than to the total tritium. This seems to indicate that tritium was indeed removed from carbon 7. On the basis of these experiments it can be concluded that the reduction with dithionite is indeed preceded by an intramolecular rearrangement. The enzymatic reduction, on the other hand, proceeds by the direct addition of hydride ion from NADPH to carbon 6.

Mechanism of the enzymatic reduction of folate

The next question to be answered was: How is folate reduced by dihydrofolate reductase? Several possibilities had to be considered.

(1) NADPH is located on the enzyme with the nicotinamide ring perpendicular to the pteridine ring with its carbon 4 between C-6 and C-7 of folate. In this way NADPH transfers hydrogen from the A side to C-6 and from the B side to C-7.

(2) The reduction of folate proceeds through a transfer of a hydride from NADPH (either A or B side) to carbon 7. H_2-Folate is formed first. This compound is subsequently reduced by another molecule of NADPH to H_4-folate.

(3) The reduction proceeds through an intermediate other than H_2-folate. To check which of these possibilities is true, the reduction of folate by dihydrofolate reductase was carried out, in one case with NADPH tritiated at the A side and in another case at the B side. To obtain the specifically labelled NADPH, NADP ($4-H^3$) was reduced with either glucose-6-phosphate dehydrogenase or isocitrate dehydrogenase. In the former reaction, hydrogen is introduced on the B side, thus the label moves to the A side. In the latter case the opposite is true. The

enzymatic reduction of folate led in each case to the formation of H_4-folate. This product was isolated and purified as described above for 7-methyl-H_4-folate. To determine the distribution of tritium, H_4-folate was oxidized to H_2-folate [17]. Tritium from carbon 6 was eliminated during this reaction. H_2-Folate thus obtained was purified by recrystallization before determination of

Table 4. Transfer of tritium from A and B sides of NADPH, respectively, during the enzymatic reduction of folate.

Reaction	Relative specific activity				
	NADP	H_4-folate*	H_2-folate (C-7)	H_4-folate − H_2-folate (C-6)	Folate
NADPH³-A + H_2-Folate	—	100	4·4	96	0
NADPH³-A + Folate	152	100	15	85	11
NADPH³-A + Folate	124	100	17	83	—
NADPH³-B + Folate	124	2·3	—	—	—
S_2O_4 = + Folate + ³H_2O			15		11·6

NADPH³-A and NADPH³-B = NADPH labelled with tritium on A or B side, respectively.
* The actual specific activities were, from top to bottom: $38·6 \times 10^{-3}$, $8·7 \times 10^{-3}$, $21·7 \times 10^{-3}$ and $0·5 \times 10^{-3}$ curie/mole.
— These values were not determined.

its radioactivity. To make sure that the radioactivity of H_2-folate is not due to some contaminants, the compound was further oxidized to folate. The latter compound was purified by chromatography on DEAE cellulose. Comparison with a synthetic H_2-folate labelled at C-7 indicates that during the latter oxidation about 20-30% of tritium (instead of a theoretically expected 50%) is eliminated.

The results of the experiments described above are summarized in Table 4. When H_2-folate is reduced with NADPH³-A, tritium is transferred to carbon 6. After reoxidation to H_2-folate only 4% of tritium was retained. Upon further oxidation even this small quantity disappeared. Thus, in this case tritium was incorporated only at C-6. When folate is reduced with NADPH³-A, 80% of tritium from NADPH is found in H_4-folate (lines 2 and 3); 84% of this amount is found at C-6 and 16% at C-7. It can be seen that 75% of tritium at C-7 is retained upon oxidation of H_2-folate to folate, indicating that it was truly incorporated into this position (compare with the last line of Table 4). The fact that the distribution of tritium between C-6 and C-7 is 84 to 16 and not 50 to 50 indicates merely that greater isotope discrimination occurs during the transfer of hydrogen to C-7 than to C-6. This phenomenon may be related to the observation that the activation energy with H_2-folate as substrate is higher than that with folate as substrate. In contrast, when folate is reduced with NADPH[3]-B, only a negligible amount of radioactivity is incorporated in H_4-folate. On the basis of these experiments it may be concluded that: The first step in the reduction of folate is transfer of hydrogen from A side of NADPH to

6

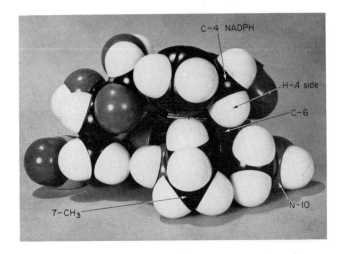

7

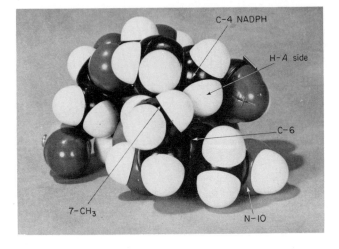

Figure 6 and Figure 7. Suggested positioning of NADPH and two isomers of 7-methyl-H_2-folate in the active complex with the enzyme.

carbon 7. H_2-Folate is thus formed which is subsequently reduced to H_4-folate. It has to be emphasized that in each case the same side of NADPH is involved in the reaction.

Possible location of NADPH on the enzyme

It has been mentioned previously that both isomeric forms of 7-methyl-H_2-folate are bound to dihydrofolate reductase with about the same strength. Yet one of the isomers is reduced to 7-methyl-H_4-folate 70 times faster than the other. Since it has been shown that the reduction of 7-methyl-H_2-folate involves transfer of hydride ion from NADPH to carbon 6, the question arises why the configuration on carbon 7 should affect this reaction. The difference in the rate of reaction between H_2-folate and its 7-methylderivative is to be expected. The 7-methyl group does not seem to disturb the affinity of the analogue to the enzyme, but certainly may have an effect on the electron distribution in the pyrazine ring. This effect, however, should be identical for both isomers. One possible explanation of this phenomenon is that the 7-methyl group may interfere with the proper positioning of NADPH with respect to 7-methyl-H_2-folate. We may imagine that NADPH rests with its nicotinamide ring parallel and on top of the pyrazine ring. In this configuration hydrogen on the A side of carbon 4 touches directly carbon 6 of 7-methyl-H_2-folate (Fig. 6). It can be seen from the model presented in Fig. 7 that, if the 7-methyl is facing NADPH, this configuration is greatly distorted, though the direct contact between hydrogen at C-4 of NADPH and C-6 of the pteridine is still possible.

Kinetic studies with NADPH in the presence of folate and H_2-folate, respectively

It has been thought that additional information concerning the binding of NADPH to the enzyme could be obtained from kinetic studies. The following alternatives had to be considered:

(1) NADPH which reduces both folate as well as H_2-folate is bound to the same site on the enzyme. If NADPH is indeed located with respect to H_2-folate as presented in the model, it can be easily imagined that by turning the nicotinamide ring horizontally by $60°$ its hydrogen at C-4 could be brought in contact with C-7 of folate. Such movement could be brought about by slight conformational changes of the enzyme. In this case the single binding site for NADPH would be available on the enzyme and the conformation of the enzyme would change depending on whether folate or H_2-folate is the substrate.

(2) The other alternative was that two different sites for NADPH are available, one specific for reduction of folate, the other for H_2-folate. If this alternative is true, the further question arises: In the case when folate is the substrate, do both NADPH molecules bind to the enzyme simultaneously or in

sequence, i.e. first folate is reduced to H_2-folate, then the second molecule of NADPH reduces H_2-folate to H_4-folate? To answer these questions the effect of NADPH concentration on the rate of reduction of folate and H_2-folate, respectively, has been studied at different temperatures. In these experiments folate and H_2-folate, respectively, were present at optimal concentrations. The K_m and V_{max} values at different temperatures were determined. It has been noted that with both substrates (folate and H_2-folate) the changes of K_m values followed closely the changes of V_{max} values. Thus it appears that we are dealing here with a steady state rather than with an equilibrium system. Under such circumstances the K_m values do not represent true dissociation constants of the

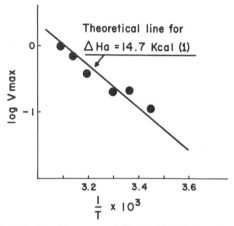

Figure 8. Plot of log V_{max} versus $1/T$ with H_2-folate as the substrate.

enzyme-NADPH complex and cannot be used for evaluation of thermodynamic parameters. Some information could be obtained, however, from the analyses of V_{max} values. It has to be pointed out that V_{max} values calculated from the plots of $1/v$ versus $1/\text{NADPH}$ in the presence of optimal concentration of H_2-folate should be identical with those calculated from the plots of $1/v$ versus $1/H_2$-folate in the presence of optimal concentration of NADPH. This is because in each case the V_{max} value represents the velocity at the optimal concentration of both the substrate and the cofactor. That this is indeed true in our case is demonstrated in Fig. 8. The experimental points represent the values of log V_{max} plotted against $1/T$. These values of V_{max} were obtained from plots of $1/v$ versus $1/\text{NADPH}$ at optimal concentration of H_2-folate. The slope of the line fitted to the experimental points was taken from our earlier paper. In this case, however, the V_{max} values were determined from the plots of $1/v$ versus $1/H_2$-folate at optimal NADPH concentrations. Although there was some pH difference between the earlier (pH 5·35) and the present (pH 6) studies, the fit is remarkably good. When the effect of NADPH concentration on the rate of reduction of folate was studied the situation was more complicated. First of all, if the reaction involves sequential addition of NADPH to the enzyme, the normal $1/v$ versus $1/NADPH$ plot should be satisfactory. This is because in the reaction sequence the first reaction seems to be the rate-limiting one.

(1) Folate + NADPH + H$^+$ $\xrightarrow{\text{Enz.}}$ H$_2$-folate + NADP

(2) H$_2$-folate + NADPH + H$^+$ $\xrightarrow{\text{Enz.}}$ H$_4$-folate + NADP

Thus only the kinetics of this reaction are being studied. If, however, the reaction involves simultaneous addition of NADPH then the following equation is true:

$$\text{Folate} + 2\,\text{NADPH} + 2\text{H}^+ + \rightarrow \text{H}_4\text{-folate} + 2\,\text{NADP}$$

In this case the equilibrium equation for the interaction of NADPH and the enzyme takes the following form:

$$\frac{[\text{Enz.}] \times [\text{NADPH}]^2}{[\text{Enz.} - (\text{NADPH})^2]} = K$$

and the plot of $1/v$ versus $1/NADPH^2$ should satisfy the Michaelis Menton equation. The V_{max} values at different temperatures were thus calculated by both methods, $1/v$ versus $1/NADPH$ and $1/v$ versus $1/NADPH^2$ and their logarithms were plotted versus $1/T$ (Fig. 9). At the temperature of 40°C ($T = 313°$, $1/T = 3.19 \times 10^{-3}$) only the $1/v$ versus $1/NADPH^2$ plot gave a sensible V_{max} and K_m value. At other temperatures both ways of plotting were possible but in general a better fit of the straight line between the experimental points was obtained by plotting $1/v$ versus $1/NADPH^2$ at higher temperatures

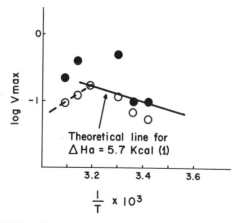

Figure 9. Plot of log V_{max} versus $1/T$ with folate as the substrate.
O—Determined from the plots $1/v$ versus $1/S^2$.
●—Determined from the plots $1/v$ versus $1/S$.

and $1/v$ versus $1/$NADPH at lower temperatures. The differences, however, were not great enough to decide objectively which way of plotting is applicable. The principle, mentioned earlier, that the V_{max} values should be the same no matter which of the two reactants is the variable one, was applied to distinguish between the real and unreal V_{max} values. The slope of the line fitted to the experimental points was taken from our earlier paper. In this case the V_{max} values were determined from the plots of $1/v$ versus $1/$folate at optimal NADPH concentration. It appears that at $20°$ and $25°C$ the theoretical line fits the experimental points obtained from linear plots ($1/v$ versus $1/$NADPH). At higher temperatures, however, the points obtained from the plots of $1/v$ versus $1/$NADPH^2 fall closer to the theoretical line than those obtained from linear plots. This observation could be interpreted as an indication that between $25°$ and $30°C$ the sequential addition of NADPH to the enzyme-folate complex changes into the simultaneous one. Other interpretations, however, are also possible and therefore this point cannot be established with certainty. Further it can be seen that above $40°C$ the rate of the reduction starts to decrease. There is nothing surprising about the fact that the reaction rate decreases with increasing temperature above $40°C$. This can be explained by the progressive denaturation of the enzyme at elevated temperature. It is surprising however that this denaturation occurs only with folate as substrate and not with H_2-folate. Since the site of binding of folate and H_2-folate to the enzyme is supposedly the same it appears that NADPH occupies two different positions, one appearing to be more heat sensitive than the other. It has been observed that when both folate and NADPH were at optimal concentrations, no decrease of activity between $40°$ and $50°C$ occurred. Thus it appears that the protection against thermal denaturation depends on the concentration of NADPH. The relative strength of binding of NADPH to the corresponding sites on the enzyme may be the deciding factor in the selective protection of these sites against thermal denaturation.

CONCLUSIONS

Following conclusions can be drawn from the above studies. Two NADPH molecules are involved in the reduction of folate to H_4-folate, the first one transfers the hydride ion to position 7, the other one to position 6. There are indications that both molecules may be bound to the enzyme-folate complex simultaneously. If this is the case, they must be far enough from each other so that the binding of one does not interfere with the binding of the other. It has been shown that the methyl group in position 7 of 7-methyl-H_2-folate interferes with the binding of NADPH. Thus it is not likely that two bulky groups like that of nicotinamide could be located on the same side of the folate molecule. It must then be assumed that folate is in between two NADPH molecules lined up with their 4 positions towards C-6 and C-7 of folate, respectively. At low temperatures the coiling of the enzyme protein is so tight that only the substrate and one molecule of NADPH could fit at one time. With increasing temperature the coiling becomes less tight and thus at 30°C it could be possible to accommodate simultaneously folate and two molecules of NADPH. With further increase of the temperature the progressive uncoiling leads to gradual denaturation. NADPH seems to protect the site responsible for the reduction of H_2-folate better than that responsible for the reduction of folate.

The need for comparative studies of the denaturation process of different dihydrofolate reductases is evident.

ACKNOWLEDGEMENT

This investigation was supported in part by Research Grant CA-02906 from the National Cancer Institute of the United States Public Health Service.

REFERENCES

1. Zakrzewski, S. F., Hakala, M. T. and Nichol, C. A., *Molec. Pharmac.* 2 (1966) 423.
2. Morales, D. R. and Greenberg, D. M., *Biochim. biophys. Acta* 85 (1964) 360.
3. Bertino, J. R., Perkins, J. P. and Johns, D. G., *Biochemistry, N.Y.* 4 (1965) 839.
4. Kaufman, B. T. and Gardiner, R. C., *J. biol. Chem.* 241 (1966) 1319.
5. Greenberg, D. M., Bui-Duy Tam, Jenny, E. and Pages B., *Biochim. biophys. Acta* 122 (1966) 423.
6. Perkins, J. P., Hillcoat, B. L. and Bertino, J. R., *J. biol. Chem.* 242 (1967) 4771.
7. Sirotnak, F. M., Donati, G. J. and Hutchison, D. J., *J. biol. Chem.* 239 (1964) 2677
8. Kessel, D. and Roberts, D., *Biochemistry, N.Y.* 4 (1965) 2631.
9. Blakley, R. L. and Hillcoat, B. L., *J. biol. Chem.* 241 (1966) 2995.
10. Burchall, J. J. and Hitchings, G. H., *Molec. Pharmac.* 1 (1965) 126.
11. Ferone, R., Burchall, J. J. and Hitchings, G. H., *Fedn Proc. Fedn Am. Socs exp. Biol.* 27 (1968) 390.
12. Jaffe, J. J., McCormack, J. J. Jr., and Gutteridge, W. E., *Fedn Proc. Fedn Am. Socs exp. Biol.* 27 (1968) 660.
13. Futterman, S., *J. biol. Chem.* 228 (1957) 1031.
14. Silverman, M. and Noronha, J. M., *Biochem. biophys. Res. Commun.* 4 (1961) 180.
15. Pastore, E. J. and Friedkin, M., *J. biol. Chem.* 237 (1962) 3802.
16. Blakley, R. L., Ramarastri, B. V. and McDougall, B. M., *J. biol. Chem.* 238 (1963) 3075.
17. Zakrzewski, S. F., *J. biol. Chem.* 241 (1966) 2962.
18. Pastore, E. J. and Williamson, K. L., *Fedn Proc. Fedn Am Socs exp. Biol.* 27 (1968) 764.
19. Boothe, J. H., Mowat, J. H., Waller, C. W., Angier, R. B., Semb, J. and Gazzola, A. L., *J. Am. chem. Soc.* 74 (1952) 5407.
20. Zakrzewski, S. F. and Sansone, A., *J. biol. Chem.* 242 (1967) 5661.
21. Zakrzewski, S. F. *J. biol. Chem.* 241 (1967) 2957.

FEBS Symposium, Volume 16, 1969, pp. 65-80

The Application of Antifolics to the Study of Folate Interconverting Enzymes of Different Origin

K. SLAVÍK, V. SLAVÍKOVÁ, K. MOTYČKA and E. HERMANOVÁ

*Laboratory of Protein Metabolism, School of Medicine,
Charles University; and Institute of Haematology and
Blood Transfusion, Prague, Czechoslovakia*

SUMMARY

A comparative study has been performed on the effect of various tetrahydrofolate analogues on thymidylate synthetase variants from *E. coli*, calf thymus and Sarcoma 180. Both animal enzyme variants differ from the bacterial one in the reactivity of the 2,4-diaminopyrimidine moiety of tetrahydroaminopterin derivatives and by different interaction of the *p*-aminobenzoylglutamic acid residue with the enzyme. The enzyme from Sarcoma 180 differs from the calf thymus enzyme in its different mode of binding of the *p*-aminobenzoic acid part of tetrahydrofolate, by a stronger binding of the 2,4-diaminopyrimidine moiety, and by a different effect of the substituents at the atom N_5. The results provide some evidence for different arrangements of reactive areas of thymidylate synthetase of differing origin. Several new types of folic acid analogues— isohomofolic acid, azahomofolic acid and azahomoaminopterin—were prepared. Tetrahydroderivatives of isohomofolic acid and azahomoaminopterin are weak inhibitors of calf thymus thymidylate synthetase. Azahomoaminopterin and related compounds are strong cytostatics for HeLa cells in tissue culture but they are relatively non-toxic for mice. This group of compounds appeared to provide a suitable tool for investigating the binding specifity of folate reductase.

INTRODUCTION

The principal mode of action of the known folic acid antimetabolites has been exhaustively investigated in the course of the past twenty years, but little attention has been paid to the differences in their interaction with folate interconverting enzymes of different origin. Hitchings and Burchall [1] pin-pointed the sites in 2,4-diaminopteridine molecules essential to the growth inhibition of certain bacteria, and other sites where species differences could be observed. Baker and Ho [2, 3] compared the inhibitory effect of some 1,2-dihydro-S-triazines for folate reductase from pigeon liver and *E. coli* and they found considerable differences between the bacterial and animal variants. In order to provide more information on this subject, the interaction of several tetrahydrofolate analogues with enzymes controlling, or at least limiting, DNA synthesis has been investigated.

The purpose of this study was to determine whether an enzyme catalysing essentially the same reaction in different types of cells differs in the arrangement of the binding sites and catalytic groups. Structural analogues of natural substrates or coenzymes seemed to be suitable tools for this purpose because their different mode of binding to the enzyme variants would provide indirect evidence for the different arrangements of the active centres of the variants studied.

Thymidylate synthetases of different origin, i.e. *E. coli,* calf thymus and Sarcoma 180, were used as models for this study because this enzyme seems to regulate, or at least to limit, DNA synthesis. Different tetrahydrofolate analogues were applied for this comparative study of enzyme variants because some information about the coenzyme and inhibitor specifity has already been provided by Friedkin *et al.* [4, 5] and our previous experiments [6].

EXPERIMENTAL PART

Materials

Tetrahydroaminopterin, tetrahydroamethopterin, their $3',5'$-dichloroderivatives, $3',5'$-dichlorotetrahydrofolic acid, tetrahydrofolic acid, 4-aminotetrahydro-pteroic acid, $2',4'$-diaminotetrahydropteridine, C^7-methyltetrahydrofolic acid, N^5-methyltetrahydrofolic acid, and N^5-formyltetrahydrofolic acid were prepared from recrystallized commercial preparations by catalytic hydrogeniza-tion in glacial acetic acid as described previously [6, 7], and subsequent precipitation of the products by a 20-fold excess of anhydrous ether in a large chromatographic chamber filled with carbon dioxide. The preparations thus obtained were checked for purity (especially for the presence of dihydroderiva-tives) by chromatography on a DEAE celulose column using a linear gradient of water and 2M ammonium bicarbonate for elution. In this way all tetrahydro-derivatives were found to be almost 90% pure and they contained about 5-7% dihydroderivatives [8].

Azahomotetrahydrofolic acid, azahomotetrahydroaminopterin, and iso-homotetrahydrofolic acid (Fig. 1) were synthetized in our laboratory by a route described elsewhere [8, 9].

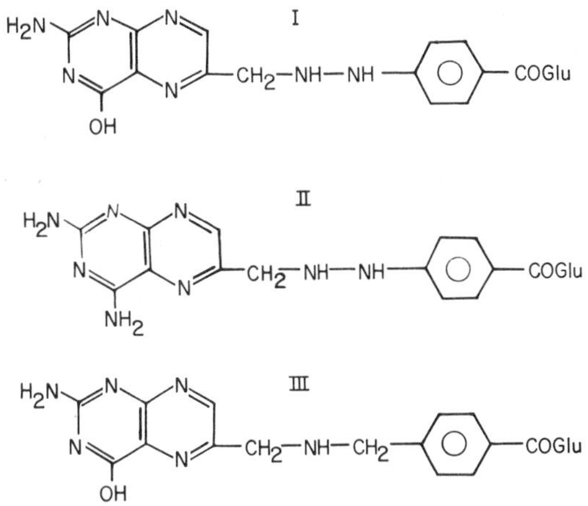

Figure 1. Formulas of some new folate analogues used for the comparative study of enzyme inhibition.
  I. Azahomofolic acid (NHF)
  II. Azahomoaminopterin (NHAP)
  III. Isohomofolic acid $(CH_2{}^{10}F)$

Enzyme preparations

Thymidylate synthetase from *E. coli* was prepared from bacteria harvested at the end of the logarithmic growth phase as described in our earlier communication [6].

The calf thymus enzyme was prepared from organs frozen in dry ice immediately after collection, in the following manner:

150 g of thymus was homogenized in 800 ml of 0·1M Tris-HCl buffer pH 7·5 and centrifuged at 35,000 g. The turbid and viscous supernatant was freed of nucleic acids and clarified by addition of 200 ml of 5% streptomycine sulphate solution. The clear supernatant was fractioned by addition of solid ammonium sulphate and the fraction between 40-60% saturation, containing the enzyme, was separated by centrifugation. The precipitate was dissolved in 50 ml 0·1M Tris-HCl buffer pH 7·5 and kept in the frozen state. The preparation was stable for 2-3 weeks in the frozen state.

The Sarcoma 180 enzyme and thymidylate synthetase from other tumours were partially purified in a similar manner. The ascitic form of all tumours investigated, transplanted on H strain mice, were used as the starting material. The ascitic cells were separated from the ascitic fluid (collected 9 days after transplantation) by centrifugation, then washed twice with saline, disrupted by homogenization in a Potter-Elvehjem homogenizer, and the enzyme purified in the same manner as that from thymus.

Determination of enzyme activity

The enzyme activity was assayed by the modified spectrophotometric method of Wahba and Friedkin [10].

For the *E. coli* enzyme the incubation mixture contained $0.83\,\mu$mole of tetrahydrofolic acid, $48.3\,\mu$moles of Tris-HCl buffer, pH 7.4, $13.5\,\mu$moles of formaldehyde, $25\,\mu$moles of $MgCl_2$, $50\,\mu$moles of mercaptoethanol, and $1\,\mu$mole of deoxyuridylic acid, in a total volume of 1.1 ml. The reaction was started by the addition of deoxyuridylate and was continued for 15 min at 20°C. The change in optical density at 338 nm was measured in a Beckman DU spectrophotometer; the incubation mixture without deoxyuridylate served as blank.

For the thymus and Sarcoma 180 enzymes the incubation mixture contained $0.25\,\mu$mole of tetrahydrofolic acid, $48.3\,\mu$moles of Tris-HCl buffer, pH 7.4, $0.5\,\mu$mole of formaldehyde, $50\,\mu$moles of mercaptoethanol, and $1\,\mu$mole of deoxyuridylic acid, in a total volume of 1.1 ml. The measurement was performed in the same way as for the bacterial enzyme.

Assay for coenzyme activity

The analogues to be tested for their coenzyme activity were added in place of tetrahydrofolic acid at equimolecular amounts to the incubation mixture, containing $0.75\,\mu$mole of the analogue, $1.5\,\mu$moles of [^{14}C]formaldehyde ($3.2\,\mu$C), $150\,\mu$moles of mercaptoethanol, $3\,\mu$moles of deoxyuridylic acid, and $150\,\mu$moles of sodium barbital buffer, pH 7.6, in a total volume of 3.5 ml. After an incubation for 1 hour at 22°C, the mixture was deproteinized with an equal volume of 20% trichloroacetic acid and, after removal of protein by centrifugation, the supernatant was extracted three times with 10 ml portions of ether. The aqueous phase was brought to pH 8 with 2N ammonia and 0.05 ml of bacterial alkaline phosphatase solution (2000 units) were added in order to convert nucleotides to nucleosides, and incubated at 22°C for 30 min. Then 0.25 ml of 2% ferric chloride solution in 2N HCl was added and the mixture heated for 30 min at 100°C in order to destroy excess of formaldehyde and radioactive tetrahydrofolate derivatives.

Finally the mixture was evaporated to dryness in a flash evaporator, the residue dissolved in 0.2 ml water, and $2\,\mu$moles of thymidine added as a carrier.

The solution was transferred quantitatively to a preparative paper chromatogram on Whatman 3 MM paper and chromatographed with *n*-butanol saturated with 5% aqueous ammonia. After detection, the thymidine spot was eluted into 1 ml water, the eluate evaporated to dryness, dissolved in 0.2 ml water and counted in the Nuclear Chicago scintillation counter. The incubation mixture without deoxyuridylate served as the blank.

The coenzyme activities were compared with that of tetrahydrofolic acid whose activity was taken as 100%.

Determination of the inhibition constants

The inhibition constants for the various tetrahydrofolic acid analogues were calculated from the following equations:

$$\frac{1}{v} = \frac{K}{V}\left(1 + \frac{I}{K_I}\right)\frac{1}{A} + \frac{1}{V}$$

$$\text{for competitive inhibition (1)}$$

$$\frac{1}{v} = \frac{K}{V}\left(1 + \frac{I}{K_I}\right)\frac{1}{A} + \frac{1}{V}\left(1 + \frac{I}{K_I}\right)$$

$$\text{for non-competitive inhibition (2)}$$

$$\frac{1}{v} = \frac{K}{V}\left(\frac{1}{A}\right) + \frac{1}{V}\left(1 + \frac{I}{K_I}\right)$$

$$\text{for uncompetitive inhibition (3)}$$

where A = substrate concentration, I = inhibitor concentration, K = Michaelis constant, K_I = inhibition constant, V = maximal reaction velocity, and v = experimentally determined velocity [11].

RESULTS

The three species-different variants of thymidylate synthetase in enzymes from *E. coli,* calf thymus and mice Sarcoma 180 were compared mainly for their interaction with some analogues of tetrahydrofolic acid.

As regards the basic properties, the bacterial enzyme (*E. coli*) differs from both animal variants. The bacterial enzyme is activated by Mg^{2+} and SH reagents, whereas the animal variants are not. High concentrations of formaldehyde inhibit the animal variants but not the *E. coli* one. As shown in Fig. 2, tetrahydrofolate inhibits at higher concentrations both the thymus and tumour variants (from different types of ascitic tumours), whereas the *E. coli* enzyme is not affected.

Very little information about the individual differences has been obtained by a comparison of the artificial coenzyme activities of different tetrahydrofolate analogues (Table 1) for the thymus and *E. coli* variants. Minor changes in the molecule of tetrahydrofolate led either to the complete disappearance, or a decrease to a negligible fraction, of the coenzymatic activity in all enzyme variants studied. No significant differences could be observed between the animal and *E. coli* variants.

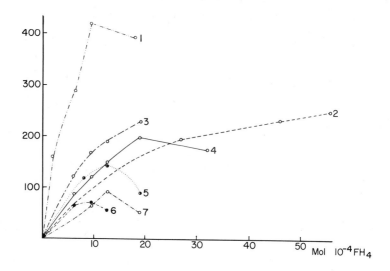

Figure 2. The effect of concentration of tetrahydrofolate on the activity of thymidylate synthetase originating from various sources.
1. Thymus enzyme
2. Enzyme from *E. coli* B
3. Enzyme from Sarcoma 180 (ascitic form)
4. Enzyme from Walker carcinoma
5. Enzyme from Ehrlich carcinoma
6. Enzyme from ascitic tumour P 288 (cortisol sensitive)
7. Enzyme from ascitic tumour P 1798
Ordinate: concentration of tetrahydrofolate Abscissa: Δ OD 338 nm after 20 min incubation.

Table 1. Comparison of coenzymic activities of some analogues of tetrahydrofolic acid on variants of thymidylate synthetase.

Compound	% of coenzymic activity of the enzyme	
	from *E. coli*	from S 180
Tetrahydrofolic acid	100	100
3'5'-dichlorotetrahydrofolic acid	0·6	0·95
C^7-methyltetrahydrofolic acid	1·4	4·7
Tetrahydrobiopterin	2·9	0
N^5-formyltetrahydrofolic acid	0	0
Tetrahydropteroylaspartic acid	1·6	0

More information could be obtained by determining the inhibitory activity of the derivatives tested. First, differences between the *E. coli* enzyme on the one hand, and both animal variants (i.e. the thymus and Sarcoma 180 enzyme) on the other, were demonstrated.

A qualitative difference could be shown in the case of 3',5'-dichlorotetra-hydrofolate, which appears to inhibit both the thymus and Sarcoma 180 enzymes with tetrahydrofolate (Fig. 3), whereas it does not inhibit the bacterial enzyme. Another difference has been shown in the case of 2,4-diaminotetrahydro-

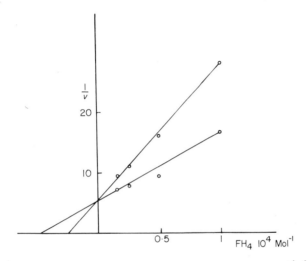

Figure 3. The type of inhibition of thymus thymidylate synthetase by 3',5'-dichlorotetra-hydrofolic acid demonstrated by the Lineweaver-Burk plot. Inhibitor concentration $5 \cdot 5 \times 10^{-5}$M. The reciprocal velocity is expressed in M^{-6} dihydrofolate formed per minute.

pteridine, which does not inhibit the *E. coli* enzyme, but is a non-competitive inhibitor of the thymus and Sarcoma 180 enzyme (Fig. 4).

Quantitatively both animal variants differ from the *E. coli* enzyme only in the case of inhibition with tetrahydroaminopterin, which is about 10 times a stronger inhibitor of both animal variants as compared with the bacterial one (Table 3).

As regards the type of inhibition, several differences could be observed between the animal and bacterial variants. Both the Sarcoma 180 and thymus enzymes are inhibited competitively with 3',5'-dichlorotetrahydroamethopterin, whereas the bacterial one is inhibited in a non-competitive manner. The quantitative differences in the K_I values are not striking (Table 2). This, however, assumes that the mentioned derivative inhibits the animal enzyme by competition with tetrahydrofolate whereas the bacterial variant is inhibited in a different manner.

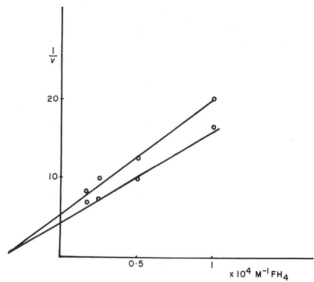

Figure 4. The type of inhibition of thymus thymidylate synthetase by the Lineweaver-Burk plot. Inhibitor concentration 5.5×10^{-5}M.

Up to the present, only the bacterial variant on the one hand, and two selected animal variants on the other, have been compared. Although the calf thymus enzyme is species specific with respect to that originating from Sarcoma 180, some differences between these two enzymes should be pointed out here.

All 4-aminoanalogues of tetrahydrofolate represented in Table 3 show a several-fold stronger inhibitory effect on the Sarcoma 180 enzyme than on the thymus variant. This makes it probable that the 2,4-diaminopteridine moiety is bound more tightly to the tumour variant.

The second difference can be shown in the case of N^5-methyltetrahydrofolate, which inhibits the thymus enzyme but not the Sarcoma 180 one. Other differences between the thymus and Sarcoma 180 enzymes can also be demonstrated in a different type of inhibition by tetrahydroamethopterin, which

Table 2. Inhibition of thymidylate synthetase from different sources by N^{10}-methyl-3′ 5′-dichlorotetrahydroaminopterin.

Source of Enzyme	K_I (M)	Type of Inhibition
E. coli	2.8×10^{-4}	non-competitive
Calf Thymus	3.4×10^{-4}	competitive
Sarcoma 180	9.2×10^{-5}	competitive

Table 3. The inhibition constants, concentrations causing 50% inhibitions, and type of inhibition of various tetrahydrofolate analogues for thymidylate synthetase of different origin.

Inhibitor	Thymus			E. coli			Sarcoma 180		
	C_i 50%	K_I	Type	C_i 50%	K_I	Type	C_i 50%	K_I	Type
Tetrahydroaminopterin	6.4×10^{-5}			1.0×10^{-5}	1.1×10^{-5}	non-competitive	6.0×10^{-6}	1.5×10^{-7}	non-competitive
Tetrahydroamethopterin	5.2×10^{-7}	2.0×10^{-6}	uncompetitive	3.5×10^{-6}	1.9×10^{-6}	non-competitive	2.4×10^{-7}	5.7×10^{-5}	competitive
Dichlorotetrahydroaminopterin	3.4×10^{-4}	1.4×10^{-4}	competitive	2.8×10^{-4}	8.0×10^{-5}	non-competitive	8.2×10^{-5}		
4-Aminotetrahydropteroic acid	1.2×10^{-3}	1.55×10^{-3}	non-competitive	6.7×10^{-4}	6.9×10^{-4}	non-competitive	2.5×10^{-4}		
2,4-Diaminotetrahydropteridine	1.25×10^{-3}	1.31×10^{-3}	non-competitive	5.0×10^{-4}	—	—	1.75×10^{-4}		
N^5Formyltetrahydrofolic acid	5.7×10^{-4}	6.0×10^{-4}	competitive	4.1×10^{-4}	2.5×10^{-4}	non-competitive	(1.54×10^{-4})		
N^5Methyltetrahydrofolic acid	6.8×10^{-4}			5×10^{-4}	0	—			
N^5Formyltetrahydroaminopterin	2.3×10^{-4}				—	—			
N^{10}Formyltetrahydroaminopterin	2.95×10^{-4}	1.05×10^{-4}	non-competitive		0	—			
Dichlorotetrahydrofolic acid	1.94×10^{-4}	1.4×10^{-4}	competitive	5×10^{-4}	0	—	8.9×10^{-5}		non-competitive
C^9Methyltetrahydrofolic acid				8.3×10^{-5}	7.9×10^{-5}	non-competitive	1.32×10^{-4}		
N^{10}Methyltetrahydrofolic acid				1.7×10^{-4}	6.3×10^{-5}	competitive	1.1×10^{-4}		
Tetrahydropteroylaspartic acid				5×10^{-4}	0	—	(7.7×10^{-5})		
C^7Methyltetrahydrofolic acid				3.6×10^{-4}	5.6×10^{-4}	non-competitive	2.3×10^{-4}		

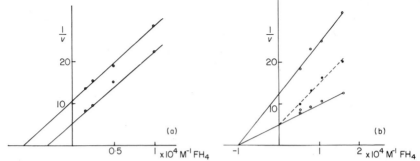

Figure 5. The type of inhibition of thymus (a) and Sarcoma 180 enzyme (b) by tetrahydroamethopterin (——) and $3',5'$-dichlorotetrahydroamethopterin (-----). Concentration of the inhibitors: tetrahydroamethopterin $2\cdot3 \times 10^{-7}$M for the Sarcoma 180 enzyme and $3\cdot4 \times 10^{-6}$M for the thymus enzyme.
$3',5'$-dichloroamethopterin was used in the concentration 1×10^{-4}M for the Sarcoma 180 enzyme.

is an uncompetitive inhibitor of the thymus enzyme and a non-competitive inhibitor of the Sarcoma 180 variant (Fig. 5). It is noteworthy that the inhibitory effect of tetrahydroamethopterin does not differ appreciably with the thymidylate synthetases isolated from various types of tumours, as shown in Table 4.

The foregoing findings stimulated further investigations in this area, for which other types of tetrahydrofolate analogues were necessary. Several new analogues with structural changes in the C_1-bearing moiety have been synthesized and applied to thymidylate synthetase specificity studies. From a group of substances prepared in our laboratory, the following will be discussed here: Azahomotetrahydrofolic acid (I), its 4-aminoanalogue-azahomotetrahydroaminopterin (II), and isohomotetrahydrofolic acid (III), (Fig. 1 shows the non-hydrogenated forms).

Concerning the basic biological properties of this group of substances, all of them proved to be relatively strong growth inhibitors of HeLa cells in tissue culture, but they showed only very little toxicity for mice, exceeding values of 50-100 mg/kg (administered in a single dose) as described elsewhere [8].

For thymidylate synthetase investigations the tetrahydroderivatives of the

Table 4. Inhibitory effect of tetrahydroamethopterin for some ascites mouse tumours.

Tumour	C_I 50% mole/1	K_I (M)	Type of inhibition with FH$_4$
Sarcoma 180	$2\cdot4 \times 10^{-7}$	$1\cdot5 \times 10^{-7}$	non-competitive
Tumour P 288, Cortisol-sensitive	$1\cdot95 \times 10^{-7}$	$2\cdot2 \times 10^{-7}$	non-competitive
Tumour P 1798	$1\cdot9 \times 10^{-7}$		
Walker's carcinoma	$2\cdot0 \times 10^{-7}$		

Table 5. Inhibition constants of azahomotetrahydrofolate, azahomoaminopterin and isohomotetrahydrofolate for thymidylate synthetase originating from different sources.

Inhibitor	Thymus	S 180	E. coli
Azahomotetrahydrofolic acid	no inhibition	$2\cdot25 \times 10^{-4}$	$2\cdot2 \times 10^{-4}$
Azahomotetrahydroaminopterin	$3\cdot0 \ \times 10^{-4}$	$4\cdot62 \times 10^{-6}$	$7\cdot7 \times 10^{-5}$
Isohomotetrahydrofolic acid	$2\cdot24 \times 10^{-4}$	$4\cdot8 \ \times 10^{-5}$	$1\cdot2 \times 10^{-4}$

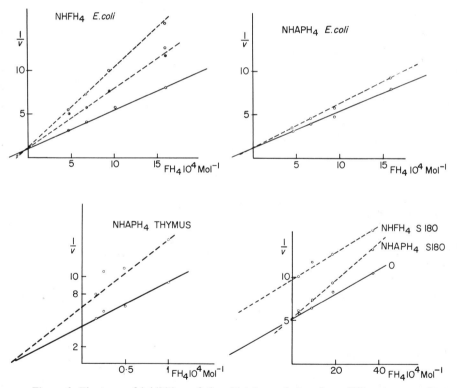

Figure 6. The type of inhibition of thymidylate synthetase from different sources by azahomotetrahydrofolate (NHFH$_4$) and azahomoaminopterin (NHAPH$_4$) demonstrated by the Lineweaver-Burk plot.

Azahomotetrahydrofolate was used in the concentrations $2\cdot4 \times 10^{-4}$M and $1\cdot2 \times 10^{-4}$M for the *E. coli* enzyme and $2\cdot4 \times 10^{-4}$M for the Sarcoma 180 enzyme.

Azahomoaminopterin was used in the concentrations $2\cdot2 \times 10^{-4}$M for the thymus and *E. coli* enzymes and $2\cdot2 \times 10^{-6}$M for the Sarcoma 180 enzyme.

76   K. SLAVÍK, *et al.*

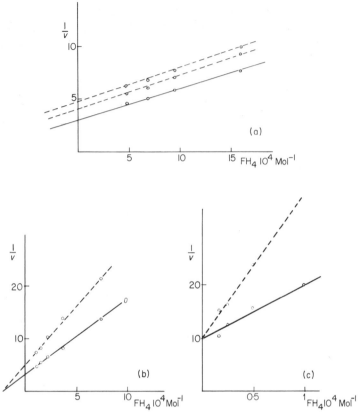

Figure 7. The type of inhibition of thymidylate synthetase from different sources by isohomotetrahydrofolate demonstrated by the Lineweaver-Burk plot.
(a) *E. coli* enzyme
(b) Sarcoma 180 enzyme
(c) Thymus enzyme
Inhibitor concentrations used were 2.2×10^{-5}M for the Sarcoma 180 enzyme, $5\text{-}10^{-5}$M and 1.2×10^{-4}M for the *E. coli* enzyme and 3.5×10^{-4}M for the thymus enzyme.

foregoing were applied, because the non-hydrogenated compounds do not inhibit the enzyme at concentrations of 5×10^{-4}M.

Concerning the *quantitative inhibitory effect* of these new antifolics, azahomotetrahydrofolate did not inhibit the thymus enzyme at 10^{-4}M but it appeared to be a weak inhibitor of the *E. coli* and Sarcoma 180 enzymes (Table 5).

Azahomotetrahydroaminopterin—the 4-aminoanalogue of the former substance—appeared to be a relatively weak inhibitor of the thymus and *E. coli* enzymes, but a stronger inhibitor by several orders of magnitude of the Sarcoma 180 enzyme.

Analogous behaviour was observed in the case of isohomotetrahydrofolic acid, which proved to be a weak inhibitor of the *E. coli* and thymus enzymes, but a considerably stronger inhibitor of the Sarcoma 180 enzyme.

The nature of the inhibition was also quite different, using thymidylate synthetases of different origin (Fig. 6).

Azahomotetrahydrofolate was a competitive inhibitor of the *E. coli* enzyme with tetrahydrofolate but an uncompetitive inhibitor of the Sarcoma 180 enzyme.

Azahomoaminopterin inhibited the thymus enzyme in a non-competitive way but it was a competitive inhibitor of the *E. coli* enzyme and also of the enzyme from Sarcoma 180.

Isohomotetrahydrofolic acid inhibited thymidylate synthetase from thymus competitively with tetrahydrofolate; with the *E. coli* enzyme the inhibition was uncompetitive and with the Sarcoma 180 enzyme non-competitive (Fig. 7).

DISCUSSION

In our previous study [6] concerning the interaction of thymidylate synthetase from *E. coli* with various tetrahydrofolate analogues, some conclusions were drawn about the sites in the molecule of tetrahydrofolate interacting with the binding sites and catalytic groups of the enzyme. The elimination or modification of the glutamate moiety, C^7N^8 reduced double bond, and halogenation of the *p*-aminobenzoic acid led to loss of the coenzymic activity but did not lead to any significant inhibitory effect of the analogues.

Analogous structural changes in the molecule of tetrahydroaminopterin, which is a potent inhibitor of the enzyme, led to a strong decrease of the inhibitory activity of 4-aminoanalogues of tetrahydrofolate. In contrast, structural changes in the one carbon-bearing moiety, represented by atoms N^5, C^9 and N^{10} in tetrahydrofolate, led not only to disappearance of the coenzyme activity but also to the appearance of the inhibitory effect. These findings suggested that in the *E. coli* enzyme variant the glutamate carboxyls, *p*-aminobenzoate moiety and C^7N^8 reduced double bond represent the groups interacting with binding sites, whereas the N^5-C^9-N^{10} site interacts probably with the catalytic groups (Fig. 8).

In the case of 4-aminoanalogues, the 2,4-diaminopteridine moiety seems not to be directly bound to the bacterial enzyme because 2,4-diaminotetrahydropteridine does not exert any inhibitory effect.

Both animal variants studied differ to a certain extent in the inhibitory effect of tetrahydrofolate analogues. The inhibitory effect of 2,4-diaminotetrahydropteridine on both variants, and a considerably stronger inhibitory effect of tetrahydroaminopterin and all similar 4-aminoanalogues, support the opinion that the animal enzyme variants bind directly the 2,4-diaminotetrahydro-pteridine moiety in contrast to the bacterial one.

Another difference exists in the inhibitory effect of 3',5'-dichlorotetrahydro-folate for both animal variants studied, whereas this compound is inactive against the bacterial variant. This fact indicates that the *p*-aminobenzoate is bound by animal thymidylate synthetase in a manner different from the binding to the bacterial variant.

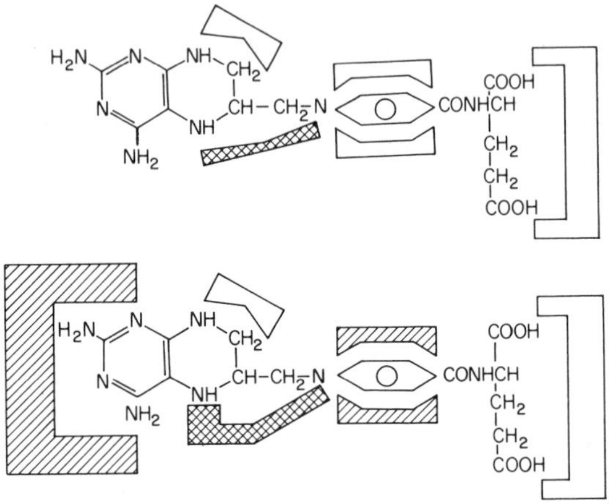

Figure 8. The proposed sites in the molecule of tetrahydroaminopterin interacting with the binding sites and catalytic groups of thymidylate synthetase from *E. coli* (above) and thymus and Sarcoma 180 (below).

☐ areas interacting with the binding sites both in the bacterial and animal enzyme variants

▨ areas interacting with the binding sites of the animal variants in a different manner from the bacterial variant

▩ areas interacting with the catalytic groups

This opinion is also supported by the fact that the mode of inhibition by dichlorotetrahydroamethopterin is different, i.e. non-competitive in the *E. coli* variant and competitive in the thymus enzyme.

Some individual differences have been found in the effect of N^5-methyltetra-hydrofolate which does not inhibit the *E. coli* enzyme but does inhibit the thymus enzyme. N^5-formyltetrahydrofolate inhibits the *E. coli* and Sarcoma 180 enzymes, but does not affect the thymus variant. This fact supports the opinion that the interaction of the one carbon moiety-bearing group is different with thymidylate synthetase originating from different sources (Fig. 8).

Concerning the differences between the thymus and Sarcoma 180 enzymes, the most striking fact is the considerably stronger inhibitory effect of all 4-aminoanalogues tested on the tumour enzyme as compared to the thymus variant. It may be concluded from this that the 2,4-diaminopyrimidine moiety is bound to the tumour enzyme more strongly than to the thymus one.

Another difference can be demonstrated by the above mentioned inhibitory effect of N^5-formyltetrahydrofolate on the tumour variant whereas the thymus enzyme is not affected by this analogue. This implies that the one carbon-bearing moiety in the tetrahydrofolate molecule is bound in a different way to the thymus and tumour enzymes. Additional evidence for differences in this reactive area is provided by the different interaction of thymidylate synthetase with three analogues with a prolonged bridge between the pteridine and p-aminobenzoate moieties: azahomotetrahydrofolic acid, azahomoaminopterin and isohomotetrahydrofolic acid. As has been demonstrated in the Results (above), considerable individual differences exist both in the degree and type of inhibition of the E. coli, thymus and Sarcoma 180 thymidylate synthetases. The differences in the extent and type of inhibition are especially remarkable between the thymus and Sarcoma 180 variants.

The above data concerning the inhibition analysis are too scanty to permit more detailed conclusions about the nature of binding, or sites of interaction with the enzyme. Nevertheless, this group of antimetabolites has been reported here as an example of the application of tetrahydrofolate analogues as tools for studying the species differences of the enzyme variants, even in cases where the enzyme cannot be isolated in a highly purified form and its structure is not known. It can only be concluded for certain that there exist species differences of enzyme variants which are detectable by differences in binding of substrate analogues. More information in this area, with the aid of a larger group of analogues, could represent a rational basis for proposed structures of antimeta-bolites interacting with the selected variant of the target enzyme.

REFERENCES

1. Hitchings, G. H. and Burchall, J. J., *Adv. Enzymol.* **27** (1965) 417.
2. Baker, B. R., "Design of Active Site Directed Inhibitors", John Wiley and Sons, New York, London, Sydney, 1967.
3. Baker, B. R. and Ho, T. B., *J. pharm. Sci.* **55** (1966) 470.
4. Friedkin, M., Plante, L. T. and Crawford, E. J., *Fedn Proc. Fedn Am. Socs exp. Biol.* **24** (1965) 541.
5. Plante, L. T., Crawford, E. J. and Friedkin, M., *J. biol. Chem.* **242** (1967) 1466.
6. Slavík, K. and Zakrzewski, S. F., *Molec. Pharmacol.* **3** (1967) 370.

7. Slavík, K., Slavíková, V. and Kolman, Z., *Colln Czech. chem. Commun.* **25** (1960) 1929.
8. Slavík, K., Slavíková, V., Motyčka, K., Hermanová, E., Souček, J., Tomsová, Z., Špundová, M. and Nováková, E., *Molec. Pharmacol.* **5** (1969) 137.
9. Slavík, K., Tomsová, Z., Šmídová, J. and Špundova M., unpublished.
10. Wahba, A. J. and Friedkin M., *J. biol. Chem.* **237** (1962) 3794.
11. Cleland, W. W., *Biochim. biophys. Acta* **67** (1963) 173.

FEBS Symposium, Volume 16, 1969, pp. 81-95

Hydroxylation of Drugs in the Organism

R. T. WILLIAMS

*Department of Biochemistry, St. Mary's
Hospital Medical School, London, England*

Hydroxylation is one of the most widespread of the biochemical reactions of drugs and other foreign compounds in the animal body. It is also the most intensely studied of these reactions. In general, it is a reaction which can lead eventually to the detoxication and elimination of a drug because the introduction of a hydroxyl group into the compound gives it a centre by which conjugation, particularly with glucuronic acid, can occur. It would therefore appear that in the animal body hydroxylation is a step in the detoxication and inactivation of a drug or any other foreign compound, according to the general scheme:

$$\text{Drug} \longrightarrow \text{hydroxylated drug} \longrightarrow \text{conjugated drug}$$

A simple and well-known example is acetanilide, an old antipyretic drug, whose main metabolic fate follows the above general scheme:

| Acetanilide | *p*-acetamidophenol | *p*-acetamidophenyl glucuronide |

The detailed mechanisms and the pharmacological and toxicological consequences of the hydroxylation of foreign compounds *in vivo* are dealt with in the succeeding papers in this Symposium. In this paper, the general aspects of the biological effects resulting from the hydroxylation of drugs and of the types of compounds undergoing hydroxylation, together with the possible pathways, will be reviewed. Hydroxylation *in vivo* can occur at carbon or nitrogen atoms, but this paper will be largely concerned with *C*-hydroxylation.

THE PHARMACOLOGICAL CONSEQUENCES OF HYDROXYLATION

Drugs are metabolized in the body usually in two phases, each of which is catalysed by specific kinds of enzymes. The first phase involves reactions

Table 1. Hydroxylation and biological activity.

Parent drug	Activity	Hydroxylated drug	Activity
Phenobarbitone $C_4H_2N_2O_2(Et)(C_6H_5)$	Hypnotic, sedative	4-Hydroxyphenobarbitone $C_4H_2N_2O_2(Et)(C_6H_4OH)$	None
Meprobamate $MeC(CH_2OCONH_2)_2C_3H_7$	Tranquillizer	Hydroxymeprobamate $MeC(CH_2OCONH_2)_2CH_2CHOHCH_3$	None
Antipyrine $Ph.NCOCH:CMeN.Me$	Analgesic, antipyretic	4-Hydroxyantipyrine $PhNCO.C(OH):CMe.N.Me$	None?
Acetanilide $AcNHC_6H_5$	?	4-Hydroxyacetanilide $AcNHC_6H_4OH$	Analgesic, antipyretic
Trichloroethylene $Cl_2C=CHCl$	Short acting analgesic and anaesthetic	Trichloroethanol $Cl_3C.CH_2OH$	Hypnotic, more toxic
Amphetamine $CH_3CH(NH_2)CH_2C_6H_5$	Stimulant	4-Hydroxyamphetamine $CH_3CH(NH_2)CH_2C_6H_4OH$	Less toxic, less stimulant but more pressor activity
Phenacetin $AcNHC_6H_4OEt$	?	4-Acetamidophenol $AcNHC_6H_4OH$	Analgesic, antipyretic
Heroin $C_{17}H_{17}NO(OAc)_2$	Narcotic	Morphine $C_{17}H_{17}NO(OH)_2$	Narcotic, analgesic, less toxic i.v., but more toxic intracerebrally
Flexin $C_7H_3NOClNH_2$	Muscle relaxant, uricosuric	1) Chlorzoxazole $C_7H_3NOCl.OH$ 2) Hydroxyflexin $C_7H_2NOCl(NH_2)(OH)$	(1) Muscle relaxant, not uricosuric (2) Inactive

classified as oxidations, reductions and hydrolyses, and the second, those classified as syntheses. In each phase, the compound is made more polar, and as a rule, the products of phase II are more polar than those of phase I. Hydroxylation is usually classified as a phase I oxidation and it is this concept of hydroxylation which is to be discussed at this meeting. However, it should be realized that hydroxy compounds can also be produced in the organism by the processes of reduction and hydrolysis, as will be shown later.

The hydroxylation of a drug may alter its biological activity in three possible directions. The hydroxylated product may be (a) less active than the parent drug or even inactive, (b) more active than the parent drug which in some cases may initially have no activity at all, or (c) different in activity from the parent drug. Where the hydroxylated drug is more active or of different activity from the parent drug, there is considerable interest, since the formation of such a metabolite may explain the toxicity, pharmacological activity or therapeutic effectiveness of the parent drug, and may lead to the production of new drugs or compounds of technological value. Examples of drugs or other foreign compounds undergoing hydroxylation in the organism and resulting in altered biological activity in the three directions mentioned are given in Table 1.

PATHWAYS OF FORMATION OF HYDROXY COMPOUNDS *in vivo*

Drugs and other foreign compounds may be converted enzymically into hydroxy compounds in the body by several pathways. These pathways may be (1) oxidative, (2) reductive, or (3) hydrolytic in nature. There is also a fourth possibility and that is by tautomeric change, which may or may not be enzyme assisted.

(1) Oxidative pathways of hydroxylation

The formation of hydroxy compounds *in vivo* can occur by the apparent addition of oxygen to (a) aromatic rings, (b) cycloalkane rings, (c) aliphatic carbon chains, and (d) suitable amino groups (see Table 2).

(a) *Aromatic rings.* The most widely studied biological hydroxylation process is that of the hydroxylation of carbocyclic and heterocyclic aromatic systems, and the commonest form of this reaction is the replacement of H by OH in such systems. This type of hydroxylation is usually carried out by enzymes—aromatic hydroxylases—occurring in the endoplasmic reticulum of the liver cells and requiring molecular oxygen and a source of reduced NADP [1]. These hydroxylations are orientated and tend to occur at the carbon atoms of the highest electron density, although this is not invariably true [2]. The extent of these

Table 2. Oxidative pathways of hydroxylation *in vivo*.

Type of compound	General formula	Hydroxy product	General formula
Aromatic system	ArX (where X = H, F, Cl, Br, NO_2, NH_2, CO_2H, CH_2OH)	Phenol	ArOH
Alicyclic system	CH_2 (ring)	Secondary alcohol	CHOH (ring)
Aliphatic chains	$R-CH_2-R^1$	Secondary alcohol	$R-CHOH-R^1$
Methyl groups	$-Y-CH_3$ (Y=C, O, N, S)	Primary alcohol	$-Y-CH_2OH$
Amino groups	$-NH_2$ $-NHCOCH_3$	Hydroxylamine	$-NHOH$ $-N(OH)COCH_3$

hydroxylations appears to be species dependent probably because the availability or activity of the aromatic hydroxylases varies with species, and furthermore, hydroxylation may be in competition with another reaction of the compound which also varies with species [3].

In unsubstituted aromatic systems there is a tendency for mono-hydroxylation to occur in more than one position, but the extent of hydroxylation in any position appears to be related to the chemical reactivity of that position. Hydroxylation tends to occur to the greatest extent at the most reactive position. Thus, indole [4] is hydroxylated mainly at the 3-position, coumarin [5] at 3, quinoline [6] at 3, pyrene [7] at 3 and 3,4-benzopyrene [7] at 5, which are the most reactive centres in these molecules. Some aromatic compounds, however, appear to be hydroxylated mainly at centres of secondary reactivity, e.g. fluorene, chrysene, 1,2-dibenzanthracene, 1,2:5,6-dibenzanthracene, and it is suggested that in these cases the most reactive centres are involved in attachment to the tissues (see review by Parke and Williams [8]).

When an aromatic system contains a substituent, the position of hydroxylation is influenced by this substituent. Thus, to take simple cases, aniline, which contains the o-p-directing NH_2 group and which is extensively hydroxylated in vivo, is hydroxylated o- or p- to the NH_2 group [9]; and benzoic acid, which contains the m-directing COOH group and is only hydroxylated to a very minor extent (0·25%) in rats, is hydroxylated o-, m- and p- to the COOH group [10]. These rules apply fairly generally to all aromatic systems containing substituent groups and can be used to predict the main position of hydroxylation in vivo of substituted aromatic compounds, whether they are carbocyclic or heterocyclic. However, hydroxylations at positions other than those predicted by these simple rules can occur as a result of the "N.I.H. shift" mentioned below.

Hydroxylation of aromatic systems can also occur by the replacement of substituent groups and examples are known of the replacement by OH of F, Cl, Br, NO_2, NH_2, CH_2OH and COOH groups in biological systems. Thus, 4-hydroxy-2,6-dichloroaniline is a minor urinary metabolite in rabbits of 2,4,6-trichloro-aniline and -nitrobenzene, and 4-hydroxy-2,5-dichloronitrobenzene of 2,4,5-trichloro-nitrobenzene. The replacement of Cl by OH has been termed "hydroxyldechlorination" by Betts et al. [11]. The replacement by OH of an NO_2 group occurs with 2,6-dichloro-4-nitroaniline, whose main metabolite in rats is 4-amino-3,5-dichlorophenol [12].

The enzymic replacement of F, Cl and Br (and of ^3H and ^2H in suitable compounds) has been reported by Guroff et al. [13] to occur in aromatic compounds such as 4-fluoro-, 4-chloro- and 4-bromo-phenylalanine and 4-fluoro-phenylacetic acid. In this type of reaction several products may be formed, including those in which the halogen, whilst being replaced by OH, is shifted to the next (*ortho*) carbon atom thus:

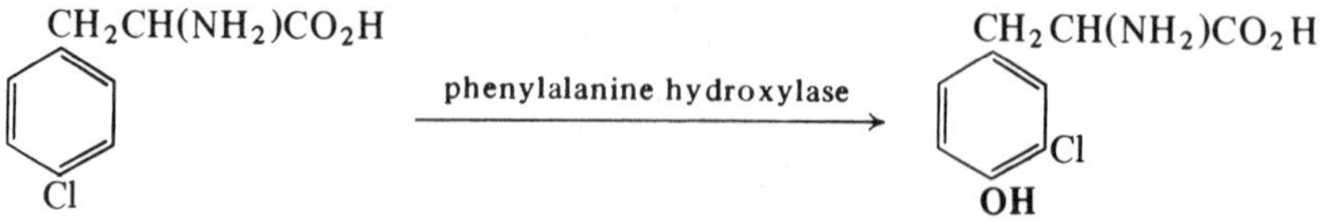

$$CH_2CH(NH_2)CO_2H \xrightarrow{\text{phenylalanine hydroxylase}} CH_2CH(NH_2)CO_2H$$

This reaction is referred to by Guroff *et al.* [13] as the "N.I.H shift" (since it was discovered at the National Institutes of Health, Bethesda, U.S.A.) and in such a reaction a compound such as 4-chlorophenylalanine can give rise to tyrosine, 3-chlorotyrosine and 4-chloro-*m*-tyrosine (see below; R = $CH_2CH(NH_2)COOH$).

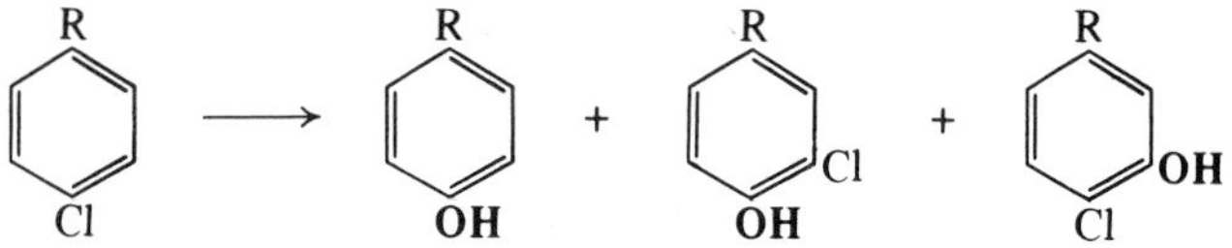

The replacement of NH_2 or COOH groups by OH has been reported to occur in micro-organisms. Thus pseudomonads contain enzymes which are capable of converting both anthranilic acid [14] and salicylic acid [15, 16] to catechol:

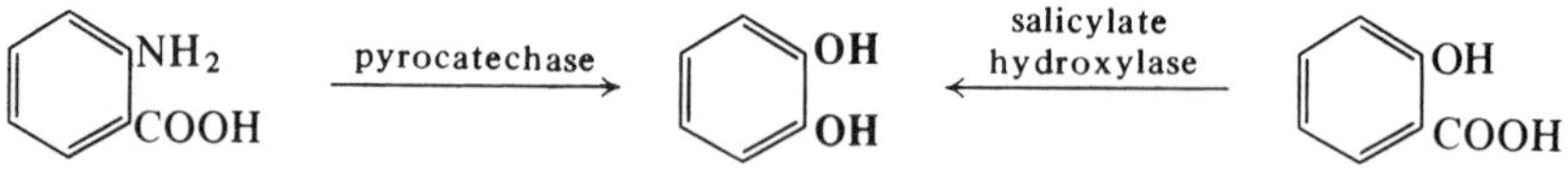

The replacement of a hydroxymethyl group by OH has been reported to occur in guinea pig liver microsomes, for Sloane [17, 18] has shown that both benzyl alcohol and *p*-aminobenzyl alcohol are converted to a small extent to phenol and *p*-aminophenol, respectively. In fact, Sloane has provided evidence that hydroxymethylation may be an intermediate in one form of aromatic hydroxylation, thus:

$$C_6H_6 \longrightarrow C_6H_5CH_2OH \longrightarrow C_6H_5OH$$

(b) *Cycloalkane rings.* Drugs and other foreign compounds containing cyclo-alkane and cycloalkene rings are also hydroxylated in the body. Steroids are a special class of alicyclic compounds but their hydroxylation will not be discussed here because not enough space is available. Many important drugs contain reduced ring systems, e.g. hexobarbitone, metrazol, quinine, morphine, LSD, meperidine, thalidomide, camphor, menthol, etc. (here one might mention the widely used sweetening agent, cyclamate or cyclohexylsulphamate) and several of these drugs undergo hydroxylation in these rings. However, studies on the hydroxylation of these systems, apart from steroids, are not yet very

Table 3. Hydroxylation of cycloalkanes in the rabbit.

Cycloalkane	Metabolites (% of dose excreted in urine)	
	More stable	Less stable
Cyclohexane	cyclohexanol (30-40) trans-1,2-cyclohexane-diol (5-8)	
Methylcyclohexane	trans-1,2-methylcyclohexanol (1·2) cis-1,3-methylcyclohexanol (11·5) trans-1,4-methylcyclohexanol (14·7) cyclohexylmethanol (0·3)	cis-1,2-methylcyclohexanol (0·5) trans-1,3-methylcyclohexanol (10·5) cis-1,4-methylcyclohexanol (2·5)
trans-Decalin	(±)-trans-cis-2-decalol (main metabolite)	trans-trans-2-decalol
cis-Decalin	(±)-cis-cis-2-decalol (main metabolite)	cis-trans-2-decalol
Tetralin	ac-1-tetralol (58) ac-2-tetralol (20)	

advanced. The study of the hydroxylation of cycloalkanes has raised interesting stereochemical problems, for the secondary alcohols produced may occur in *cis, trans* and optically active forms and therefore, questions of the thermodynamic stability of the metabolites are involved.

Cyclohexane is extensively hydroxylated in the rabbit to cyclohexanol, with *trans*-cyclohexane-1,2-diol as a minor product [19]. Methylcyclohexane is hydroxylated to seven alcohols in the rabbit [20], the amounts of each found in the urine being determined apparently by steric factors, for hydroxylation occurs mainly at the less hindered positions 3 and 4, and by the thermodynamic stability of the alcohol, for the more stable alcohols are found in the urine in largest amounts (see Table 3). In the case of *cis*- and *trans*-decalin, hydroxylation occurs at the less hindered 2-positions [21] to the more stable *cis-cis*- and *trans-cis*-2-decalols, respectively. Tetralin contains an aromatic and a partly reduced ring, and in this case, hydroxylation occurs mainly in the reduced ring at the activated methylene groups next to the aromatic ring [22] (see Table 3).

(c) *Aliphatic chains.* Many drugs contain alkyl chains including barbiturates, quinoline and acridine antimalarials such as chloroquine and mepacrine, phenothiazines such as chlorpromazine and phenergan, etc. Most of the studies on the hydroxylation of alkyl chains have been carried out on alkylbenzenes and barbiturates and from these studies the pathways of the hydroxylation of these chains have been elucidated.

In general, alkyl chains may be hydroxylated *in vivo* at the ω- and (ω-1)-positions, and if the alkyl chain is attached to a benzene ring, hydroxylation may occur also at the α-position next to the aromatic ring. ω-Hydroxylation, however, is not often detected since the product found is usually an aromatic acid. Illustrative examples of these reactions are given in Table 4.

These hydroxylations, like those of aromatic rings, are carried out mainly by liver microsomal enzymes. However, from a study of the enzymic oxidation of secobarbital (5-allyl-5-(1'—methylbutyl)barbiturate), Ide *et al.* [23] have suggested that whereas the (ω-1)-hydroxylation of this compound has the usual requirement of $NADPH_2$ and oxygen, the ω-hydroxylation requires in addition to these, an unidentified factor which occurs in the soluble fraction of liver homogenates.

(B = barbiturate ring system.)

Table 4. Hydroxylation of alkyl chains.

Compound	Hydroxylated product	Ref.
$\begin{array}{c} NH{-}CO\diagdown\quad CH_2CH_3 \\ OC\quad\quad C \\ NH{-}CO\diagup\quad CH_2CH_3 \end{array}$ Barbitone (veronal)	$\begin{array}{c} NH{-}CO\diagdown\quad CH_2CH_3 \\ OC\quad\quad C \\ NH{-}CO\diagup\quad CH_2CH_2OH \end{array}$	26
⬡CH_2CH_3 Ethylbenzene	⬡$CHOHCH_3$	27
$CH_3 . C . (CH_2OCONH_2)_2$ $\quad\quad\mid$ $\quad CH_2CH_2CH_3$ Meprobamate	$CH_3 . C . (CH_2OCONH_2)_2$ $\quad\quad\mid$ $\quad CH_2CHOHCH_3$	28
⬡$CH_2CH_2CH_3$ Propylbenzene	$\begin{cases} C_6H_5CHOHCH_2CH_3 \\ C_6H_5CH_2CHOHCH_3 \end{cases}$	29
$\begin{array}{c} NH{-}CO\diagdown\quad CH_2CH_3 \\ OC\quad\quad C \\ NH{-}CO\diagup\quad CH_2CH_2CH_2CH_3 \end{array}$ Neonal	$\begin{array}{c} NH{-}CO\diagdown\quad CH_2CH_3 \\ OC\quad\quad C \\ NH{-}CO\diagup\quad CH_2CH_2CHOHCH_3 \end{array}$	30
⬡$CH_2CH_2CH_2CH_3$ Butylbenzene	$\begin{cases} C_6H_5CHOHCH_2CH_2CH_3 \\ C_6H_5CH_2CH_2CHOHCH_3 \end{cases}$	29

Dealkylations are probably special cases of ω- and $(\omega$-1)-hydroxylation and demethylation and de-ethylation probably proceed as follows:

$$RCH_3 \longrightarrow RCH_2OH \longrightarrow RH + HCHO$$
$$RCH_2CH_3 \longrightarrow RCHOHCH_3 \longrightarrow RH + CH_3CHO$$

Dealkylation, however, occurs less readily as the length of the alkyl chain increases [24] and in ethers with chains longer than propyl, $(\omega$-1)-hydroxylated products predominate over dealkylated products [25] thus:

$$RCH_2CH_2CH_2CH_3 \longrightarrow RCH_2CH_2CHOHCH_3$$

If the longer alkyl chain is removed, then it probably occurs by ω-oxidation followed by β-oxidation.

The intermediate alcohols in N- and O-demethylation or de-ethylation have not been detected except in a few cases such as N-methylglutethimide. In this case, the glucuronide of N-hydroxymethylglutathimide (see below) was detected in the urine of dogs receiving the drug [31].

The hydroxymethyl group formed during the *in vivo* oxidation of C-methyl groups to COOH have been detected in several cases, e.g. π-hydroxycamphor is a minor metabolite of camphor [32].

Camphor π-Hydroxycamphor

(2) Reductive pathways of hydroxylation

Hydroxy compounds can be formed *in vivo* by the reduction of aldehydes, ketones, and quinones (see Table 5). These reactions are not regarded as hydroxylations in the usual sense of the word but nevertheless they yield compounds containing hydroxyl groups.

Table 5. Formation of hydroxyl groups by reduction *in vivo*.

Chemical type	Hydroxylated product
Aldehydes RCHO	Primary alcohol RCH_2OH
Ketones R . CO . R'	Secondary alcohol R . CHOH . R'
Quinones	1,4-Dihydroxy phenols

Epoxides*	Glutathione conjugate

*Hydroxylation by addition of glutathione

(a) *Aldehydes.* Aldehydes are normally oxidized in the body to the corresponding carboxylic acids, but in some cases the aldehydes yield both the corresponding carboxylic acids and primary alcohols. The classical example is chloral (see Table 6) which normally occurs as the hydrate. Both trichloroacetic acid and trichloroethanol are metabolites of this drug [33]. Butylchloral hydrate $(CH_3CHClCCl_2CH(OH)_2)$ is also reduced in the dog to 2,2,3-trichlorobutanol which is excreted conjugated with glucuronic acid [34].

(b) *Ketones.* Many aliphatic and alicyclic ketones are reduced in the animal body to secondary alcohols. This is a well-known metabolic reaction of ketones (see Tables 5 and 6).

(c) *Quinones.* The reduction of quinones to dihydric phenols also occurs in some instances (see Tables 5 and 6) but many quinones are resistant to reduction *in vivo*, e.g. anthraquinone which is actually hydroxylated to 2-hydroxyanthraquinone [35].

(d) *Epoxides.* Epoxides have been postulated as intermediates in the formation of mercapturic acids *in vivo*. It is believed that mercapturic acid-forming aromatic systems such as naphthalene are epoxidized by a liver microsomal

Table 6. Hydroxylation resulting from biological reduction.

Compound	Hydroxy metabolite	Ref.
$Cl_3C . CHO$ Chloral	$Cl_3C . CH_2OH$ Trichloroethanol	33
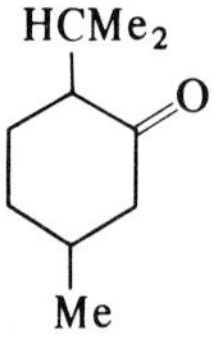 HCMe$_2$ ... Me	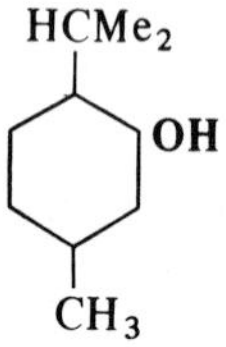 HCMe$_2$ ... CH$_3$ Neomenthol	39
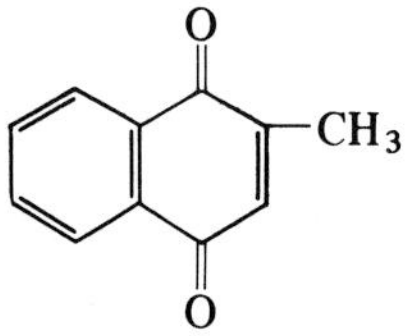 Menadione	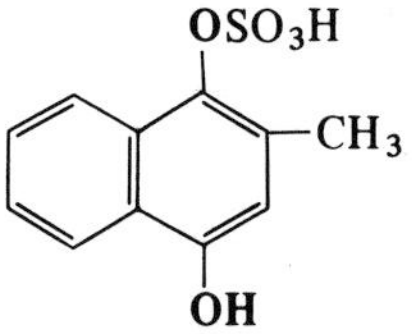 Ester sulphate of 1,4-dihydroxy- 2-methylnaphthalene	40

oxidase requiring oxygen and NADPH$_2$. The epoxide then reacts with glutathione, the process being catalysed by glutathione S-epoxidetransferase which
occurs in the supernatant fraction of liver homogenates [36]. The product is a
glutathione conjugate which contains a hydroxyl group. Further metabolic
changes result in the production of a premercapturic acid, an example of which
is shown below [37].

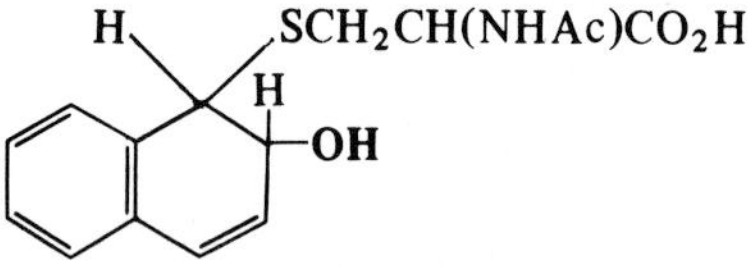

Naphthyl premercapturic acid

This is another example of a metabolic process which is not a direct
hydroxylation but nevertheless produces a hydroxy compound as a metabolic
product. Hydroxy acetylcysteine derivatives are also metabolites of bromo-
paraffins, e.g. 1-bromobutane [38].

$C_4H_9Br \longrightarrow$

$C_4H_9SCH_2CH(NHAc)CO_2H + CH_3CH_2CHOHCH_2SCH_2CH(NHAc)CO_2H$

(3) Hydrolytic pathways of hydroxylation

To complete this brief survey of the processes which lead to hydroxy compounds in the body, mention must be made of the very common hydrolytic pathways. Any ester which is hydrolysed in the body must give rise to a hydroxy compound which may be a phenol or an alcohol (1ry, 2ndry or 3ry) depending upon the nature of the ester (see Table 7). Lactones which are internal esters behave similarly, giving rise to hydroxy acids.

Table 7. Hydroxy compounds produced by hydrolysis *in vivo.*

Drug*	Hydroxy product
Aspirin	Salicylic acid
Procaine	$Et_2NCH_2CH_2OH$ Diethylaminoethanol
3-Hydroxycoumarin	o-Hydroxyphenylpyruvic acid (excreted as o-hydroxyphenyl- acetic acid)[5]

* A large number of drugs are esters and many are hydrolysed *in vivo* to alcohols or phenols.

There may be other pathways of biological hydroxylation of minor importance, but of most interest at the present time are those involving aromatic rings, microsomal enzymes and cytochrome P450, as we shall see from the subsequent papers in this Symposium.

REFERENCES

1. Gillette, J. R., *Prog. Drug Res.* **9** (1963) 11-73.
2. Diner, S., in "Electronic Aspects of Biochemistry" (edited by B. Pullman), Academic Press, New York, 1964, 237-281.
3. Williams, R. T., *Fedn Proc. Fedn Am. Socs exp. Biol.* **26** (1967) 1031.

4. King, L. J., Parke, D. V. and Williams, R. T., *Biochem. J.* **98** (1966) 266-277.
5. Kaighen, M. and Williams, R. T., *J. mednl pharm. Chem.* **3** (1961) 25-43.
6. Smith, J. N. and Williams, R. T., *Biochem. J.* **60** (1955) 284.
7. Conney, A. H., Miller, E. C. and Miller, J. A., *J. biol. Chem.* **228** (1957) 753.
8. Parke, D. V. and Williams, R. T., *Rep. Prog. Chem.* **55** (1958) 376-388.
9. Parke, D. V., *Biochem. J.* **77** (1960) 493.
10. Acheson, R. M. and Gibbard, S., *Biochim. biophys. Acta* **59** (1962) 320.
11. Betts, J. J., Bray, H. G., James, S. P. and Thorpe, W. V., *Biochem. J.* **66** (1957) 610.
12. Maté, C., Ryan, A. J. and Wright, S. E., *Fd cosmet. Toxicol.* **5** (1967) 657-663.
13. Guroff, G., Daly, J. W., Jerina, D. M., Renson, J., Witkop, B. and Udenfriend, S., *Science, N.Y.* **157** (1967) 1524.
14. Mehler, A. H., *in* "Oxygenases" (edited by O. Hayaishi), Academic Press, New York, 1962, p. 90.
15. Yamamoto, S., Katagiri, M., Maeno, H. and Hayaishi, O., *J. biol. Chem.* **240** (1965) 3408.
16. Katagiri, M., Maeno, H., Yamamoto, S. and Hayaishi, O., *J. biol. Chem.* **240** (1965) 341.
17. Sloane, N. H., *Biochim. biophys. Acta* **81** (1964) 408.
18. Sloane, N. H., *Biochim. biophys. Acta* **107** (1965) 599.
19. Elliott, T. H., Parke, D. V. and Williams, R. T., *Biochem. J.* **72** (1959) 193.
20. Elliott, T. H., Tao, R. C. C. and Williams, R. T., *Biochem. J.* **95** (1965) 70.
21. Elliott, T. H., Robertson, J. S. and Williams, R. T., *Biochem. J.* **100** (1966) 403.
22. Elliott, T. H., Hanam, J., Parke, D. V. and Williams, R. T., *Biochem. J.* **92** (1964) 52P.
23. Ide, H., Yoshimura, H. and Tsukamoto, H., *Chem. pharm. Bull.*, *Tokyo* **15** (1967) 411-419.
24. McMahon, R. E., Culp, H. W., Mills, J. and Marshall, F. J., *J. med. Chem.* **6** (1963) 343.
25. Yoshimura, H., Tsugi, H. and Tsukamoto, H., *Chem. pharm. Bull.*, *Tokyo* **14** (1966) 939-947.
26. Goldschmidt, S. and Wehr, R., *Hoppe-Seyler's Z. physiol. Chem.* **308** (1957) 9-19.
27. Smith, J. N., Smithies, R. H. and Williams, R. T., *Biochem. J.* **56** (1954) 320.
28. Ludwig, B. J., Douglas, J. F., Powell, L. S., Meyer, M. and Berger, F. M., *J. mednl pharm. Chem.* **3** (1961) 53.
29. El Masri, A. M., Smith, J. N. and Williams, R. T., *Biochem. J.* **64** (1956) 50.
30. Maynert, E. W., *J. biol. Chem.* **195** (1952) 397.
31. Keberle, H., Reiss, W., Schmidt, K. and Hoffmann, K., *Archs int. Pharmacodyn. Thér.* **142** (1963) 125.
32. Asahina, Y. and Ishidate, M., *Ber. dt. chem. Ges.* **66** (1933) 1673.
33. Marshall, E. K. and Owens, A. H., *Johns Hopkins Hosp. Bull.* **95** (1954) 1.
34. Külz, E., *Pflügers Arch. ges. Physiol.* **28** (1882) 506.
35. Sato, T., Fukuyama, T., Yamada, H. and Suzuki, T., *J. Biochem.*, *Tokyo* **43** (1956) 21.

36. Boyland, E. and Williams, K., *Biochem. J.* **94** (1965) 190.
37. Boyland, E. and Sims, P., *Biochem. J.* **68** (1958) 440.
38. James, S. P. and Jeffrey, D. J., *Biochem. J.* **93** (1964) 16P.
39. Williams, R. T., *Biochem. J.* **34** (1940) 690.
40. Richert, D. A., *J. biol. Chem.* **189** (1951) 763.

FEBS Symposium, Volume 16, 1969, pp. 97-107

General Biological Aspects of N-Hydroxylation

H. UEHLEKE

*Institute of Pharmacology, University of Tübingen,
Tübingen, Germany*

Sixty years ago W. Heubner was engaged in exploring the biological effects of arylamines like aniline. Aromatic amines are powerful met-haemoglobin-forming agents in animals but they are not effective *in vitro*. At that time the metabolic activation of aromatic amines was already assumed.

The known metabolite of aniline p-aminophenol was thought to be the causative agent because it produced ferri-haemoglobin with erythrocytes in the test tube. But Heubner [1] found that *ortho*- and *para*-substituted anilines were still effective in producing met-haemoglobin *in vivo*. In these cases the formation of o- or p-aminophenols in their metabolism is not possible.

It was also known that *in vitro* phenylhydroxylamine is a very powerful oxidant for haemoglobin. *In vivo* it is at least 10 times more active in oxidizing haemoglobin compared with p-aminophenol. Consequently, Heubner proposed the possible N-hydroxylation of arylamines and called it a "Giftung" (toxification reaction). In spite of many attempts it took another 50 years to substantiate the biochemical N-hydroxylation and the corresponding metabolites in the animal and *in vitro* with liver preparations (for reviews see refs. 29-32).

N-Oxidation of aromatic amines was first demonstrated when Kiese [2] in Tübingen found minute concentrations of nitrosobenzene in the blood of dogs dosed with aniline. In attempts to localize the transformation in the body we demonstrated N-oxidation activity in isolated liver and lung of cat [3, 4].

In 1959 we found that isolated rat liver microsomes catalyse N-hydroxylation of aniline and N-methylaniline in the presence of NADPH and O_2. Consequently this reaction was included in the well known mixed function oxidases in the liver microsomal fraction.

While we were engaged in the elucidation of this toxicological question, some support came from another direction. The Millers in the U.S.A. worked on the metabolism of carcinogenic aromatic amines. After feeding rats with N-acetyl-aminofluorene they found a new metabolite in the urine with the structure of N-hydroxy-N-acetylaminofluorene [5]. Immediately, the Millers considered N-hydroxylation to be an essential activation step in arylamine carcinogenesis.

Aminofluorene and 2-naphthylamine are also *N*-hydroxylated *in vitro* by isolated liver microsomes [6-8, 37].

By means of partition experiments we demonstrated that the primary oxidation products of arylamines are the hydroxylamines, which might be oxidized further—especially in the blood—to form the nitroso-compounds [9].

The *N*-hydroxylation system was not inhibited by metal complexing agents like EDTA, phenanthroline or α, α-dipyridyl [10]. Therefore, I was rather astonished to observe inhibition of microsomal *C*-hydroxylation of aniline, using

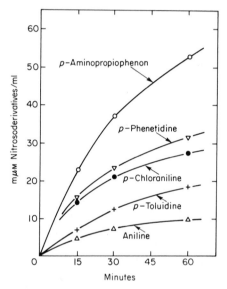

Figure 1. *N*-hydroxylation of anilines in suspensions of rat liver microsomes with NADPH. From Uehleke, 1962, Ref. 10.

80% CO and 20% O_2. But *N*-hydroxylation was not even completely blocked by flushing the incubation flasks with CO. In 1961 this fact was in contrast with the general opinion that metals were not involved in microsomal oxidations. Kampffmeyer and Kiese [11] thoroughly investigated this phenomena of CO inhibition and concluded that different enzymes must be responsible for *C*- and *N*-hydroxylation of aniline and *N*-ethylaniline. Nevertheless, *N*-dealkylation by microsomes, and simultaneous *N*-oxidation, is a complicated reaction [4, 38]. Therefore, K_M-values for this reaction in non-purified systems are difficult to interpret and represent no proof for different enzymes, but only for possible different mechanisms or cofactors.

The velocity of *N*-hydroxylation of various substituted anilines is very different. *p*-Substitution nearly always increases the velocity (Fig. 1). There is no clear correlation between the basicity of the amino group and the velocity of microsomal *N*-hydroxylation (Fig. 2). Ring substitution in the *m*-position with acyl groups extensively reduces the oxidative attack at the amine nitrogen.

N-alkylated anilines, like *N*-methyl or *N*-ethyl, are better substrates for the microsomal *N*-hydroxylation system [4, 10]. But dealkylation and *N*-oxidation velocities are reduced when the side chain increases to 3 and 4 carbon units. At the same time the formation of *N*-oxidation products decreases. In contrast, *p*-*C*-hydroxylation velocity increases with longer side chains [12].

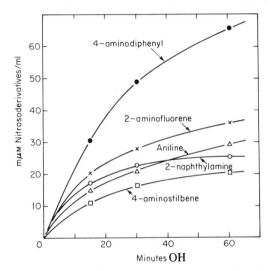

Figure 2. *N*-hydroxylation of aniline and several carcinogenic arylamines in suspensions of rat liver microsomes. From Uehleke, 1963, Ref. 37.

SPECIES DIFFERENCES

Toxicologists have for some time been aware of the rather divergent toxicity of various arylamines in single animal species in respect to general toxicity and to the formation of ferri-haemoglobin. Apart from many other factors (absorption, acetylation, glucuronidation, reduction, general stability of *N*-oxidation products and properties of erythrocytes), *N*-hydroxylation itself revealed considerable variations in microsomal fractions of the livers of different animal species. In Fig. 3, *C*- and *N*-hydroxylation of two substrates (*N*-butylaniline and *p*-chloroaniline) have been compared. Guinea pigs were found to be very active in *N*-hydroxylation; chicken liver microsomes revealed the highest activity for *C*-hydroxylation [13], but Table 1 shows that the mode of comparison is rather difficult. Guinea pigs are considered to be insensitive to the carcinogenic action of arylamines. Therefore, this observation was explained by the inability of guinea pigs to *N*-hydroxylate the amines. Furthermore, guinea pigs are reported to excrete no *N*-oxidation products in the urine after feeding *N*-acetylamino-fluorene [14]. As we have seen, *N*-hydroxylation is very active in guinea pigs.

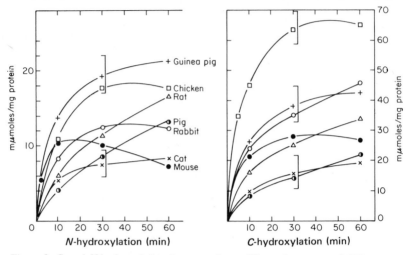

Figure 3. *C*- and *N*-hydroxylation in suspensions of liver microsomes of different animal species. Substrates: *N*-butylaniline and *p*-chloroaniline. From Debackere and Uehleke, 1964, Ref. 13.

Table 1. Comparison of the maximal velocity of *N*-hydroxylation of *p*-chloroaniline in suspensions of liver microsomes and the concentration of *N*-oxidation products formed after 60 min incubation. Debackere and Uehleke [13].

	N-hydroxylation of *p*-chloroaniline by liver microsomes		
	A V_{max} calc. mμmole/mg/min	B mμmole/mg 60 min	ratio A/B
Mouse	5·6	7·3	0·77
Rat	1·1	16·6	0·066
Guinea pig	6·5	21·2	0·33
Rabbit	2·0	12·3	0·16
Pig	0·7	13·1	0·05
Cat	1·0	8·2	0·12
Chicken	2·7	17·6	0·15

STIMULATION AND INHIBITION OF *N*-HYDROXYLATION

Administration of a variety of foreign compounds frequently leads to a marked increase of drug metabolism in living animals and in suspensions of isolated liver microsomes [15, 16]. Stimulation of drug metabolism occurs at different levels [17]: increase of the relative liver weight, increase of the endoplasmic reticulum in the liver cells (microsomal fraction), and increase of the specific activity of isolated microsomes. The latter is based partly upon the increase of the concentrations of the oxygen activating cytochrome P_{450}.

N-hydroxylation of primary arylamines was only slightly increased with rat liver microsomes after pretreatment with DDT, phenobarbital and methylcholanthrene, alone and in combination [17, 18]. By contrast, liver and kidney

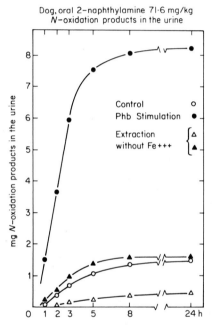

Figure 4. Total urinary excretion of the *N*-oxidation products of 2-naphthylamine in a normal and in a phenobarbital-pretreated beagle dog. From Uehleke and Brill, 1968, Ref. 22.

microsomes of rabbits were several-fold more active for *N*-hydroxylation after pretreatment with phenobarbital [19, 20].

After phenobarbital pretreatment of rabbits the specific activity (mμmoles metabolite formed per milligram of microsomal proteins in a given time) of isolated microsomes for *N*-hydroxylation of 4-aminobiphenyl or 2-aminonaphthalene was increased 3-4 times. Simultaneously, 30% liver enlargement and 60% increase of the microsomal yields per gramme of liver was observed. A corresponding metabolic increase of about 6-8 times should be expected from these data in the living animal.

We have tested this calculation in dogs with 2-naphthylamine. The excretion of N-hydroxylated 2-naphthylamine or the conjugates in the urine was considered doubtful until Boyland and Manson [21] isolated small amounts of hydroxyl-amino- and nitrosonaphthalene by means of ether extraction and Thin Layer Chromatography (TLC). Pretreatment of beagle dogs with phenobarbital (8 x 40 mg/kg) led to a dramatic increase in the metabolic N-hydroxylation of 2-naph-thylamine (Fig. 4). We isolated the N-oxidation products in the form of the nitrosonaphthalene (5—9 mg) by means of CCl_4 extraction and simple separation by column chromatography [22, 23].

There are only a few scattered data on inhibition of N-hydroxylation in animals by drugs. Anaesthesia with barbiturates or urethane seems to reduce the velocity of N-hydroxylation. Substrate competition *in vitro* is based on competition for the oxygen activating system in the microsomes.

ORGANS

N-hydroxylation of aromatic amines is not restricted to the liver. In earlier experiments [4, 10] we found N-hydroxylation in the isolated perfused lung and liver of cat using N-methylaniline as the substrate. We repeated similar experiments with rabbit lung and liver because of the higher activities of these animals. On the left side in Fig. 5 dealkylation and p-C-hydroxylation are related to the total organ. But the lung is more active if the turnover is related to organ weight.

Remmer [24] found a comparable activity of barbiturate metabolism in the 9000 x g supernatant of homogenates of rabbit lung and liver.

Ernster [25], at a recent symposium, expressed the view that the mixed function system in kidney microsomes might differ from that of the liver. We

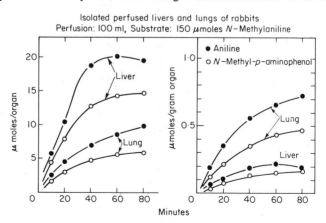

Figure 5. N-dealkylation and p-C-hydroxylation in isolated perfused livers and lungs of rabbits. From Uehleke, 1968, Ref. 27.

Table 2. Specific activities and cytochrome concentrations. m μmoles of metabolites formed by 1 mg of microsomal proteins of rabbit organs in 10 min. Substrates 3 μmoles/ml, 37°C, air. Mean of n experiments, N = normal, S = stimulated rabbits. Uehleke [27].

| Substrates | | N-Methylaniline | | | 4-Aminobiphenyl | Cytochromes $\Delta E_{450-490m\mu}$/mg Prot. | |
Reactions	n	C-Hydroxylation	N-Dealkylation	N-Hydroxylation	N-Hydroxylation	P_{450}	b_5
Liver $\frac{N}{S}$	12 9	42·3 79·5*	28·6 73·8*	19·4 15·2	8·6 26·4*	0·12 0·31*	0·14 0·16
Kidney $\frac{N}{S}$	6 5	5·8 9·2*	4·9 13·5*	3·1 5·2	3·4 8·9*	0·026 0·086*	0·056 0·120*
Lung $\frac{N}{S}$	4 4	7·2 8·6	3·8 5·2	4·1 3·9	2·1 2·6	0·024 0·030	0·031 0·040
Small Intestine $\frac{N}{S}$	5 4	0·9 1·0	1·2 1·8	— —	0·5 0·5	0·022 0·020	0·026 0·028
Brain $\frac{N}{S}$	3 3	— —	0·6 0·7	— —	— —	? —	0·004 —
Pig Urinary Bladder N	6	?	1·6	—	0·9	?	0·009

* These numbers are significantly different (P < 0·05) compared with the controls.

investigated the microsomal cytochrome substrate interaction with kidney microsomes of phenobarbital-stimulated rabbits (Fig. 6). There is no difference in the spectral changes between liver and kidney microsomes after addition of aniline (type II) or methylcholanthrene (type I) [28]. In addition to liver and lung, N-hydroxylation was also detected in the microsomal fraction of kidney [20] and to a minor degree in brain, intestine and the urinary bladder mucosa

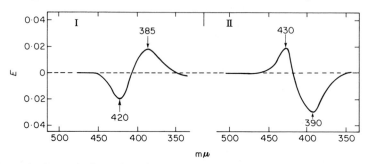

Figure 6. Spectral absorption changes in suspensions of rabbit kidney microsomal suspensions after addition of hexobarbital $10^{-3}M(I)$ and aniline $10^{-3}M(II)$. Difference spectrum against suspensions without substrates. Rabbits were stimulated with phenobarbital. From Uehleke and Greim, 1968, Ref. 20.

[26, 27]. Sometimes the activities of the microsomal fractions of extrahepatic tissues are too small to be estimated properly. Therefore, in Table 2 the activities are also indicated for microsomes of phenobarbital-stimulated animals. N-hydroxylation, and other drug reactions, are increased markedly in liver and kidney only.

TOXICOLOGICAL ASPECTS OF N-HYDROXYLATION

N-oxidation reactions cover a large field of toxicology and side effects of drugs. Many drugs and foreign compounds contain aromatic amino and nitro groups and they are metabolized to the corresponding hydroxylamino and nitroso compounds. It should be pointed out that N-hydroxylation generally occurs along with other reactions (e.g. C-ring-hydroxylation, etc.) to only a minor extent.

(a) Formation of ferri-haemoglobin

Arylhydroxylamines are very powerful haemoglobin-oxidizing metabolites. One molecule of arylhydroxylamine is able to oxidize hundreds of haemoglobin molecules in a cyclic process even *in vitro* (but not with purified haemoglobin!) when oxygen and carbohydrate substrates are available [29, 31, 32, 39].

The biochemical mechanisms are presented in detail in the paper of Dr. Wagner in this Symposium (p. 161).

Side effects of phenacetine, typical after high or chronic doses, are haemolysis, formation of ferri-haemoglobin, and kidney discolouration. The deacetylation product, p-phenetidine, seems to be partly responsible. After application of phenacetine in several species, the concentrations of phenetidine in liver and kidney are considerably higher than in the blood. Kidney microsomes from phenobarbital-stimulated rabbits were nearly as active in N-hydroxylating phenetidine as normal liver microsomes [34].

Certain sulphonamides also produce ferri-haemoglobin. Therefore we investigated the metabolism of sulphanilamide in relation to N-hydroxylation [33]. N-oxidation products of sulphanilamide were isolated by extraction of microsomal suspensions incubated with sulphanilamide and $NADPH_2$. The N_4-hydroxy-sulphonamides are the metabolites responsible for the formation of ferri-haemoglobin (Table 3).

Table 3. Formation of ferri-haemoglobin by different possible metabolites of sulphanilamide. Suspensions of cattle erythrocytes 50-60 mg Hb/ml, 37°C, substrates 5 μmoles/ml; under air or nitrogen. Thauer *et al.* [33].

		Air	Nitrogen
Sulphanilamide	H_2N—⟨ ⟩—SO_2NH_2 (positions 5,6,4,1,3,2)	○	○
2-Hydroxy-sulphanilamide	H_2N—⟨ ⟩—SO_2NH_2	○	○
3-Hydroxy-sulphanilamide	H_2N—⟨HO ⟩—SO_2NH_2	○	○
p-Hydroxylamino-benzenesulphonamide	$HOHN$—⟨ ⟩—SO_2NH_2	+	○
p-Nitrosobenzene-sulphonamide	ON—⟨ ⟩—SO_2NH_2	+	○
p,p'Disulphonamidoazoxybenzene	H_2NO_2S—⟨ ⟩—$N{=}N$(→O)—⟨ ⟩—SO_2NH_2	○	○

(b) Binding to proteins and allergy

The very reactive arylhydroxylamines are partly bound to different proteins. This might lead to the formation of antigens. We tested the production of antibodies with guinea pigs after i.p. injections of phenetidine with an adjuvans. The Dale-Schultz test with the isolated uteri of the guinea pigs revealed a positive reaction [35].

Aniline-type molecules belong to the most powerful allergens for humans. A variety of drugs, industrial compounds, dyes, cosmetics, etc. fall in this class.

(c) N-Hydroxylation and carcinogenesis

It is now generally accepted that the N-hydroxy products of several carcinogenic arylamines are more effective than the parent amines or the aminophenols formed in the organism.

It is not clear whether the hydroxylamines or any conjugates are the transport forms that are further activated or liberated in the susceptible organ. Some facts are not in agreement with this proposal. We thus have to consider that N-hydroxylation activity is present in many organs, even in the urinary bladder mucosa. Recently we have demonstrated that arylamines and their N-hydroxy derivatives are rapidly absorbed from the urinary bladder of dogs [36]. Hence the bladder implantation of these compounds may give invalid results.

Nevertheless, we feel that carcinogenesis by arylamines is likely to be the first mechanism that might be clarified at the molecular level (see paper of Prof. Boyland in this Symposium, p.183).

REFERENCES

1. Heubner, W., *Arch. exp. Path. Pharmak.* **72** (1913) 239.
2. Kiese, M., *Arch. exp. Path. Pharmak.* **235** (1959) 354.
3. Uehleke, H., *Arch. exp. Path. Pharmak.* Abstr. **241** (1961) 150. 26. Tag der Deutschen Pharmakol. Ges., Würzburg, 1960.
4. Kiese, M. and Uehleke, H., *Arch. exp. Path. Pharmak.* **242** (1961) 117.
5. Cramer, J. W., Miller, J. A. and Miller, E. C., *J. biol. Chem.* **235** (1960) 885.
6. Uehleke, H., *Biochem. Pharmac.* **8** (1961) 23.
7. Uehleke, H., *Experientia* **17** (1961). 557.
8. Uehleke, H., *Experientia* **24** (1968) 108.
9. Uehleke, H., *Fifth Int. Congr. Biochem,* Moscow, 1961, Abstr. S. 399, 18-55, Pergamon Press, 1961.
10. Uehleke, H., *Proc. First Int. pharmac. Meet.,* Stockholm, 1961. **6,** 31, Pergamon Press, 1962.
11. Kampffmeyer, H. and Kiese, M., *Arch. exp. Path. Pharmak.* **250** (1965) 1.
12. Uehleke, H., *in* "Redoxfunktionen cytoplasmatischer Strukturen", Symp. p. 97, Wiener Akad. Ärztl. Fortb., Wien 1962.

13. Debackere, M. and Uehleke, H., *Proc. Eur. Soc. Study Drug Toxic.* **IV** (1964) 40.
14. Miller, E. C. and Miller, J. A., *Pharmac. Rev.* **18** (1966) 805.
15. Remmer, H., *Proc. Eur. Soc. Study Drug Toxic.* **IV** (1964) 57.
16. Conney, A. H., *Pharmac. Rev.* **19** (1967) 317.
17. Uehleke, H., *Arch. Pharmak. exp. Path.* **259** (1967) 66.
18. Uehleke, H., *Third Int. pharmac. Meet.*, Sao Paulo, 1966. Abstr. 81.
19. Uehleke, H. and Nestel, K., *Pharmak. exp. Path.* **257** (1967) 151.
20. Uehleke, H. and Greim, H., *Arch. Pharmak. exp. Path.* **259** (1968) 199 and **261** (1968) 152.
21. Boyland, E. and Manson, D., *Biochem. J.* **101** (1966) 84.
22. Uehleke, H. and Brill, E., *Biochem. Pharmac.* **17** (1968) 1459.
23. Uehleke, H., Geipert, F., Schnitger, F., Brill, E., Radomski, J. L. and Deichmann, W. B., *Arch. Pharmak. exp. Path.* **260** (1968) 213.
24. Remmer, H., *in* "Redoxfunktionen cytoplasmatischer Strukturen", Symp. p. 75, Wiener Akad. Ärztl. Fortb., Wien 1962.
25. Ernster, L., *in* "Biochemie des Sauerstoffs", p. 184, 19. Kolloquium der Ges. für Biologische Chemie, Moosbach, 1968. Springer-Verlag, Heidelberg, 1968.
26. Uehleke, H., *Life Sci.* **5** (1966) 1489.
27. Uehleke, H., *Proc. Eur. Soc. Study Drug Toxic.* **X** (1969) 94.
28. Schenkman, J. B., Remmer, H. and Estabrook, R. W., *Molec. Pharmac.* **3** (1967) 113.
29. Bodanski, O., *Pharmac. Rev.* **3** (1951) 144.
30. Heubner, W., *Erg. ges. Physiol.* **43** (1940) 1.
31. Uehleke, H., *Fortschr. Arzneimitt. Forsch.* **8** (1964) 195.
32. Kiese, M., *Pharmac. Rev.* **18** (1966) 1146.
33. Thauer, R. K., Stöffler, G. and Uehleke, H., *Arch. exp. Path. Pharmak.* **252** (1965) 32.
34. Uehleke, H., unpublished, Tübingen (1967).
35. Uehleke, H., *Z. Immun. Forsch. exp. Ther.* **123** (1962) 447.
36. Uehleke, H., *Arch. Pharmak. exp. Path.* **261** (1968) 218.
37. Uehleke, H., *Biochem. Pharmac.* **12** (1963) 219.
38. Kiese, M. and Uehleke, H., *Naturwissenschaften* **48** (1961) 379.
39. Burger, A., Wagner, J., Uehleke, H. and Götz, E., *Arch. Pharmak. exp. Path.* **256** (1967) 333.

FEBS Symposium, Volume 16, 1969, pp. 109-124

Mechanisms of Oxidation by Enzymes in the Endoplasmic Reticulum

J. R. GILLETTE

Laboratory of Chemical Pharmacology, National Heart Institute,
National Institutes of Health,
Bethesda, Maryland, U.S.A.

List of non-usual abbreviations and definitions

Type 1 spectral change, the difference spectrum characterized by a trough at about 420 nm and a peak at about 385 nm; type 2 spectral change, the difference spectrum characterized by a peak at about 430 nm and a trough at about 395 nm; K_s, the concentration of a substance that causes one half the maximal type 1 or type 2 spectral change; K_m, the concentration of a substance that causes one half the maximal rate of metabolism; A_{max}, the maximal absorbancy of a type 1 (A_{490}-A_{420}) or a type 2 (A_{430}-A_{490}) spectral change; SKF 26754A, aminoethyl diphenylpropylacetate HCl; SKF 8742A, monoethyl-aminoethyl diphenylpropylacetate HCl; SKF 525A, diethylaminoethyl diphenyl-propylacetate HCl; DPEA, 2,4-dichloro-6-phenylphenoxyethylamine; Lilly 390-378-23B, 2, 4-dichloro-6-phenoxyethyl monomethylamine; Lilly 327-169-22B, 2,4-dichloro-6-phenylphenoxyethyl dimethylamine.

During the past several years, it has become increasingly evident that the vast majority of lipid-soluble drugs and other foreign compounds are oxidized by NADPH-dependent enzymes in liver microsomes (for reviews, see refs. 1-3). The versatility of these enzymes is virtually unique, for they catalyze a variety of different oxidative reactions, such as sidechain oxidation, aromatic hydroxy-lation, deamination, N-, S- and O-dealkylation, N- and S-oxidation, dehalo-genation and the conversion of organothiophosphonates to organo-phosphates.

In many instances, drugs are metabolized by more than one of these reactions and hence may be converted to a wide variety of metabolites. For example, the commonly used depressant, chlorpromazine, undergoes N-oxidation, sulfoxi-dation, aromatic hydroxylation and three types of N-dealkylation. Since many of the metabolites arising from the metabolism of drugs possess biological activity, and indeed may be more potent than the parent drug, one of the objectives of the biochemical pharmacologist has been to identify the various metabolites and to determine the dominant reactions. Attainment of this objective, however, is more complicated than it might seem. Not only the absolute rates but the relative rates of the various reactions vary with the compound, the animal species, the strain [4], and even the individual [5]. Moreover, there are sex differences [4], age differences [6], and diurnal variations [7] in the rate of drug metabolism. The rates of drug metabolism may be varied by removal of the adrenals [8, 9], or the hypophysis [10], or by pretreating the animals with thyroxine [9, 11], epinephrine [9, 12], alloxan [9, 13], or carbon tetrachloride [14-16]. The rates may be altered by sham operation [17] or starvation [18, 19]. The activities of the microsomal enzymes may be inhibited by various substances or enhanced by pretreatment of the animals with diverse substances including inhibitors (for reviews, see refs. 2, 3, 20). The rates of metabolism of drugs in the smooth-surfaced microsomes also differ from those in the rough-surfaced microsomes [21, 22].

Table 1. Relationship between ethylmorphine metabolism and various components in rabbit liver microsomes.

Component	Smooth	Rough	Smooth / Rough
Ethylmorphine demethylation (nmole/mg/min)	2·8	0·56	5·65
Cytochrome P-450 (nmole/mg)	0·93	0·32	3·53
Cytochrome c reductase (nmole/min/mg)	170	78	2·23
Cytochrome P-450 reduction (nmole/min/mg)	5·96	1·25	5·55

It is currently believed that most of the reactions are catalyzed by cytochrome P-450 or the recently discovered cytochrome P-446 [23-26]. In support of this view, carbon monoxide inhibits all of the reactions, with the possible exception of N-oxide formation and sulfoxide formation. In addition, the partition coefficients, where they have been measured, are similar to those obtained by Cooper et al. [27]. It is also believed that NADPH cytochrome c reductase reduces the carbon monoxide-sensitive cytochromes either directly or indirectly through an unidentified carrier. The sequence of events, however, has been a matter of conjecture. A revised version of the mechanism proposed by Brodie et al. [1] is shown in Fig. 1. In this mechanism, NADPH reduces cytochrome c reductase which in turn reduces cytochrome P-450. The reduced cytochrome P-450 then combines with oxygen to form an "active oxygen" complex which in turn oxidizes the drug.

The findings that various substances cause type 1 and type 2 spectral changes in liver microsomes, even in the absence of NADPH or dithionite [28-30], has led to the view that the substrates combine with the oxidized as well as the reduced forms of cytochrome P-450 and cytochrome P-446. Thus the mechanism of the carbon monoxide-sensitive reactions may be as complex as that shown in Fig. 2.

During the past few years, we have carried out studies to determine how the components of the enzyme systems differ with species and sex and how they were affected by various treatments. We hoped that these studies might provide a better concept not only of the mechanisms of alteration but also of the mechanism of the drug-metabolizing enzymes. In this paper, I shall summarize our findings which show that differences in any of the components cause alterations in the rate of drug metabolism. Most of the studies have been carried out with ethylmorphine, which causes a type 1 spectral change, and aniline, which causes a type 2 spectral change. Ethylmorphine undergoes N-demethylation and little, if any, O-deethylation [31]. The N-demethylation of this drug is enhanced by pretreatment of rats with phenobarbital but is not altered by pretreatment with 3-methylcholanthrene [23]. Since phenobarbital pretreatment selectively increases the amount of cytochrome P-450 and 3-methylcholanthrene selectively increases the amount of cytochrome P-446 [25, 26], the N-demethylation of ethylmorphine is presumably catalyzed by cytochrome P-450 but not cytochrome P-446. In contrast, the hydroxylation of aniline is enhanced by pretreatment of animals with either phenobarbital or 3-methylcholanthrene [20] and thus may be metabolized by either cytochrome P-450 or cytochrome P-446.

Relationships between the demethylation of ethylmorphine and the anaerobic reduction of cytochrome P-450

A variety of experiments have shown that the metabolism of ethylmorphine is more closely related to the rate of cytochrome P-450 reduction than to the total amount of cytochrome P-450 or to the rate of cytochrome c reduction. Fouts and his co-workers [21, 22] have reported that many drugs are metabolized more rapidly by smooth-surfaced microsomes from rabbit liver than by rough-surfaced microsomes. As shown in Table 1, Holtzman et al. [32] found that the difference in the metabolism of ethylmorphine was not related to differences in the amount of cytochrome P-450, or the activity of NADPH cytochrome c reductase, but was related to the rate of cytochrome P-450 reduction by NADPH in a 100% carbon monoxide atmosphere.

Adrenalectomy of male rats has been shown to impair the metabolism of a wide variety of drugs [8, 9]. Recently, Castro et al. [33] showed that adrenalectomy decreases the activity of cytochrome c reductase, the rate of cytochrome P-450 reductase, the amount of cytochrome P-450, and the magnitude of the type 1 spectral change caused by ethylmorphine (Table 2). However, cortisone in adrenalectomized rats reversed the impairment of ethylmorphine metabolism, cytochrome c reductase and cytochrome P-450 reductase,

Table 2. Effect of cortisone treatment on ethylmorphine demethylation and various components of the electron transport system in liver microsomes of adrenalectomized male rats.

Component	Sham operated	Adrex	Adrex + cortisone
			% of sham value
Ethylmorphine demethylation (nmole/mg/min)	4·5	56	124
Cytochrome P-450 (nmole/mg)	1·27	81	75
Cytochrome c reductase (nmole/mg/min)	113	69	113
Cytochrome P-450 reductase (nmole/mg/min)	7·4	68	140
Spectral change (Type 1) (OD x 10^3)	9	73	76

but not the decrease in cytochrome P-450 or the spectral change. Thus the effects of cortisone on ethylmorphine demethylation were more closely related to a decrease in the rates of cytochrome c reduction and cytochrome-450 reduction than to the other parameters studied.

Castro and Gillette [34] found that species differences in the metabolism of ethylmorphine may be attributed to differences in both V_m and K_m. Davies *et al.* [35] confirmed these findings (Table 3, columns 1 and 6) but found very little species differences in the amount of cytochrome P-450 or in the activity of cytochrome c reductase (Table 3, columns 3 and 4). Although there was a species difference in the magnitude of the type 1 spectral change, this was not related to the species difference in the rate of ethylmorphine metabolism (Table 3, cf. columns 1 and 5). Indeed, the only parameter that seemed to be related to the demethylation of ethylmorphine was the rate of cytochrome P-450 reduction under anaerobic conditions (Table 3, cf. columns 1 and 2). Even this parameter, however, could not be related to the demethylase activity in

Table 4. Ethylmorphine demethylation and apparent extinction coefficients for cytochrome P-450 in liver microsomes from male and female rats.

Sex	N	V_{max} mμmoles HCHO mg protein/min	$E_{P\text{-}450}$* $mM^{-1}\ cm^{-1}$
Male	5	9·20 ± 0·84	97·4 ± 4·5
Female	5	2·50 ± 0·44	91·5 ± 5·5

$$*E_{P\text{-}450} = \frac{OD_{450\text{-}490}\ m\mu}{\text{Total heme} - \text{cytochrome } b5}$$

Table 3. Species differences in ethylmorphine demethylation and component of liver microsomes.

Species	Sex	(1) V_m for ethylmorphine demethylation mμmol/min/mg	(2) Cytochrome P-450 reduction mμmol/mg/min	(3) Cytochrome c reductase mμmol/mg/min	(4) Cytochrome P-450 mμmol/mg	(5) Type 1 spectral change (ΔOD/mg) $\times 10^3$	(6) K_m* mM	(7) K_s mM
Mouse	Male	13·2	11·2	144	1·23	6	1·1	0·9
Mouse	Female	18·0	12·3	166	0·86	9	0·9	0·6
Rat	Male	11·6	8·35	150	0·82	15	0·32	0·25
Rat	Female	4·5	7·3	145	0·67	10	0·56	0·35
Rabbit	Male	4·0	3·04	130	1·05	17	2·05	0·95
Rabbit	Female	4·3	3·41	150	1·09	12	2·08	0·90
Guinea Pig	Male	5·4	3·82	132	1·10	19	1·25	1·08
Guinea Pig	Female	5·0	4·2	145	1·28	16	1·31	1·32

* Ethylmorphine demethylation.

114   J. R. GILLETTE

microsomes of male mice and female rats. Moreover, the sex difference in
metabolism is not due to differences in the relative amounts of cytochrome
P-450 and cytochrome P-446, for Greene and Stripp [36] in my laboratory have
found little sex difference in the apparent extinction coefficient of cytochrome
P-450 (Table 4).

The effects of various substances on the rate of cytochrome P-450 reduction

A number of investigators have shown that various substrates stimulate the
oxidation of NADPH by liver microsomes in air [37-40]. If the rate-limiting step
of the oxidation of drugs were the rate of cytochrome P-450 reduction, it would
be difficult to account for this stimulatory effect unless the substrates altered
the rate of cytochrome P-450 reduction. Accordingly, Gigon et al. [41] found
that substances that cause type 1 spectral changes enhance the rate of reduction
of the cytochrome. In contrast, those substances that cause type 2 spectral
changes slow the rate of cytochrome P-450 reduction (Table 5). The effects on
the anaerobic cytochrome P-450 reduction were similar to the effects of NADPH
oxidase activity; type 1 substances enhanced NADPH oxidation whereas type 2
substances either had no effect or inhibited it (Table 6).

These findings raised the possibility that the stimulatory effects of ethylmorphine were more closely related to the maximal velocity of ethylmorphine
metabolism than is the endogenous cytochrome P-450 reduction. To evaluate
this possibility, Gigon et al. [41] studied the effects of ethylmorphine on

Table 5. Effect of drug substrates in hepatic microsomal cytochrome P-450
reduction by NADPH in male rats.

| | Cytochrome P-450 reduction nmol/min/mg protein | | |
Drug substrates	Control	In the presence of substrate	% of control
Type 1 substrates and inhibitors			
Ethylmorphine	10·7	18·9	177
Hexobarbital	7·2	12·3	170
SKF 525-A	8·2	18·0	221
Aminopyrine	8·0	11·4	142
Imipramine	7·7	12·6	162
Type 2 substrates and inhibitors			
Aniline	10·1	4·5	45
Nicotinamide	7·6	4·5	59
DPEA	8·0	2·9	36

Table 6. Effect of drug substrates on NADPH oxidation by rat liver microsome.

Substrate	Type	NADPH oxidation nmoles/min/mg protein
None		18·0
Ethylmorphine	1	32·1
Hexobarbital	1	29·0
SKF 525-A	1	39·6
Aniline	2	20·5
Nicotinamide	2	19·1
DPEA	2	13·9

cytochrome P-450 reduction in liver microsomes from male and female rats (Table 7). In the absence of ethylmorphine there was only a slight, though significant, sex difference in the rate of reduction of cytochrome P-450, but in the presence of ethylmorphine the rate of reduction was 69% greater in liver microsomes from males than in those from females. Thus, the 3-fold sex difference in the metabolism of ethylmorphine was not related to the total rate of P-450 reduction, either in the presence or the absence of ethylmorphine. It seemed possible, however, that only a part of the cytochrome P-450 in the microsomes of females may be involved in the metabolism of ethylmorphine and that the stimulatory effect of ethylmorphine on cytochrome P-450 reduction might be proportional to the active fraction of the cytochrome. Accordingly, the sex differences in the substrate-induced increase in the rate of cytochrome P-450 reduction was closely related to the sex difference in ethylmorphine metabolism. These findings thus suggest the possibility that ethylmorphine combines with the cytochrome P-450 in liver microsomes to form a complex which is more readily reduced by NADPH cytochrome P-450 reductase than is cytochrome P-450 in the absence of the substrate.

Table 7. Relationship between the rates of ethylmorphine demethylation and cytochrome P-450 reduction in microsomes from male and female rats.

Conditions for P-450 reduction	Male		Female	
	P-450* Reduction	P-450 red* Demethylation†	P-450* Reduction	P-450 red* Demethylation†
Control	10·5	0·97	8·2	2·48
Ethylmorphine	19·1	1·77	11·4	3·33
Ethylmorphine minus control	8·6	0·80	3·2	0·97

* P-450 reduction (nmole/min/mg.) $E = 91 \text{ mM}^{-1} \text{ cm}^{-1}$.
† V_m, ethylmorphine demethylation (nmole/min/mg.) Male, 10·8; female 3·3.

An extinction coefficient of $91 \text{ mM}^{-1}\text{cm}^{-1}$ was used to convert the data from absorbancy to nmoles of cytochrome P-450. With this value the stoichiometric relationship between the rate of the ethylmorphine-induced cytochrome P-450 reduction and the rate of ethylmorphine demethylation approached the theoretical value of 1:1 for a mixed oxygenase system (Figs. 1 and 2). In view of the studies of Hildebrandt *et al.* [26], however, it is possible that the conversion factor should be $50 \text{ mM}^{-1}\text{cm}^{-1}$ rather than $91 \text{ mM}^{-1}\text{cm}^{-1}$, and that the stoichiometric relationship between the substrate-induced cytochrome P-450 reduction and ethylmorphine demethylation would approach 1·5-2:1. The interpretation of these findings must thus await further investigation.

It has been suggested that the stimulatory effects of a substrate on NADPH oxidation are stoichiometrically related to the rate of oxidation of the substrate

Table 8. Inhibition of NADPH oxidation in mouse liver microsomes by carbon monoxide.

Atmosphere	NADPH oxidation ΔOD 340 mμ/min
14% O_2−86% N_2	0·068
14% O_2−56% N_2−30% CO	0·031
% Inhibition	55%

[37, 38]. However, it should be pointed out that the increase in the rate of NADPH oxidation caused by a substrate of cytochrome P-450 enzymes may not necessarily correspond stoichiometrically to the rate of substrate oxidation. The reason for this conclusion is evident from the following considerations. In the absence of a substrate the total rate of NADPH oxidation (R_t) is due to the rate of NADPH oxidation through both the active cytochrome P-450 enzyme (R_p) and other pathways (R_o), i.e. $R_t = R_p + R_o$. In the presence of substrate the total rate of NADPH oxidation $(R\ )$ is due to the rate of decomposition of the O_2-cytochrome P-450-substrate complex (R_{ps}) and the rate of NADPH oxidation through other pathways (R_o), i.e. $R_{ts} = R_{ps} + R_o$. Thus the difference in the total rates of NADPH oxidation in the presence and absence of the substrate does not represent the rate of decomposition of the O_2-cytochrome P-450 complex and hence the rate of substrate oxidation, but represents the difference in the rates of decomposition of the O_2-cytochrome P-450-substrate complex and O_2-cytochrome P-450, i.e. $R_{ts} - R_t = R_{ps} - R_p$. Thus the magnitude of the difference between the total rate of NADPH oxidation in the presence and absence of the substrate should approach the rate of substrate oxidation only when R_p is negligible. However, Sasame [3, 42] in my laboratory has found that endogenous NADPH oxidation by liver microsomes is blocked by CO about 55% (Table 8), suggesting that R_p is probably not negligible, and thus that the change

1.   NADPH + cytochrome c reductase + H^+ $\rightleftharpoons$ $NADP^+$
                                                                  + H_2-cytochrome c reductase

2. H_2-cytochrome c reductase + cytochrome P-450 (Fe^{+3}) $\xrightarrow{\text{carrier?}}$
        cytochrome c reductase + cytochrome P-450 (Fe^{+2}) + $2H^+$ + e^-

3.   Cytochrome P-450 (Fe^{+2}) + O_2 $\rightleftharpoons$ cytochrome $-$ P-450 (FeO_2)

4.   Cytochrome P-450 (FeO_2)
                    + substrate $\rightleftharpoons$ cytochrome P-450 (FeO_2) $-$ substrate

5a.   Cytochrome P-450 (FeO_2) $-$ substrate + $2H^+$ + e^- $\rightarrow$
                    cytochrome P-450 (Fe^{+3}) + oxidized substrate + H_2O

5b.   Cytochrome P-450 (FeO_2) + $2H^+$ + e^- $\rightarrow$ cytochrome P-450 (Fe^{+3}) + H_2O_2

Figure 1. A revised version of the mechanism of drug oxidation proposed by Brodie, Gillette and LaDu.

in the rate of NADPH oxidation observed on the addition of substrates should be less than the rate of substrate oxidation. Claims of a stoichiometric relationship between the rate of substrate metabolism and the magnitude of the difference in the rate of NADPH oxidation should thus be accepted with caution. Actually, discrepancies between the effects of a substrate on the rate of NADPH oxidation and the rate of substrate metabolism may be considerably greater than hitherto supposed. Sasame [3, 42] in my laboratory found that the

1.   NADPH cytochrome c reductase + H^+ $\rightleftharpoons$ $NADP^+$
                                                              + H_2-cytochrome c reductase

2.   Cytochrome P-450 (Fe^{+3})
                    + substrate $\rightleftharpoons$ cytochrome P-450 (Fe^{+3}) $-$ substrate

3a. H_2-cytochrome c reductase + cytochrome P-450 (Fe^{+3}) $\xrightarrow{\text{carrier?}}$
        cytochrome c reductase + cytochrome P-350 (Fe^{+2}) + $2H^+$ + e^-

3b. H_2-cytochrome c reductase + cytochrome P-450 (Fe^{+3}) $-$ substrate
        $\xrightarrow{\text{carrier?}}$ cytochrome c reductase
                    + cytochrome P-450 (Fe^{+2}) $-$ substrate + $2H^+$ + e^-

4.   Cytochrome P-450 (Fe^{+2})
                    + substrate $\rightleftharpoons$ cytochrome P-450 (Fe^{+2}) $-$ substrate

5a.   Cytochrome P-450 (Fe^{+2}) + O_2 $\rightleftharpoons$ cytochrome P-450 (FeO_2)

5b.   Cytochrome P-450 (Fe^{+2}) $-$ substrate
                    + O_2 $\rightleftharpoons$ cytochrome P-450 (FeO_2) $-$ substrate

6.   Cytochrome P-450 (FeO_2)
                    + substrate $\rightleftharpoons$ cytochrome P-450 (FeO_2) $-$ substrate

7a.   Cytochrome P-450 (FeO_2) + $2H^+$ + e^- $\rightarrow$ cytochrome P-450 (Fe^{+3}) + H_2O_2

7b.   Cytochrome P-450 (FeO_2) $-$ substrate + $2H^+$ + e^- $\rightarrow$
                    cytochrome P-450 (Fe^{+3}) + oxidized substrate + H_2O

Figure 2. A possible mechanism of drug oxidation by liver microsomes.

Table 9. Lack of correlation between NADPH and hexobarbital oxidation by rabbit liver microsomes.

	N	NADPH oxidized mμmoles $\pm$ SD	Hexobarbital oxidized mμmoles $\pm$ SD
Hexobarbital	4	327 $\pm$ 9	106 $\pm$ 17
Control	4	149 $\pm$ 6	–
Difference		178	106 $\pm$ 17

hexobarbital-induced increase in NADPH oxidation by rabbit liver microsomes was about 50% greater than the amount of hexobarbital metabolized (Table 9). The reason for this discrepancy is unknown, but it suggests the possibility that a part of the reduced cytochrome P-450-hexobarbital complex formed from the oxidized cytochrome P-450-hexobarbital complex does not result in oxidation of the drug. If this is the case, then it seems possible that some type 1 substances may enhance NADPH oxidation and cytochrome P-450 reduction without being metabolized. In any event, it is evident that type 2 substrates will not cause stoichiometric increases in NADPH oxidation and that studies based solely on the effects of substances on NADPH oxidation by liver microsomes should be interpreted with care.

Relationship between type 1 and type 2 spectral changes and effects on nitro-reductase

Since the enzymatic reduction of p-nitrobenzoate is also mediated by cytochrome P-450 [3, 43, 44], it seemed likely that substances which caused spectral changes might alter nitro-reductase activity. As shown in Table 10, compounds that cause type 2 spectral changes inhibited the reduction of p-nitrobenzoate; substances, such as SKF-8742-A and Lilly-390-378-23B, that cause both type 1 and type 2 spectral changes, also inhibited nitro-reduction, but to a lesser extent [44]. In contrast, all the substances that cause only type 1 spectral changes enhanced rather than inhibited the reaction. In attempting to determine a value for K_I, however, it was found that DPEA exerted an unusual effect on nitro-reductase. A Dixon plot of the data obtained with various concentrations of DPEA was non-linear (Fig. 3), and reciprocal plots of the data obtained with various concentrations of p-nitrobenzoate revealed that DPEA inhibited nitro-reduction by a mixed mechanism. These findings are thus reminiscent of partial mixed inhibition and suggest that the reduction of p-nitrobenzoate was either catalyzed by several enzymes, at least one of which was not inhibited by DPEA, or was catalyzed by a single enzyme that was only partially blocked by DPEA.

Table 10. The effects of various substances on the reduction of p-nitrobenzoate by mouse liver microsomes.

Substance	Type of spectral change		Relative nitroreductase activity
	Type 1	Type 2	
SKF 26754 A		+	58
SKF 8742 A	+	±	79
SKF 525 A	+		136
DPEA		+	41
Lilly 390-378-23B	+	+	73
Lilly 327-169-22B	+		118
Aniline		+	80
Hexobarbital	+		123
Ethylmorphine	+		125
Aminopyrine	+		105

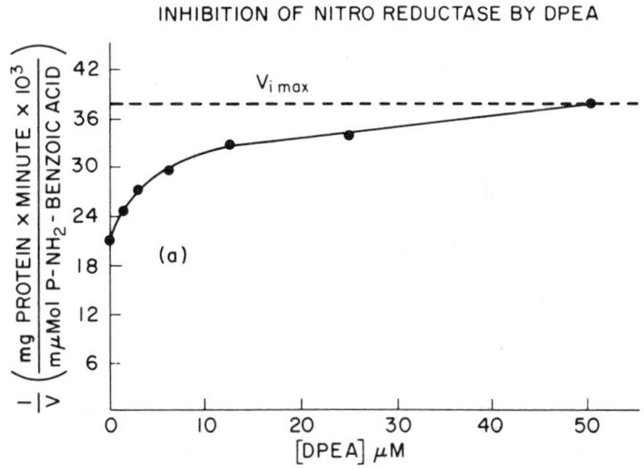

INHIBITION OF NITRO REDUCTASE BY DPEA

Figure 3. Dixon plot of the inhibitory effects of DPEA on p-nitrobenzoic acid reduction by mouse liver.

The effects of type 1 and type 2 compounds as inhibitors of oxidative reactions

Reports [28, 30] that there is a close correlation between the K_s and the K_m values for a number of substrates suggested the possibility that the spectral changes were visible representations of Michaelis complexes. It therefore seemed possible that the two types of spectral changes represented two enzymes, one visualized by a type 1 spectral change, and the other visualized by a type 2 spectral change. Alternatively, the spectral changes represent two sites, on a single enzyme; one site manifested by a type 1 spectral change and the other manifested by a type 2 spectral change. According to both views, substances which cause a type 1 spectral change should competitively inhibit the oxidation of each other and those that cause type 2 spectral changes should competitively inhibit each other. According to the second view, substances that cause type 2 spectral changes might inhibit the metabolism of a type 1 substrate non-competitively, but never competitively.

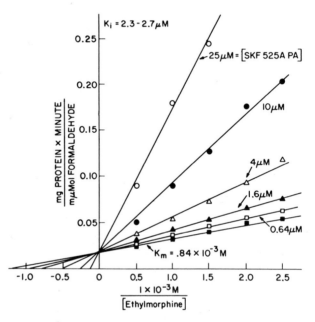

Figure 4. The effects of various concentrations of SKF-26754A (SKF-525A PA) on ethylmorphine N-demethylation by mouse liver microsomes in the presence of 20 mM nicotinamide.

There are a number of facts which make it difficult to accept this simple concept of the interrelationships between spectral changes and drug oxidation. Schenkman *et al.* [47] showed that nicotinamide inhibits aminopyrine demethylation by a competitive mechanism. Sasame [42] in my laboratory confirmed these results, but found that nicotinamide inhibits the demethylation of ethylmorphine predominantly by a non-competitive mechanism. Thus a type 2 substance may inhibit the demethylation of type 1 substrates either competitively or non-competitively, depending on the substrate. Moreover, he [45] showed that the hydroxylation of aniline is inhibited uncompetitively by SKF-26754A and DPEA, even though all three substances cause type 2 spectral changes [44, 45]. In addition, SKF-26754A inhibits the N-demethylation of ethylmorphine competitively (Fig. 4), whereas DPEA inhibits the reaction non-competitively at low concentrations (0·4-4·0 μM) and both non-competitively and competitively at high concentrations of the inhibitor (>25 μM). The dual effects of DPEA are especially evident when nicotinamide is added to incubation mixtures (Fig. 5).

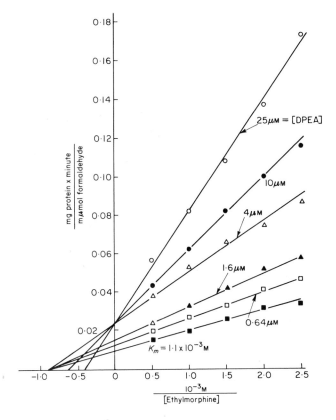

Figure 5. The effects of various concentrations of DPEA on ethylmorphine N-demethylation by mouse liver microsomes in the presence of 20mM nicotinamide.

The competitive inhibition of ethylmorphine demethylation by SKF-26754A was unexpected for this inhibitor is very avidly bound to liver microsomes. Indeed, A_{max} (type 2) is obtained when the free concentration of SKF-26754A is about 0·2 μM, even though the total concentration of cytochrome P-450 in the incubation mixtures is usually about 1 μM in suspensions of 1·0 mg microsomal protein per ml [45]. Thus it seems likely that SKF-26754A exerts its competitive inhibitory effect by altering the affinity of the enzyme for the substrate rather than by competing with the substrate for the same site on the enzyme. Accordingly SKF-26754A alters the K_s for the type 1 spectral change caused by ethylmorphine [45], even though high concentrations of ethylmorphine do not decrease the magnitude of the type 2 spectral change caused by SKF-26754A [42].

In conclusion, these findings suggest that the mechanism for drug metabolism is more complicated than has been hitherto suspected. Liver microsomes apparently contain a population of cytochrome P-450 enzymes, and not just a composite of cytochrome P-450 and cytochrome P-446. In general, type 1 substrates that are slowly metabolized will combine with a relatively small proportion of the cytochrome P-450 enzymes, whereas substrates which are rapidly metabolized combine with a relatively large proportion of them. The overall kinetics of the reaction, however, will depend on a number of factors including not only the proportion of the cytochrome P-450 which binds the substrate but also the equilibrium constant for formation of the complexes between the substrate, and the oxidized form of the active portion of the cytochrome P-450, the rate of reduction of the cytochrome P-450-substrate complex, and perhaps the steady state constants (K_m) for the dissociation of the reduced cytochrome P-450-substrate and O_2-cytochrome P-450-substrate complexes. With some substrates, such as ethylmorphine, the rate limiting step of the reaction may be the rate of reduction of the oxidized cytochrome-P-450-substrate complex, but this need not be the case for other substrates. Type 1 and type 2 substances may inhibit the reactions in a number of ways. They may compete with the substrate for the same binding site of cytochrome P-450, they may decrease the affinity of cytochrome P-450 for the substrate, or they may slow the rate of reduction of the cytochrome P-450-substrate complex.

The findings presented here also suggest that a number of relationships which have been reported to account for the kinetics of drug metabolism may not be universally applicable. With some substrates, such as hexobarbital [30] and cyclohexane [46], the K_m and V_{max} of drug oxidation are apparently related to the K_s and A_{max} of the spectral change, but with other substrates, such as ethylmorphine, no such relationship exists. With some substrates, such as ethylmorphine, the stimulatory effects on cytochrome P-450 reduction may be related to rate of their metabolism. It is possible that the stimulatory effects of type 1 substances on NADPH oxidation may be superficially related to the oxidation of drugs, but as shown in this paper the stoichiometric relationships between the hexobarbital-induced NADPH oxidation and hexobarbital metabolism clearly do not fit the 1:1 relationship required by the mixed-function oxidase mechanism. It is evident that much more work needs to be done to account for these discrepancies.

REFERENCES

1. Brodie, B. B., Gillette, J. R. and La Du, B. N., *A. Rev. Biochem.* **27** (1958) 427.
2. Gillette, J. R., *Prog. Drug Res.* **6** (1963) 13.
3. Gillette, J. R., *Adv. Pharmac.* **4** (1966) 219.
4. Quinn, G. P., Axelrod, J. and Brodie, B. B., *Biochem. Pharmac.* **1** (1958) 152.
5. Brodie, B. B., Burns, J. J. and Weiner, M., *Medna. exp.* **1** (1959) 290.
6. Fouts, J. R. and Adamson, R. H., *Science, N.Y.* **129** (1959) 897.
7. Radzialowski, F. M. and Bousquet, W. F., *Life Sci.* **6** (1967) 2545.
8. Remmer, H., *Arch. exp. Path. Pharmak.* **233** (1958) 184.
9. Kato, R. and Gillette, J. R., *J. Pharmac. exp. Ther.* **150** (1965) 285.
10. Conney, A. H., Miller, E. C. and Miller, J. A., *Cancer Res.* **16** (1956) 450.
11. Conney, A. H. and Garren, L., *Biochem. Pharmac.* **6** (1961) 257.
12. Fouts, J. R., *Fedn Proc. Fedn Am. Socs exp. Biol.* **21** (1962) 1107.
13. Dixon, R. L., Hart, L. G. and Fouts, J. R., *J. Pharmac. exp. Ther.* **133** (1961) 7.
14. Smuckler, E., Arrhenius, E. and Hultin, T., *Biochem. J.* **103** (1967) 57.
15. Castro, J. A., Sasame, H. A., Sussman, H. and Gillette, J. R., *Life Sci.* **7** (1968) 129.
16. Dingell, J. V. and Heimberg, M., *Biochem. Pharmac.* **17** (1968) 1269.
17. Fouts, J. R., Dixon, R. L. and Shultice, R. W., *Biochem. Pharmac.* **7** (1961) 265.
18. Dixon, R. L., Shultice, R. W. and Fouts, J. R., *Proc. Soc. exp. Biol. Med.* **103** (1960) 333.
19. Kato, R. and Gillette, J. R., *J. Pharmac. exp. Ther.* **150** (1965) 279.
20. Conney, A. H., *Pharmac. Rev.* **19** (1967) 317.
21. Fouts, J. R., *Biochem. biophys. Res. Commun.* **6** (1961) 373.
22. Gram, T. E., Rogers, L. A. and Fouts, J. R., *J. Pharmac. exp. Ther.* **155** (1967) 479.
23. Sladek, N. E. and Mannering, G. J., *Biochem. biophys. Res. Commun.* **24** (1966) 668.
24. Alvares, A. P., Schilling, G., Levin, W. and Kuntzman, R., *Biochem. biophys. Res. Commun.* **29** (1967) 521.
25. Remmer, H., Estabrook, R. W., Schenkman, J. B. and Greim, H., *Arch. Pharmak. exp. Path.* **259** (1968) 98.
26. Hildebrandt, A., Remmer, H. and Estabrook, R. W., *Biochem. biophys. Res. Commun.* **30** (1968) 607.
27. Cooper, D. Y., Levin, S., Narasimhulu, S., Rosenthal, O. and Estabrook, R.W., *Science, N.Y.* **147** (1965) 400.
28. Remmer, H., Schenkman, J. B., Estabrook, R. W., Sasame, H. A., Gillette, J. R., Narasimhulu, S., Cooper, D. Y. and Rosenthal, O., *Molec. Pharmac.* **2** (1966) 187.
29. Imai, Y. and Sato, R., *Biochem. biophys. Res. Commun.* **22** (1966) 620.
30. Schenkman, J. B., Remmer, H. and Estabrook, R. W., *Molec. Pharmac.* **3** (1967) 113.
31. Mannering, G. J., personal communication.
32. Holtzman, J. L., Gram, T. E., Gigon, P. and Gillette, J. R., *Fedn Proc. Fedn Am. Socs exp. Biol.* **27** (1968) 838.

33. Castro, J. A., Greene, F. E., Gigon, P., Sasame, H. A. and Gillette, J. R., *Fedn Proc. Fedn Am. Socs exp. Biol.* 27 (1968) 350.
34. Castro, J. A. and Gillette, J. R., *Biochem. biophys. Res. Commun.* 28 (1967) 426.
35. Davies, D., Gigon, P. and Gillette, J. R., *Pharmacologist* 9 (1967) 203.
36. Greene, F. E., Stripp, B. and Gillette, J. R., unpublished results.
37. Trivus, R. H., and Spirtes, M. A., *Fedn Proc. Fedn Am. Socs exp. Biol.* 24 (1965) 152.
38. Orrenius, S., Dallner, G. and Ernster, L., *Biochem. biophys. Res. Commun.* 14 (1964) 329.
39. Blake, D. E., Bousquet, W. F. and Miya, T. S., *Fedn Proc. Fedn Am. Socs exp. Biol.* 23 (1964) 535.
40. Das, M. L., Orrenius, S. and Ernster, L., *Eur. J. Biochem.* 4 (1968) 519.
41. Gigon, P., Gram, T. E. and Gillette, J. R., *Biochem. biophys. Res. Commun.* 31 (1968) 558.
42. Sasame, H. A., unpublished observations.
43. Gillette, J. R. and Sasame, H. A., *Fedn Proc. Fedn Am. Socs exp. Biol.* 24 (1965) 152.
44. Sasame, H. A. and Gillette, J. R., *Pharmacologist* 9 (1967) 202.
45. Sasame, H. A., *Mechanisms of Inhibition of NADPH-Dependent Enzymes in Liver Microsomes.* Ph.D. dissertation, George Washington University, Washington, D.C., U.S.A.
46. Ullrich, V., Schädelin, J. and Staudinger, Hj., this volume, p. 261.
47. Schenkman, J. B., Ball, J. A. and Estabrook, R. W., *Biochem. Pharmac.* 16 (1967) 1071.

FEBS symposium, Volume 16, 1969, pp. 125-141

The Induction of Hydroxylating Enzymes by Drugs

H. REMMER

Department of Toxicology, University of Tübingen,
Tübingen, Germany

During the last 12 years many investigators have described the induction of microsomal liver enzymes which metabolize foreign compounds; several names which come to mind are: Conney *et al.* [1], Burns *et al.* [2], Gillette [3], Kato [4], Fouts [5], and Orrenius [6]. But it was Conney *et al.* [7] who first described this outstanding phenomenon when studying the influence of methylcholanthrene on the metabolism of several carcinogens in the liver. The same phenomenon was discovered independently in the course of investigations of drug tolerance [8, 9], but few authors have pointed out the fact that this strange type of enzyme induction is merely one easily detectable part of the striking action of numerous lipid-soluble compounds on the liver.

I. Methods for studying activation of drug metabolism

Pharmacologists employ methods which can be easily used for studying drug metabolism. These simple procedures give sufficient information about the capacity of compounds for inducing drug-metabolizing enzymes *in vivo*. So far pharmacologists are in a more favourable position than biochemists. The higher activity of drug-metabolizing enzymes measured *in vitro* can be checked by *in vivo* experiments determining either the elimination rate of the drug or the duration of drug action.

In a typical example, a dog received orally a single dose of 200 mg/kg tolbutamide, the well-known antidiabetic agent (Fig. 1). Six days later we injected i.v. as a test drug the anaesthetic hexobarbital and followed the decline of the hexobarbital concentration in the blood. We compared the considerably faster elimination rate of hexobarbital with that observed before treatment with tolbutamide. Fourteen days after administration of tolbutamide we repeated the injection of hexobarbital. The elimination rate had returned to a nearly normal level.

Much easier and less time-consuming was the determination of sleeping time in rats which received the same anaesthetic as test substance (Fig. 2).

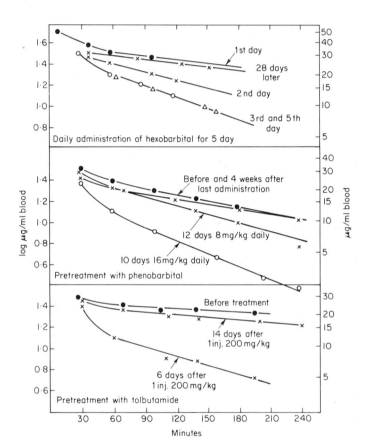

Figure 1. Decrease of hexobarbital concentration (30 mg/kg i.v.) in the blood of dogs after pretreatment with hexobarbital, phenobarbital, and tolbutamide.

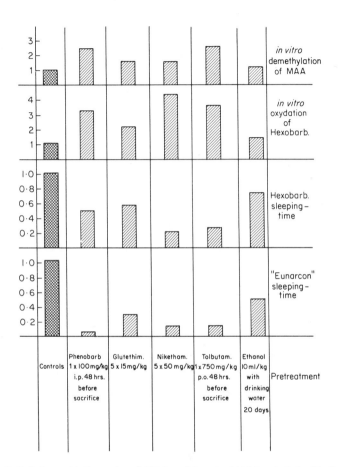

Figure 2. Relative oxidation rates of MAA and hexobarbital incubated with liver-supernatant, and relative sleeping time after i.p. injection of two short-acting barbiturates after pretreatment with four drugs differing chemically and pharmacologically; values of controls = 1·0
MAA=monomethylaminoantipyrine; Eunarcon=Na-N-methyl-5-isopropyl-5-(2′bromoallyle) barbiturate.

The first column indicates the normal sleeping time after hexobarbital and another similar barbiturate. The sleeping time usually lasts for about 45 minutes. The rats had been pretreated with inducing agents as indicated in Fig. 2.

All of these compounds caused a considerable shortening of the sleeping time. It should be noted that alcohol also had a small but significant effect on sleeping time.

The duration of drug action depends either on the speed of excretion or on the rate of metabolism. Butler and co-workers found that hexobarbital is not excreted in an unchanged form [10]. From the stimulating work of Brodie and his group we know that hexobarbital is oxidized by microsomal liver enzymes [11]. So we assumed that the faster decline of hexobarbital concentration in the dog, and the shorter duration of hexobarbital action in rats, was due to an enhanced breakdown. This was easily proved by determining the oxidation rate *in vitro.* We incubated liver microsomes with hexobarbital or MAA as substrates. The latter was oxidatively *N*-demethylated and the correlation between *in vivo* and *in vitro* experiments was striking. The higher the oxidation rate the shorter was the action of barbiturates.

II. Compounds and properties of compounds activating drug metabolism

The activation of metabolism is not limited to those two reactions shown here. Nearly all more or less lipid-soluble foreign substances and several endogenous compounds such as steroids can be hydroxylated by this completely unspecific enzyme system. Therefore, we should not be surprised to find all types of compounds, not related either chemically or pharmacologically, listed under those substances which have activating properties. Table 1 includes related substances which do not have this peculiar property. The list is far from being complete as there are numerous other compounds having the same activating action.

The best known activating drug is phenobarbital. Hexobarbital, which is metabolized most rapidly, is not able to induce its own metabolism in rats if it is administered daily, as is usually done, because its action is too short. If, however, it is administered several times a day, so that it is able to act on the enzyme system for a longer period of time, it exerts the same effect as phenobarbital.

There is a second point which should be considered. That is the dependence of magnitude of activation on the solubility of the compound. Two sulphonamides which are more water- than lipid-soluble have no effect. If however, lipid solubility predominates, they are activating agents.

Surprisingly, alkaloids such as morphine, pethidine, nicotine, and atropine do not have activating properties.

Carcinogenic polycyclic hydrocarbons have provoked a little confusion. Some compounds, such as related hydrocarbons and aniline are hydroxylated much

Table 1. Compounds stimulating the activity of drug-metabolizing enzymes.

Pharmacological action	Compounds tested as enzyme stimulator	Effect	References
Anaesthetic gases	Nitrous oxide	+	34
	Ether	+	34
	Chloroform	+	35
	Divinylether	0	35
	Halothane	0	35
Hypnotics and sedatives	Urethane	+	36, 37, 38, 39
	Carbromal (Adalin)	++	36, 37
	Barbiturates	+++	36, 9, 1, 40, 38, 41, 4
	Pyridione (Persedon)	++	36, 37
	Methyprylone (Noludar)	++	36, 37
	Glutethimide (Doriden)	+++	36, 37, 38, 41
	Thalidomide	0	42
	Ethanol	+/−	36, 37
	Chloral hydrate	+/−	43, 35
	Chlorbutanol (Chloretone)	+	38, 44
	Chloralose	+/−	36
	Ethinamate (Valamid)	0	36, 37
	Hydroxydione (Viadril)	0	43
Anticonvulsants	Diphenylhydantoin (Dilantin)	++	36, 37, 43
	Methylphenylethylhydantoin (Mesantoin)	++	36, 37
	Paramethadione (Paradione)	++	36, 37
	Trimethadione (Tridione)	0	36, 37
	Primidone (Mysoline)	++	43
Tranquillizers	Chlorpromazine	++	43
	Triflupromazine	++	43
	Promazine	0	43
	Chlordiazepoxide	++	45
	Hydroxyzine	+	46
Analgesics	Phenylbutazone	+++	1
	Aminopyrine	++	1
	Pethidine	0	36, 34
	Morphine	0	36, 34
Muscle relaxants (interneural) blocking agents)	Mephenisine	+	43
	Meprobamate	++	42, 43
	Phenaglycodol	+++	42, 4, 43
	Carisoprodol	+	43
	Zoxazolamine	0	1
Antihistaminics	Orphenadrine	++	1, 47
	Diphenhydramine	++	1, 47
	Chlorcyclizine	++	48
Central nervous system-stimulants	Nikethamide (Coramin)	+++	49, 36, 37, 41
	Bemegride	++	36, 37
	Pentylenetetrazol (Metrazol)	0	36, 37

Table 1.—*continued*

Pharmacological action	Compounds tested as enzyme stimulator	Effect	References
Psychomotoric stimulants, hypoglycemic agents	Imipramine (Tofranil)	++	50
	Iproniazid	++	51
	Tolbutamide (Orinase)	+++	37, 36
	Chlorpropamide	++	46
	Carbutamide	++	36, 37
	Sulphaethidol	0	36, 37
	Sulphanilamide	0	36, 37
Inhibitors of cholesterol biosynthesis, androgenics and gestagenics	Triparanol	++	46
	SKF-525A	++	46, 52
	Nortestosteron	+	55
	Norethandrolone	+	54
	Norethynodrel	+	53
Insecticides	Chlordane	++++	56
	DDT	++++	57, 58
	α- and γ-Hexachlorcyclohexane	++++	59, 57, 56
	Dieldrin	+++	57, 56
	Aldrin	+++	58
	Heptachlor	+++	58
	Heptachlor epoxide	++	58
	Pyrethrums	0	58
	Piperonyl butoxide	0	58
Carcinogenic polycyclic hydrocarbons	3-Methylcholanthrene	+++	60
	3,4-Benzpyrene	+++	61
	1,2,5,6-Dibenzanthracene	+	62

faster after pretreatment with these carcinogens [1]. But this is not true for most of the well-known drugs. The expected faster hydroxylation rate cannot be observed since the enzyme is inhibited by the binding of the carcinogens or unknown metabolities to the enzyme having obviously a greater affinity for carcinogenic hydrocarbons (unpublished results).

Steroids have a very small activating action, but the mechanism of inducing a higher rate of hydroxylation seems to be different from that observed after administration of the above-mentioned foreign compounds.

In summary, activation of drug-hydroxylating enzymes is dependent on the following characteristics of the compounds:

(1) the length of time the agent stays in the liver cells;

(2) the ratio of lipid- to water-solubility;

(3) peculiar physico-chemical features which are not yet known;

(4) the affinity of the inducing agent or its metabolite for the enzyme. Any induction of the enzyme may be counteracted by an inhibition of the reaction rate.

III. Induction of cytochrome-P_{450}

I have spoken about activation and avoided the term induction since I did not give any evidence that an increase in the hydroxylation rate is really due to an increase in the amount of enzyme.

After pretreating rats daily for three days with phenobarbital, cytochrome-P_{450} increased 6-fold, while after a similar treatment with benzpyrene it rose only 2½-fold (Fig. 3). There was a significant but much smaller increase of a band at 426 mμ which signified the amount of cyt.-b_5 present in the microsomes. However, these rats were starved for 48 hours before sacrifice. Starvation alone doubled cyt.-P_{450} in female rats, and increased the hydroxylation rate 20-50% (Fig. 4). This may be why the inducing action of phenobarbital is much smaller in fed than in starving animals.

Further evidence that we are dealing with a typical enzyme induction can be shown by the amount of the enzyme-substrate complex which is observed after adding hexobarbital in excess to microsomal preparations of induced and control rats *in vitro*. The methods used are described in detail elsewhere [12-14].

It might be objected that an increase of this haem pigment signifies an enhancement of a cytochromal cofactor, which is only evidence for a larger amount of the haem, but not of the enzyme.

This is why we also determined the enzyme-substrate complex as a true expression of the enzyme available in the microsomal particles for binding any suitable substrate.

Aniline (Fig. 5) and basic compounds which are bound to the sixth free ligand of the iron in the haem moved the peak of the oxidized cytochrome at 420 to 423 mμ; whereas hexobarbital (Fig. 6), after addition to microsomal particles, interacted with the haemoprotein, producing a second Soret peak at 395. Since the method for measuring these absolute spectra is very time-consuming, we relied on the difference spectra shown below, which are easy to measure and are a true expression of the complex formed. After adding hexobarbital, the peak at 420 decreased and absorption at 392 increased. The magnitude of the spectral changes was dependent on the amount of enzyme present in microsomes and the amount of substrate added (Fig. 7).

Induction of phenobarbital produced a 10-fold increase of the enzyme-hexobarbital complex (Fig. 8). This considerably exceeded the rise of syt.-P_{450} shown in Fig. 3. There is no change at all after adding hexobarbital if microsomes of benzpyrene-treated rats are used, because benzpyrene or its metabolites are bound to the enzyme and prevent any reaction with hexobarbital as I have mentioned earlier.

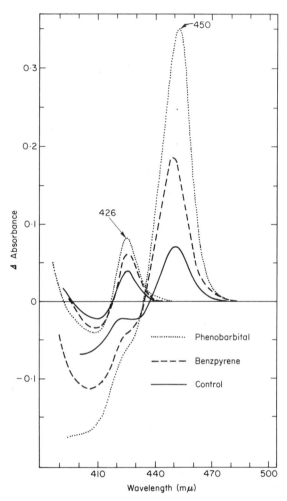

Figure 3. Difference spectra of cytochrome-P_{450} (sample cuvette: dithionite reduced + CO; reference cuvette: dithionite reduced) and cyt.-b_5 (sample cuvette: DPNH reduced; reference cuvette: no addition) measured in suspensions of microsomes containing 2 mg protein/ml, isolated from,———control rats, - - - 3,4-benzpyrene-treated rats (3 × 20 mg/kg) and, · · · phenobarbital-treated rats (3 × 80 mg/kg). The ♀ rats, 60-70 g, were starved 48 h before decapitation. The peak at 450 mμ represents the difference spectrum of cyt.-P_{450} and at 426 that of cyt.-b_5.

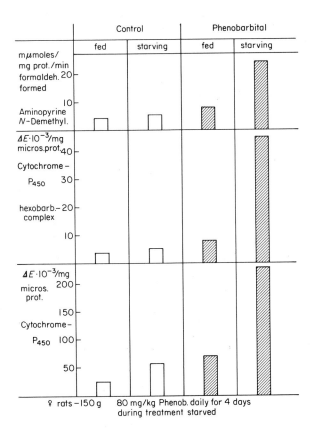

Figure 4. The effect of starvation and of pretreatment with phenobarbital on the hydroxylase in the endoplasmic reticulum.

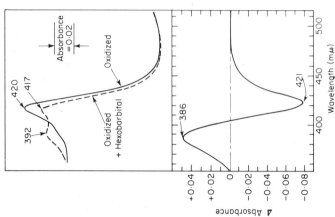

Figure 6. Formation of a second peak after reaction of hexobarbital with the oxidized cyt.-P$_{450}$ (method: see [14]). Difference spectrum (below) after addition of hexobarbital (10^{-4}M) to the sample cuvette. See legend Fig. 5.

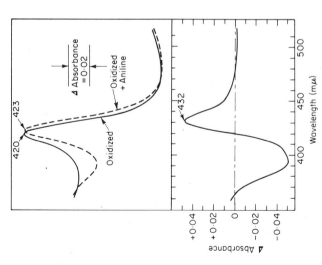

Figure 5. Shift of the absorption maximum after reaction of aniline with the oxidized cyt.-P$_{450}$ (method:see [14]). Difference spectrum (below) after addition of aniline (10^{-4}M) to the sample cuvette. Sample and control cuvette contain the same microsomal suspension (1-2 mg protein/ml).

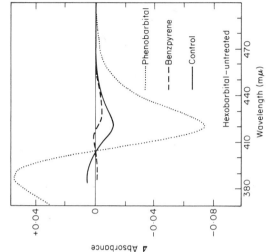

Figure 8. Binding spectra: after addition of hexobarbital to sample cuvette, microsomal suspensions in both cuvettes contain 2 mg protein/ml. Spectra show difference between oxid. cyt.-P_{450} + hexobarbital versus oxid. cyt.-P_{450}. Microsomes prepared, (a) from untreated, (b) from phenobarbital-pretreated (4 × 80 mg/kg i.p.), and (c) from benzpyrene-pretreated (4 × 20 mg/kg i.p. in corn oil) rats. All rats were starved for 48 h before sacrifice.

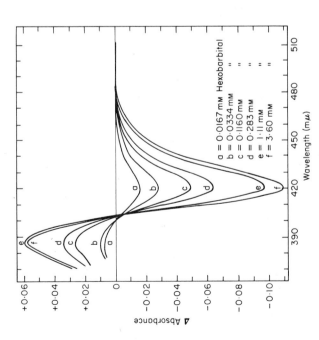

Figure 7. The effect of hexobarbital concentration on the magnitude of the difference spectrum.

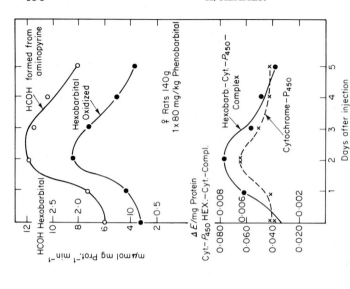

Figure 10. Time course of induction after a single dose of phenobarbital (80 mg/kg). The upper part shows the rise and fall of cyt.-P$_{450}$ and the "cytochrome-hexobarbital complex" (see Fig. 6) in microsomes prepared from rat livers up to 120 h after injection of the drugs. The lower part shows the rise and fall of the oxidation of aminopyrine and hexobarbital by the same microsomal preparations.

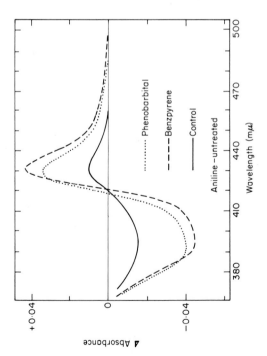

Figure 9. Binding spectra: aniline + oxid. cyt.-P$_{450}$ versus oxid. cyt.-P$_{450}$. All other conditions as in legend to Fig. 8.

The increase in the magnitude of the difference spectrum produced by the binding of aniline to haem (Fig. 9) was much less and parallels the amount of cyt.-P_{450} and the hydroxylation rate very closely [15].

After a single injection of phenobarbital to $\underset{+}{Q}$ non-starved rats we determined the time-course of induction.

The amount of cyt.-P_{450} increased only about 60% but the oxidation rate of hexobarbital and the formation of formaldehyde from aminopyrine was more than doubled (Fig. 10). As we expected, the rate corresponded very closely to the magnitude of the enzyme-substrate complex which can be formed with hexobarbital.

Similar changes occurred upon induction of rats with DDT. The increase in the oxidation rate did not correspond with the increase in cyt.-P_{450}, but again there was a close relationship between the rate of hexobarbital oxidation and the spectrum of the hexobarbital-cyt.-P_{450} complex, whereas the induction after a single dose of phenobarbital lasted only 3-4 days. It took about four weeks for the enhanced activity to return to normal after a single injection of DDT (Greim and Remmer, unpublished). The reason for this prolonged induction was the very slow metabolism of DDT which accumulates in the fat. Only 1% of the amount of DDT, present in the organism, was oxidized per day.

IV. Increase of smooth membranes during induction

The induction of cyt.-P_{450} is followed by profound changes in the liver cells. After repeated doses of phenobarbital or several other lipid-soluble drugs, the liver weight increases 20-50% [15, 16, 16a]. A typical hypertrophy of the liver occurs. This very important point cannot be discussed here. In addition, the activities of several microsomal enzymes, which I have not yet mentioned, increase several-fold at the same time as, for example, esterases, reductases and conjugases [17]. The increase of enzyme activity is much higher in the microsomes which are isolated from smooth membranes of the endoplasmic reticulum than in those isolated from rough membranes. Chemical determinations demonstrated a 2-fold rise in the protein and lipid content of the smooth membrane fraction; but microsomal enzymes which have nothing to do with the breakdown of drugs (such as glucose-6-phosphatase, nucleosidase and ATPase) are activated only slightly or not at all [17]. Several cytoplasmic enzymes, such as UDP-glucose-dehydrogenase [18], some transaminases [19], and conjugases [20, 21], and several others [16, 16a], are also induced, as well as a few mitochondrial enzymes [22]. At the same time, the oxygen consumption of the mitochondria increases [22].

The results obtained in pharmacological and biochemical experiments can be confirmed with morphological methods; the electron microscope shows only an augmentation of smooth membranes without any change in the appearance of other cell structures [15]. However, the mechanism which nature uses for increasing enzymes and membranes remains very mysterious.

V. Mechanism of enzyme induction and of increase of smooth membranes

Many experiments have been carried out with inhibitors of protein synthesis. Puromycin blocks the synthesis of the drug-hydroxylating enzyme [1], but the effect of actinomycin is not characteristic, as it inhibits only if given in lethal doses [23]. All these results seem to prove the idea that drugs induce an increased synthesis of one or several enzymes. Observations of Gelboin et al. [24] also seem to confirm this concept. Microsomes, but not ribosomes which have lost their endogenous Messenger RNA by preincubation, incorporate labelled phenylalanin under the influence of poly-U much faster if they are isolated from rats pretreated with phenobarbital. Careful experiments of Seifert et al. [25] with several systems used for in vitro protein synthesis lead to the conclusion that phenobarbital has a small but significant effect on the ribosomal level only 5 hours after administration of phenobarbital. The appreciable increase in protein synthesis which has been described by Gelboin et al. [24] can be attributed to the combined action of phenobarbital and starvation on the liver [26]. Repeated administrations of phenobarbital inhibit the overall in vitro synthesis of proteins in the endoplasmic reticulum [25].

Shuster and Jick isolated and purified the flavoenzyme which is able to reduce cyt.-C, the so-called cyt.-C-reductase of the endoplasmatic reticulum, and found a 4-fold increase of this particular enzyme after prelabelling it by injecting tritiated leucine and treating rats with phenobarbital daily [27]. The flavo-enzyme in pretreated mice did not lose the label for about 3-4 days. However, the label of the same enzyme isolated from untreated rats disappeared, as could be expected, with a t½ of about 3 days, coming close to the value found by Omura et al. [28]. Shuster and Jick [27] obtained the same results when they determined the loss of labelling from the total microsomal protein and concluded that the increase of protein in the endoplasmic reticulum is mainly due to a decrease of the protein degradation. The interpretation of these results has been challenged by Arias and Schimke [29]. Using arginine labelled only in the guanidino-group they did not find a decreased breakdown, and concluded that the inhibited loss of labelling after injecting [14C]leucine should be viewed as an increased reutilization of amino acids after pretreating rats with pheno-barbital.

Omura and Kuriyama [30] found with the pulse-labelling method a consider-able increase (300-400%) in the rate of synthesis of cyt.-c-reductase, but not of cyt.-b_5, which are located exclusively in the microsomal membranes 5 hours after injection of the inducing drug. The rate of synthesis then declined gradually.

Schulte-Hermann et al. [31], however, studying DNA-synthesis, observed an increase in the rate of mitosis and in the number of nuclei with a corresponding acceleration of [^{3}H] thymidine incorporation in DNA using as inducing agent α-hexacyclohexane. This agrees with experiments reported by Gelboin *et al.* [32] and Bresnick [33] that methylcholanthrene and phenobarbital induce RNA polymerase. The latter experiments support the concept that phenobarbital increases protein synthesis by acting on the nucleus. It is possible that it combines in the liver cell with a repressor-like substance which regulates the rate of RNA formation. But it is at present too early to describe the mechanism of phenobarbital induction exactly. We are dealing with a completely new phenomenon which can be regarded as an adaptation to foreign substances invading the organism. What can be concluded is that the rate of synthesis of several enzymes, such as cyt.-P$_{450}$ and cyt.-c-reductase, is increased very early after administration of the inducing agent. The liver hypertrophy and the growth of the endoplasmic reticulum, however, which occur during repeated treatment, seem to obey different rules. The inhibition of *in vitro* synthesis of proteins in the microsomes and ribosomes point to a decreased breakdown. This, however, points to the need for an explanation of the very unusual increase in the reutilization of amino acids.

SUMMARY

The induction of microsomal enzymes is a completely non-specific phenomenon produced by a great variety of compounds. It is characterized by an increase of cyt.-P$_{450}$, the haem as well as protein moiety. Induction of the cytochromes seems to act as a trigger which initiates an augmentation of several other enzymes associated with the smooth membranes of the endoplasmic reticulum. This is followed by liver hypertrophy with a parallel increase of all substituents of the liver cells, and can be demonstrated by combined pharmacological, morphological, and biochemical methods.

REFERENCES

1. Conney, A. H., Davison, C., Gastel, R. and Burns, J. J., *J. Pharmac. exp. Ther.* **130** (1960) 1.
2. Burns, J. J., Rose, K., Goodwin, S., Reichenthal, J., Horning, E. C. and Brodie, B. B., *Am. J. Pharm.* **113** (1955) 481.
3. Gillette, J. R. *in* "Symposium on Regulation of Enzyme Activity and Synthesis in Normal and Neoplastic Liver", Indiana, 1962.
4. Kato, R., *Medna. exp.* **3** (1960) 95.
5. Fouts, J. R., *Biochem. biophys. Res. Commun.* **6** (1961) 373.
6. Orrenius, S., *J. Cell Biol.* **26** (1965) 713.
7. Conney, A. H., Miller, E. C. and Miller, G. A., *Cancer Res.* **16** (1956) 450.
8. Remmer, H., *Naturwissenschaften* **46** (1959) 580.
9. Remmer, H., *Arch. exp. Path. Pharmak.* **235** (1959) 279.

10. Bush, M. T., Butler, T. C. and Dickison, H. L., *J. Pharmac. exp. Ther.* **108** (1953) 104.
11. Brodie, B. B., Gillette, J. R. and La Du, B. N., *A. Rev. Biochem.* **27** (1958) 427.
12. Remmer, H., Greim, H., Schenkman, J. B. and Estabrook, R. W., *in* "Methods in Enzymology", Vol. 10 (edited by R. W. Estabrook and M. E. Pullman), Academic Press, New York, 1967, p. 703.
13. Schenkman, J. B., Remmer, H. and Estabrook, R. W., *Molec. Pharmac.* **3** (1967) 113.
14. Remmer, H., Estabrook, R. W., Schenkman, J. B. and Greim, H. *Arch. Pharmak. exp. Path.* **259** (1968) 98.
15. Schenkman, J. B., Frey, I., Remmer, H. and Estabrook, R. W., *Molec. Pharmac.* **3** (1967) 516.
16. Remmer, H. and Merker, H. J., *Klin. Wschr.* **41** (1963) 276.
16a. Kunz, W., Schaude, G., Schimassek, H., Schmid, W. and Siess, M., *Proc. Eur. Soc. Study Drug Toxic.* **VII** (1966).
17. Remmer, H. and Merker, H. J., *Science, N.Y.* **142** (1963) 1657.
18. Touster, O., Hollmann, S., Pineda, O. and Shumaker, S., *Proc. First Int. pharmac. Meet.,* Stockholm, 1961.
19. Greim, H., unpublished.
20. Schellhas, H., Hornef, W. and Remmer, H., *Arch. exp. Path. Pharmak.* **251** 2 (1965) 111.
21. Remmer, H., *Arch. exp. Path. Pharmak.* **247** (1964) 461.
22. Orrenius, S. and Ernster, L., *Life Sci.* **6** (1967) 1473.
23. Orrenius, S., Ericsson, J. L. E. and Ernster, L., *J. Cell Biol.* **25** (1965) 627.
24. Kato, R., Jondorf, W. R., Loeb, L. A., Ben, T. and Gelboin, H. V., *Molec. Pharmac.* **2** (1966) 171.
25. Seifert, J., Greim, H. and Chandra, P., *Hoppe-Seyler's Z. physiol. Chem.* **349** (1968) 1179.
26. Greim, H., *Hoppe-Seyler's Z. physiol. Chem.* **349** (1968) 1774.
27. Shuster, L. and Jick, H., *J. biol. Chem.* **241** (1966) 5361.
28. Omura, T., Siekevitz, P. and Palade, G. E., *J. biol. Chem.* **242** (1967) 2389.
29. Arias, J. M. and Schimke, R. T., *in* "Symposium on Microsomes and Drug Oxidations", Bethesda, 1968.
30. Omura, T. and Kuriyama, Y., *in* "Symposium on Microsomes and Drug Oxidations", Bethesda, 1968.
31. Schulte-Hermann, R., Schlicht, I., Magour, S. and Koransky, W., *Arch. exp. Path. Pharmak.* **255** (1966) 72.
32. Gelboin, H. V., Wortham, J. S. and Wilson, R. G., *Nature, Lond.* **214**, No. 5085 (1967) 281.
33. Bresnick, E., *Molec. Pharmac.* **2** (1966) 406.
34. Remmer, H., *Proc. First Int. pharmac. Meet.,* Stockholm, 1961. 6, 235, Pergamon Press, 1962; Sympos. Redoxfunkt. cytoplasm. Funkt., 1962, p. 75.
35. Remmer, H. and W. Schmidt-Volkmar, unpublished.
36. Remmer, H., *in* CIBA Foundation Symposium on Enzymes and Drug Action (1962) p. 276.
37. Krause, W., Inaugural-Diss., Freie Universität, Berlin (1962).
38. Kato, R. and Vasanelli, P., *Biochem. Pharmac.* **11** (1962) 779.
39. Fujimoto, J. M. and Plaa, F. L., *J. Pharmac. exp. Ther.* **131** (1961) 282.

40. Remmer, H., *Arch. exp. Path. Pharmak.* **236** (1959) 7.
41. Kato, R., Chiesara, E. and Vassanelli, P., *Biochem. Pharmac.* **11** (1962) 913.
42. Kato, R., *Atti Soc. lomb. Sci. med. Biol.* **XIV** (1959) 778.
43. Kato, R. and Vassanelli, P., *Biochem. Pharmac.* **11** (1962) 779.
44. Kato, R., Chiesara, E. and Vassanelli, P., *Atti Accad. med. lomb.* **XV** (1960) 443.
45. Hoagland, D. R., Miya, T. S. and Bousquet, W. F., *Toxic. appl. Pharmac.* **9** (1966) 116.
46. Kato, R., Chiesara, E. and Vassanelli, P., *Biochem. Pharmac.* **13** (1964) 69.
47. Conney, A. H. and Burns, J. J., *Ann. N.Y. Acad. Sci.* **86** (1960) 167.
48. Conney, A. H., Michaelson, I. A. and Burns, J. J., *J. Pharmac. exp. Ther.* **132** (1961) 202.
49. Brazda, F. G. and Baucum, R., *J. Pharmac. exp. Ther.* **132** (1961) 295.
50. Dingell, J. V. and Gillette, J. R., unpublished.
51. Stock, K. and Westermann, E., *Arch. exp. Path. Pharmak.* **243** (1962) 44.
52. Serrone, D. M. and Fujimoto, J. M., *Biochem. Pharmac.* **11** (1962) 609.
53. Juchau, M. R. and Fouts, J. R., *Biochem. Pharmac.* **15** (1966) 891.
54. Novick, W. J., Stohler, C. M. and Swagzdis, J., *J. Pharmac. exp. Ther.* **151** (1966) 139.
55. Booth, J. and Gillette, J. R., *J. Pharmac. exp. Ther.* **137** (1962) 374.
56. Hart, L. G., Shultice, R. W. and Fouts, J. R., *Toxic. appl. Pharmac.* **5** (1963) 371.
57. Ghazal, A., Koransky, W., Portig, J., Vohland, H. W. and Klempau, I., *Arch. exp. Path. Pharmak.* **249** (1964) 1.
58. Hart, L. G. and Fouts, J. R., *Proc. Soc. exp. Biol. Med.* **114** (1963) 388.
59. Koransky, W., Portig, J., Vohland, H. W. and Klempau, I., *Arch. exp. Path. Pharmak.* **247** (1964) 61.
60. Conney, A. H., Miller, E. C. and Miller, J. A., *Cancer Res.* **16** (1956) 450.
61. Conney, A. H., Miller, E. C. and Miller, J. A., *J. biol. Chem.* **228** (1957) 753.
62. Acros, J. C., Conney, A. H. and Buu-Hoi, Ng. Ph., *J. biol. Chem.* **236** (1961) 1291.

FEBS Symposium, Volume 16, 1969, pp. 143-160

Metabolic Interactions of Drugs and Steroid Hormones in Rat Liver Microsomes

S. ORRENIUS and B. P. LISBOA

Department of Biochemistry, University of Stockholm,
Sweden

INTRODUCTION

Studies during the past fifteen years have revealed important similarities between the hydroxylation of drugs and steroid hormones as catalysed by the isolated liver microsomes. Both processes were soon found to be NADPH-dependent and to require the presence of molecular oxygen [1, 2]. Subsequently, it was reported that the well-known inhibitor of drug metabolism, SKF 525-A* [3, 4], also markedly depresses the rate of steroid hydroxylation in the liver microsomes. Leybold and Staudinger [5], and Colas [6] observed a sex difference in rat liver androgen hydroxylase activity similar to that earlier reported by Quinn *et al.* [7] for drug metabolism. Phylogenetic studies revealed further similarities in the distribution of drug and steroid hydroxylation activities [8, 9]. Conney and Klutch [10] reported that administration of phenobarbital into rats *in vivo* gives rise to an increase in the rate of steroid hydroxylation in the isolated liver microsomes, analogous to its stimulation of drug hydroxylation [11, 12]. This observation was another important discovery pointing to a close relationship between the oxidative metabolism of drugs and steroid hormones in the liver microsomes.

These and related findings [13] indicated the involvement of common enzyme components in the drug and steroid hydroxylation reactions as catalysed by the liver microsomes. More recent results [14-16] suggest that drug and steroid hydroxylations may in fact be functions of a common microsomal hydroxylating enzyme system of low specificity, involving as catalytic components the NADPH-cytochrome c reductase [17] and the cytochrome P-450 [18, 19]. The same enzyme system also seems to catalyse the ω-oxidation of fatty

---

* *Trivial and systematic names and non-standard abbreviations.*
Testosterone, 17β-hydroxyandrost-4-en-3-one; androstenedione, androst-4-ene-3,17-dione; 5α-dihydrotestosterone, 17β-hydroxy-5α-androstane-3-one; 5α-androstanedione, 5α-androstane-3,17-dione. PCMB, *p*-chloromercuribenzoate; SKF 525-A, β-diethylaminoethyl-diphenylpropylacetate.

acids in the liver microsomes [20]. However, although not yet supported by direct biochemical evidence, the existence of additional enzymes involved in drug and steroid hydroxylation cannot be ruled out.

It is the purpose of this paper to present evidence for the involvement of the NADPH-cytochrome c reductase and cytochrome P-450 in the liver-microsomal hydroxylation of steroid hormones, studied with testosterone as a model compound. The stimulatory effects of phenobarbital treatment on the metabolism of C_{18} and C_{19} steroids will be discussed. Data relating to the direct metabolic interaction of drugs and steroid hormones within the liver microsomes are presented. Finally, the evidence for a regulatory function of circulating steroid hormones on the level of the microsomal hydroxylating enzyme system will be summarized.*

EXPERIMENTAL

Male Sprague-Dawley rats (200-300 g) were used in all experiments. The animals were starved overnight prior to decapitation. Phenobarbital was injected intraperitoneally (80 mg of sodium phenobarbital per kg body-weight) once daily.

Liver microsomes were isolated as described by Ernster et al. [21]. The microsomes were further subfractionated into rough- and smooth-surfaced vesicle fractions according to the procedure of Dallner [22]. Submitochondrial particles were prepared from beef-heart mitochondria by the technique of Löw and Vallin [23].

Protein was determined according to the method of Lowry et al. [24]. RNA was measured as described by Dallner [22].

Incubation conditions

The incubation system for measuring testosterone hydroxylation contained, in a volume of 2 ml: liver microsomes (ca. 2 mg of protein); 0·8 mM testosterone (including 0·4 μC of [^{14}C] testosterone) dissolved in 0·5 ml propylene glycol; 50 mM tris-Cl buffer, pH 7·5; 5 mM $MgCl_2$; 1 mM $NADP^+$ and a NADPH-generating system consisting of 50 mM nicotinamide; 5 mM DL-isocitrate; 0·005 mM $MnCl_2$; and enough isocitric dehydrogenase to reduce 0·32 μmole $NADP^+$ per min. In some experiments 3 mM NADPH was added and $NADP^+$ and the NADPH-generating system were omitted. The time of incubation was 10 or 20 min and the temperature 37°C. The reaction was stopped by the addition of ether-chloroform (3:1) and the steroids were extracted into this medium (3 x 3 ml) by shaking at room temperature. After evaporation of the ether-chloroform phase, the steroids were dissolved in a minimal amount of ethanol and separated by thin-layer chromatography on silica gel, as described below.

* The results have been reported in part in a preliminary form [15, 16, 20, 42].

The oxidative demethylation of aminopyrine was assayed using the same incubation conditions, except that testosterone was omitted and 5 mM aminopyrine was added to the system. The time of incubation and the temperature were the same as described above, but the reaction was stopped by the addition of 0·5 ml 20% $ZnSO_4$ and 0·5 ml saturated $Ba(OH)_2$. The amount of formaldehyde formed was measured by the Nash reaction [25].

In most experiments air was used as the gas phase. When the effects of anaerobiosis or carbon monoxide were studied, all solutions, the suspension of microsomes, and finally the whole incubation mixture were slowly bubbled with pure N_2 or 56% N_2; 4% O_2; 40% CO; a mixture of 96% N_2; 4% O_2 bubbled through the control.

Fluorometric recording of NADPH oxidation

In a series of experiments the NADPH-linked metabolism of testosterone and aminopyrine was assayed by following the oxidation of NADPH in an Eppendorf fluorometer as described by Estabrook and Maitra [26]. The incubation mixture contained in a final volume of 3 ml was 50 mM tris-Cl buffer, pH 7·5; 1·5 mM $MgCl_2$; 0·05 mM NADPH; and ca. 2 mg of microsomal protein. Testosterone and aminopyrine were added to the final concentrations indicated in the various experiments. The temperature was 30°C.

Since liver microsomes catalyse a slow endogenous NADPH oxidation [27], occurring also in the absence of any added substrate, it was necessary to measure the rate of NADPH disappearance both in the absence and presence of added hydroxyl acceptor. The stimulation of the rate of NADPH disappearance caused by substrate addition to the incubation mixture was used as a measurement of hydroxylation activity. The reaction was started by the addition of NADPH.

Separation of testosterone metabolites

The ethanol extracts containing the metabolites formed during the incubation of testosterone with liver microsomes in the presence of NADPH were subjected to thin-layer chromatography (TLC) on silica gel GF (Merck AG, Darmstadt, Germany) using 20 x 20 cm plates under the conditions described previously [28, 29]. In the present work ascending one-dimensional TLC with single or multiple developments was employed. The following solvent systems were used: *for the steroids:* *S-1* ethyl acetate/cyclohexane 60:40; *S-2* ethyl acetate/cyclohexane/ethanol 45:45:10; *S-3* ethyl acetate/*n*-hexane/ethanol 75:20:5 and *S-4* chloroform/ethanol 95:5; *for the acetate derivatives:* *S-5* ethyl acetate/cyclohexane 50:50; *S-6* benzene/ethanol 95:5.

Steroid standards were chromatographed together with the extracts and developed by using the anisaldehyde-sulphuric acid reaction, by exposition to iodine vapours, or by observation under an UV-light lamp at λ 240 [30].

After chromatography of the radioactive extracts, 1·25 or 2·5 mm wide zones of the silica gel layer along the plate were scraped off, mixed with a scintillation solution, and analysed for radioactivity as previously described [31].

RESULTS AND DISCUSSION

It is well established that testosterone can be metabolized in the isolated rat liver microsomes under the influence of several enzymes, such as hydroxysteroid oxidoreductases and steroid ring reductases, as well as by hydroxylation [2]. Four monohydroxylated testosterone derivatives with 2β, 6β, 7α and 16α hydroxyl groups have been completely identified after incubation of rat liver microsomes in the presence of NADPH [32]. The formation of a dihydroxy-testosterone and of several saturated $C_{19}O_3$ steroids have also been reported under the same incubation conditions [32-35].

TLC separation of testosterone metabolites

Figure 1 shows the distribution of radioactivity upon thin-layer chromatography on silica gel of the steroids present in the alcohol extract after incubation of rat liver microsomes with testosterone in the presence of NADPH. Solvent system *S-1* was used to develop the chromatogram. Figure 1 also demonstrates the

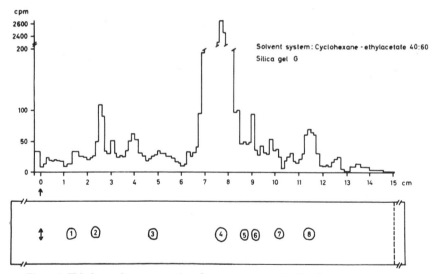

Figure 1. Thin-layer chromatography of testosterone metabolites formed during incubation of rat liver microsomes with testosterone in the presence of NADPH. Solvent system *S-1* was used to develop the chromatogram (↑↑). The chromatographic mobilities in this system of the following reference steroids are shown: 1. 16α- and 7α-hydroxytestosterone; 2. 2β-hydroxytestosterone; 3. 6β-hydroxytestosterone; 4. testosterone; 5. 5α-androstane-$3\alpha,17\beta$-diol; 6. androst-4-ene-3,17-dione; 7. androsterone; 8. 5α-androstane-3,17-dione.

Table 1. NADPH-linked metabolism of testosterone in rat liver microsomes.

Exp. no.	Starting point	Testosterone	Hydroxylated products (2β, 6β, 7α, 16α)	5α-dihydro-testosterone	5α-A-3,17-diol	A^4-3,17-dione	5α-A-3,17-dione
				Distribution of radioactivity			
1	0.64	86·3	6·10	1·81	2·16	1·15	2·06
2	0.78	86·4	6·46	1·30	1·24	1·10	2·13
3	0.79	87·2	6·34	0·97	1·37	1·11	2·29
4	0.81	86·5	6·76	0·89	1·49	1·36	2·18
5	0.77	86·5	6·76	0·87	1·31	1·25	2·17
6	0.73	87·1	6·65	0·74	1·51	0·99	1·98
7	0.88	87·1	6·30	1·57	1·17	0·76	2·30
M ± SD	0·77 ± 0·08	86·7 ± 0·38	6·48 ± 0·25	1·16 ± 0·40	1·46 ± 0·33	1·10 ± 0·19	2·16 ± 0·14

The metabolites were separated by TLC using solvent system S-1 (↑↑)

chromatographic mobilities of several known reference steroids under the same conditions. It may be noted in the chromatogram that there are unidentified radioactive peaks among the metabolites more polar than testosterone which could possibly correspond to hydroxylated 5α-dihydrotestosterone or triols [34]. The reproducibility of the TLC separation employed in these experiments is shown in Table 1. Between 6 and 7% of the added testosterone was recovered in the fraction containing hydroxylated metabolites after incubation with liver microsomes under the conditions employed.

The $C_{19}O_3$ steroids were separated from the $C_{19}O_2$ steroids by means of ascending TLC using solvent system S-3—in this system all $C_{19}O_2$ steroids have the same polarity, or are less polar than testosterone. The material containing

Table 2. Thin-layer chromatography of the acetate derivatives of several known steroid standards.

Acetate derivative of	Solvent system			
	Ethyl acetate/cyclohexane (50:50)		Benzene/ethanol (95:5)	
	R_F	R_S*	R_F	R_S
Testosterone	0·42	1·90	0·54	
2β-hydroxytestosterone	0·42	1·90	0·61	2·32
6β-hydroxytestosterone	0·36		0·52	
16α-hydroxytestosterone	0·30		0·48	
6β-hydroxyandrostenedione	0·22		0·43	
16-hydroxyandrostenedione	0·24		0·44	

* R_S (S = testosterone); R_F-values of testosterone in these systems: 0·22 (ethyl acetate/cyclohexane) and 0·26 (benzene/ethanol).

the $C_{19}O_3$ steroids, i.e. the entire area between the starting line and the incubated steroid (testosterone), was eluted with absolute ethanol according to the technique of Böttiger and Lisboa [36] and rechromatographed as free steroids or after acetylation, using several solvent systems referred to above. After acetylation of the fraction corresponding to $C_{19}O_3$ steroids, obtained by chromatography in system S-3, the acetate derivatives were subjected to TLC using two different solvent systems. Using solvent system S-5, five radioactive peaks were obtained with R_F-values of 0·20 (I), 0·32 (II), 0·35 (III), 0·42 (IV) and 0·48 (V); the peaks I, II, III and IV had the same chromatographic mobilities as the acetate derivatives of 6β-hydroxyandrostenedione, 16α-, 6β- and 2β-hydroxytestosterone, respectively (Table 2). When solvent system S-6 was used to develop the chromatogram, six radioactive peaks were recovered exhibiting R_F-values of 0·20 (I), 0·40 (II), 0·48 (III), 0·52 (IV), 0·60 (V) and 0·64 (VI); the peaks II, III, IV and V having mobility values similar to those of

6β-hydroxyandrostenedione, 16α-, 6β- and 2β-hydroxytestosterone, respectively (Table 2). The less polar material found in both chromatograms could represent 5α-androstane-triol(-s)-acetate(s).

Testosterone hydroxylation

Figure 2 shows that when the testosterone hydroxylation activity was assayed as described above, the reaction was linear with time for at least up to 40 min and also with the amount of microsomal protein added up to 4 mg. The K_m value

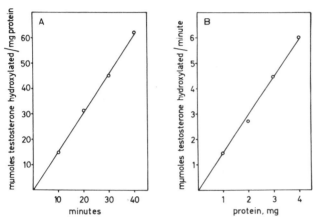

Figure 2. Testosterone hydroxylation as a function of time of incubation (A) and with varying amounts of microsomes (B).

calculated for testosterone under the incubation conditions employed was 3×10^{-5}M, which is in good agreement with that reported by Kuntzman et al. [37].

An optimal rate of testosterone hydroxylation (1·5-2 mμmoles/min/mg microsomal protein) was obtained when the incubation was carried out in the

Table 3. Hydroxylation of testosterone with various hydrogen donors.

Additions	Testosterone hydroxylation mμmoles/min/mg protein
NADPH, 3 mM	1·70
NADH, 3 mM	0·09
NADPH, 3 mM + NADH, 3 mM	1·68
NADPH, 3 mM + NADP, 1 mM	0·98
NADPH, 3 mM + NADP, 3 mM	0·63
NADH, 3 mM + NADP, 1 mM	0·18

The pyridine nucleotides were added in final concentrations as indicated.

presence of added NADPH (Table 3). Addition of NADH did not further increase the hydroxylation activity in the presence of the indicated concentration of NADPH. Analogous to the findings with drugs undergoing oxidative demethylation [38], NADP$^+$ inhibited the rate of hydroxylation of testosterone in a competitive manner, as it has been previously reported to inhibit the NADPH-cytochrome c reductase activity [39]. The low rate of testosterone hydroxylation in the presence of NADH and NADP$^+$ does not support the existence of an active transhydrogenase during these conditions.

Effects of inhibitors

Table 4 shows the requirement for molecular oxygen of the testosterone hydroxylation and aminopyrine demethylation reactions. This requirement is absolute, since the traces of activity remaining when the reactions were carried

Table 4. Inhibition by carbon monoxide of the testosterone hydroxylation and aminopyrine demethylation activities in rat liver microsomes.

Gas phase	Testosterone hydroxylation	Aminopyrine demethylation
	mμmoles/min/mg protein	
air	1·61	4·05
100% N$_2$	0·12	0·31
96% N$_2$; 4% O$_2$	1·54	3·90
56% N$_2$; 4% O$_2$; 40% CO	0·26	0·42

out under nitrogen atmosphere are completely abolished when submitochondrial particles, exhibiting a high cytochrome oxidase activity, are used, in the presence of succinate as substrate, in order to achieve complete anaerobiosis in the system. The inhibition of drug hydroxylation in the liver microsomes by carbon monoxide [40] is due to the inactivation of the reduced cytochrome P-450 [41]. This inactivation is light-reversible and maximal reversal of the oxygen-activating capacity is effected by illumination with the 450 mμ light band as shown by Cooper *et al.* [41]. More recently the inhibitory effect of CO on the hydroxylation of testosterone in the liver microsomes was demonstrated [15, 42, 43] and also found to be light-reversible [43], analogous to the findings with drug hydroxylation.

As demonstrated in Table 5, oxidized cytochrome c and p-chloromercuribenzoate strongly inhibit testosterone hydroxylation, as well as aminopyrine demethylation. Cytochrome c presumably acts by accepting electrons from the reduced flavoprotein and PCMB by blocking sulphydryl groups essential for the interaction between the flavoenzyme and the cytochrome. The partial inhibition

Table 5. Effects of various inhibitors on testosterone hydroxylation and aminopyrine demethylation activities in rat liver microsomes.

Additions	Testosterone hydroxylation	Aminopyrine demethylation
	mμmoles/min/mg protein	
None	1·50	3·72
Cytochrome c, 10^{-5}M	0·54	0·86
Cytochrome c, 10^{-5}M, cytochrome oxidase*	0·18	0·48
PCMB, 10^{-5}M	0·70	1·53
10^{-4}M	0·36	0·90
SKF 525-A, 10^{-4}M	0·76	1·71

* Added in the form of submitochondrial particles (0·2 mg protein).
The inhibitors were added in final concentrations as indicated.

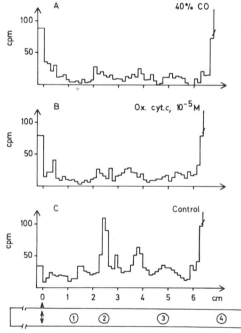

Figure 3. Effects of carbon monoxide (A) and oxidized cytochrome c (B) on the formation of $C_{19}O_3$ steroids during the incubation of rat liver microsomes with testosterone in the presence of NADPH (C = control). Separation by TLC using solvent system *S-1* (↑↑). The reference steroids also chromatographed were: 1.16α- and 7α-hydroxytestosterone; 2. 2β-hydroxytestosterone; 3. 6β-hydroxytestosterone; 4. testosterone.

of the two reactions by cytochrome c, also in the absence of added submitochondrial particles, may be explained by the contamination of the microsomal
fraction with mitochondria or mitochondrial fragments and was abolished in the
presence of 10^{-4}M KCN. In agreement with previous observations [13], Table 5
also shows that approximately half inhibition of testosterone hydroxylation and
aminopyrine demethylation was achieved with SKF 525-A.

In another series of experiments we investigated in some detail the effects of
oxidized cytochrome c, carbon monoxide, PCMB and SKF 525-A on the
chromatographic pattern of hydroxylated testosterone metabolites formed upon
incubation of rat liver microsomes with testosterone. The results obtained with
oxidized cytochrome c and carbon monoxide are shown in Fig. 3 and
demonstrate, like those obtained with PCMB and SKF 525-A, a significant
inhibition of the formation of all the major hydroxylated products from
testosterone, as separated by the TLC procedure employed.

The very similar effects of each of the inhibitors used on the testosterone
hydroxylation and aminopyrine demethylation activities in rat liver microsomes,
add strong support to the concept that both processes are catalysed by a
common enzyme system, involving as components the NADPH-cytochrome c
reductase and cytochrome P-450.

Stereospecificity of NADPH oxidation

The accumulated evidence from comparative studies of the effects of certain
inhibitors on drug and steroid hydroxylations in rat liver microsomes, strongly
suggests the involvement of a common flavoenzyme—the NADPH-cytochrome c
reductase—in both reactions. Further support for this hypothesis derives from
studies of the detritiation of NADPH, tritiated in the $4A$ or in the $4B$ position,
occurring during the oxidation of NADPH involved in the testosterone hydroxylation, aminopyrine demethylation, and cytochrome c reduction reactions [44].

Table 6. Stereospecificity of certain NADPH-linked reactions in rat liver
microsomes. (Data from Das et al. [44].)

Additions	Per cent NADPH oxidized	Per cent ^{3}H in H_2O
NADPH-$4A$-^{3}H + cytochrome c	45	56
NADPH-$4B$-^{3}H + cytochrome c	45	1
NADPH-$4A$-^{3}H	52	57
NADPH-$4A$-^{3}H + testosterone	65	68
NADPH-$4A$-^{3}H + aminopyrine	77	78
NADPH-$4B$-^{3}H	38	10
NADPH-$4B$-^{3}H + testosterone	67	14
NADPH-$4B$-^{3}H + aminopyrine	60	10

Table 6 shows that, when rat liver microsomes were incubated with cytochrome c, testosterone or aminopyrine, there was a marked detritiation of NADPH-$4A$-^{3}H, whereas there was no significant detritiation of the $4B$ analogue. Upon incubation of liver microsomes with the two tritiated forms of NADPH in the absence of added substrate, the major detritiation occurred with NADPH-$4A$-^{3}H. However, it has not been possible to exclude also a minor detritiation of NADPH-$4B$-^{3}H under these conditions.

Interaction of drugs and steroids during _in vitro_ metabolism

There are now several reports that when drugs and steroid hormones are incubated with liver microsomes, in the presence of an excess of NADPH, they inhibit each other's oxidative metabolism in a competitive manner [45, 46]. When testosterone and aminopyrine, in optimal concentrations for metabolism, were incubated with rat liver microsomes, the testosterone hydroxylation activity was inhibited by ca. 25%, whereas the rate of aminopyrine demethylation was decreased by approximately 50% in the presence of testosterone.

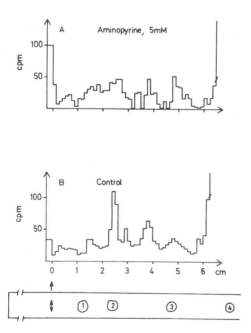

Figure 4. Effects of aminopyrine (A) on the formation of $C_{19}O_3$ steroids during the incubation of rat liver microsomes with testosterone in the presence of NADPH (B = control). Separation by TLC using solvent system _S-1_ (↑↑). The reference steroids also chromatographed were: 1. 16α- and 7α-hydroxytestosterone; 2. 2β-hydroxytestosterone; 3. 6β-hydroxytestosterone; 4. testosterone.

Analysis of the pattern of hydroxylated metabolites formed during the incubation of testosterone with rat liver microsomes, in the absence and presence of
aminopyrine, showed no significant qualitative differences (Fig. 4).

The NADPH oxidase activity of liver microsomes was first described by
Gillette and collaborators [27]. They observed that rat liver microsomes in the
presence of NADPH, but in the absence of any added hydroxyl acceptor,
catalyse a slow oxygen uptake with a concomitant formation of hydrogen
peroxide. Although the NADPH oxidase has now been studied rather extensively,
its nature remains unclear and the available evidence suggests that the NADPH
oxidation observed under these circumstances may in fact be the sum of several
different reactions functioning parallel within the microsomes [20, 38, 47, 48].

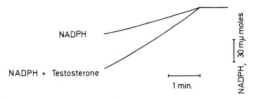

Figure 5. Stimulation by testosterone of the rate of NADPH oxidation catalysed by liver
microsomes isolated from rats treated with five injections of phenobarbital. NADPH
oxidation was recorded fluorometrically and testosterone was added to a final concentration
of 0·5 mM.

Addition of lipid-soluble compounds capable of undergoing hydroxylation,
e.g. aminopyrine or testosterone (Fig. 5), to liver microsomes in the presence of
NADPH causes an enhanced rate of NADPH oxidation. Table 7 shows the
stimulation of NADPH oxidation in the presence of aminopyrine and the
concomitant formation of formaldehyde, due to the oxidative demethylation of
the drug. When testosterone was added to the system, there was no further
stimulation of the rate of NADPH oxidation but rather a minor inhibition,
whereas the formation of formaldehyde was markedly decreased. This observation adds further support for a competition of drugs and steroids for a

Table 7. Stimulation by testosterone and aminopyrine of microsomal NADPH
oxidation.

Additions	NADPH oxidized	Formaldehyde formed
	mμmoles/min	
NADPH, 0·05 mM	10·6	–
NADPH + aminopyrine, 3 mM	30·0	17·3
NADPH + testosterone, 0·5 mM	27·1	–
NADPH + aminopyrine + testosterone	24·6	7·6

common microsomal enzyme system and points to a possible metabolic interaction of these compounds, when present together, also under *in vivo* conditions.

Drug-induced stimulation of steroid metabolism

The important observation by Conney and Klutch of an increased activity of androgen hydroxylation in liver microsomes from rats pretreated with phenobarbital or chlorcyclizine [10] has been followed by several other reports on the stimulation of oxidative steroid metabolism by drug treatment [49]. Figure 6

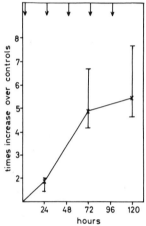

Figure 6. Stimulation of the rate of testosterone hydroxylation in isolated liver microsomes by phenobarbital administration into rats *in vivo*. The arrows indicate the phenobarbital injections.

depicts the increase in the formation of polar metabolites from testosterone in liver microsomes isolated from phenobarbital-treated male rats. The enhancement of testosterone hydroxylation equalled the phenobarbital-induced increase in the levels of the NADPH-cytochrome *c* reductase and cytochrome P-450 in

Table 8. Phenobarbital-induced increase in the formation of hydroxylated metabolites from testosterone in isolated rat liver microsomes.

Fraction containing	Treated*	Control	Ratio
	per cent added testosterone metabolized		
2β-hydroxytestosterone	6·94	2·30	3·0
6β-hydroxytestosterone	4·73	1·90	2·5
7α-hydroxytestosterone	4·80	1·71	2·8
16α-hydroxytestosterone	3·12	0·76	4·1

* Three injections of phenobarbital were given.

the liver microsomes [50] and was also parallel to an enhancement of the overall hydroxylation activity, as measured with several different drugs. The stimulatory effects of phenobarbital treatment on the rate of formation of the various hydroxylated products from testosterone in the liver microsomes were investigated. Table 8 shows that there was an enhanced formation of all the hydroxylated metabolites of testosterone recovered after TLC separation, with the maximal increase in the rate of formation of the product exhibiting the chromatographic mobilities of 16α-hydroxytestosterone. Studies of the sub-microsomal localization of the testosterone hydroxylating activity and its response to phenobarbital induction gave results similar to those obtained for the oxidative demethylation of aminopyrine, i.e. the smooth-surfaced microsomal fraction exhibited the major increase in activity (Table 9).

Table 9. Effect of phenobarbital treatment on the activities of testosterone hydroxylation and oxidative demethylation of aminopyrine in rough- and smooth-surfaced rat liver microsomes.

No. of phenobarb. treatm.	Fraction	$\frac{RNA}{Protein}$	Testosterone hydroxylation	Aminopyrine demethylation
			mμmoles/min/mg protein	
0	Total microsomes	0·16	1·61	3·34
	Rough microsomes	0·27	1·74	2·84
	Smooth microsomes	0·04	1·77	3·19
3	Total microsomes	0·19	6·85	14·82
	Rough microsomes	0·27	6·25	13·70
	Smooth microsomes	0·08	7·25	18·40

In another series of experiments we have compared the effects of phenobarbital administration to male rats *in vivo* on the oxidative metabolism of C_{19} and C_{18} steroids in the isolated liver microsomes. The results reveal that there was a marked stimulation of the rate of formation of polar metabolites using either androstenedione or norandrostenedione as substrate.

We have also recently performed an investigation of the effects of drug treatment of male rats on another important metabolic pathway for steroid hormones in the liver microsomes, i.e. the NADPH-linked 5α-reduction using the conversion of androstenedione to 5α-androstanedione as a model reaction. The results of these experiments, which will be described in detail in another section of this symposium [51], show a considerable stimulation of the 5α-reductase activity by phenobarbital treatment. However, when norandrostenedione was used as a substrate, no significant stimulation of the 5α-reductase activity was found upon phenobarbital treatment of the animals. The stimulation of the steroid 5α-reductase activity by phenobarbital treatment is of particular interest, since it does not seem to involve enzyme components common with the drug and steroid hydroxylation activities.

Interaction of drugs and steroids during *in vivo* metabolism

It is now quite obvious that several drugs and steroids influence each other's metabolism in the isolated liver microsomes. However, the physiological implications of this phenomenon have still to be established. In the intact animal several other factors, such as the distribution of the compounds within the body and the degree of protein-binding, will effect their concentrations at the metabolic site, thereby making possible interactions in metabolism difficult to study. To overcome difficulties associated with the study of drug metabolism *in vivo*, Stitzel *et al.* [52] have devised the isolated perfused liver for studying the inhibition by various drugs of each other's metabolism and reported findings similar to those obtained with the isolated liver microsomes. We have recently commenced an investigation of the interaction of drugs and steroid hormones during metabolism in the isolated perfused rat liver [53]. The preliminary results indicate a significant inhibition of drug metabolism in the presence of added steroids. Although objections can be raised as to whether drug metabolism in the isolated perfused liver is a good reflection of the conditions in the intact animal, it seems probable that such studies will provide valuable information about the metabolic interaction of drugs and steroid hormones.

Hormonal regulation of hydroxylation activity

The existence of sex differences in the rate of metabolism of many drugs is well known [1, 49]. It is also known that such sex differences can be abolished by changing the pattern of circulating steroid hormones. These and other observations have indicated a regulatory function of circulating steroid hormones on drug metabolism. We have previously reported a marked decrease in the microsomal activities of testosterone hydroxylation and aminopyrine demethylation in male rats subjected to adrenalectomy and castration [16]. The decrease in hydroxylation activity was paralleled by a similar decrease in the concentration of cytochrome P-450 in the isolated liver microsomes. These findings support the hypothesis of a regulatory control of circulating steroid hormones on the liver-microsomal hydroxylation activity and indicate that this regulation may occur by effects on the terminal oxidase involved, i.e. cytochrome P-450.

The present evidence suggests the involvement of the NADPH-cytochrome *c* reductase and cytochrome P-450 as catalytic components in the drug and steroid hydroxylation reactions in the liver microsomes. However, many problems in this connection remain to be elucidated. What is, for example, the relationship between the isolated NADPH-cytochrome *c* reductase and the native microsomal enzyme? Are there different forms of cytochrome P-450 or additional enzymes involved in drug and steroid hydroxylations and in the hydroxylations of steroid hormones in various positions? The low rate of steroid hydroxylation in the isolated liver microsomes, in spite of the high concentration of cytochrome P-450 in these particles, raises the problem as to whether there are other, and possibly better, endogenous substrates for this enzyme system. What are the possible physiological implications of the metabolic interaction of drugs and steroid hormones observed under *in vitro* conditions? Still more questions could be formulated but they will all be answered only by further experimental evidence.

SUMMARY

The hydroxylation of testosterone in rat liver microsomes has been studied with respect to catalytic components involved in the reaction. The stimulatory effects of phenobarbital treatment of rats *in vivo* on the rate of hydroxylation of C_{18} and C_{19} steroids and on the steroid 5α-reductase activity in the liver microsomes are reported. Data are presented which relate to the metabolic interaction of drugs and steroid hormones in the liver microsomes. Finally, the evidence for a regulatory function of circulating steroid hormones on the rate of hydroxylation of drugs and steroids in the liver microsomes is summarized.

ACKNOWLEDGEMENT

This work was supported by grants from the Swedish Medical Research Council and from the Swedish Cancer Society.

REFERENCES

1. Brodie, B. B., Gillette, J. R. and La Du, B. N., *A. Rev. Biochem.* **27** (1958) 427.
2. Talalay, P., *A. Rev. Biochem.* **34** (1965) 347.
3. Axelrod, J., Reichenthal, J. and Brodie, B. B., *J. Pharmac. exp. Ther.* **112** (1954) 49.
4. Cooper, J. R., Axelrod, J. and Brodie, B. B., *J. Pharmac. exp. Ther.* **112** (1954) 55.
5. Leybold, K. and Staudinger, Hj., *Biochem. Z.* **331** (1959) 389.
6. Colas, A., *Biochem. J.* **82** (1962) 390.
7. Quinn, G. P., Axelrod, J. and Brodie, B. B., *Biochem. Pharmac.* **1** (1958) 152.
8. Brodie, B. B. and Maickel, R. P., *Proc. First Int. pharmac. Meet.*, Stockholm, 1962, Symp. 6, p. 299.
9. Ozon, R. and Breuer, H., *Hoppe-Seyler's Z. physiol. Chem.* **333** (1963) 282.

10. Conney, A. H. and Klutch, A., *J. biol. Chem.* **238** (1963) 1611.
11. Conney, A. H. and Burns, J. J., *Nature, Lond.* **184** (1959) 363.
12. Remmer, H., *Arch. exp. Path. Pharmak.* **235** (1959) 279.
13. Conney, A. H., Schneidman, K., Jacobson, M. and Kuntzman, R., *Ann. N.Y. Acad. Sci.* **123** (1965) 98.
14. Ernster, L. and Orrenius, S., *Fedn Proc. Fedn Am. Socs exp. Biol.* **24** (1965) 1190.
15. Orrenius, S., *in* "Symposium on the Interaction of Drugs and Subcellular Components in Animal Cells" (edited by P. N. Campbell), Churchills, London, 1968, p. 97.
16. Orrenius, S., Gnosspelius, Y., Das. M. L. and Ernster, L., *in* "Structure and Function of the Endoplasmic Reticulum in Animal Cells" (edited by F. C. Gran), Universitetsforlaget, Oslo, 1968, p. 81.
17. Kamin, H., Masters, B. S. S., Gibson, A. H. and Williams, C. H., *Fedn Proc. Fedn Am. Socs exp. Biol.* **24** (1965) 1164.
18. Omura, T. and Sato, R., *J. biol. Chem.* **239** (1964) 2370.
19. Omura, T. and Sato, R., *J. biol. Chem.* **239** (1964) 2379.
20. Das, M. L., Orrenius, S. and Ernster, L., *Eur. J. Biochem.* **4** (1968) 519.
21. Ernster, L., Siekevitz, P. and Palade, G. E., *J. Cell Biol.* **15** (1962) 541.
22. Dallner, G., *Acta path. microbiol. scand.* 1963, suppl. 166.
23. Löw, H. and Vallin, I., *Biochim. biophys. Acta* **69** (1963) 361.
24. Lowry, O. H., Rousebrough, N. J., Farr, A. L. and Randall, R. J., *J. biol. Chem.* **193** (1951) 265.
25. Nash, T., *Biochem. J.* **55** (1953) 416.
26. Estabrook, R. W. and Maitra, P. K., *Analyt. Biochem.* **3** (1963) 369.
27. Gillette, J. R., Brodie, B. B. and La Du, B. N., *J. Pharmac. exp. Ther.* **119** (1957) 532.
28. Lisboa, B. P., *J. Chromat.* **13** (1964) 391.
29. Lisboa, B. P., *J. Chromat.* **19** (1965) 81.
30. Lisboa, B. P., *in* "Steroids and Terpenoids" (edited by R. B. Clayton), "Methods in Enzymology" (edited by S. P. Colowick and M. D. Kaplan), Academic Press, New York, 1968.
31. Gustafsson, J.-Å. and Lisboa, B. P., *Steroids* **11** (1968) 555.
32. Lisboa, B. P., Gustafsson, J.-Å. and Sjövall, J., *Eur. J. Biochem.* **4** (1968) 496.
33. Leybold, K. and Staudinger, Hj., *Biochem. Z.* **331** (1959) 389.
34. Gustafsson, J.-Å., Lisboa, B. P. and Sjövall, J., *Eur. J. Biochem.* **5** (1968) 437.
35. Gustafsson, J.-Å., Lisboa, B. P. and Sjövall, J., *Eur. J. Biochem.* **6** (1968) 317.
36. Böttiger, L.-E. and Lisboa, B. P., *Z. Klin. Chem. Klin. Biochem.* **5** (1967) 176.
37. Kuntzman, R., Lawrence, D. and Conney, A. H., *Molec. Pharmac.* **1** (1965) 163.
38. Orrenius, S., *J. Cell Biol.* **26** (1965) 713.
39. Williams, C. H. and Kamin, H., *J. biol. Chem.* **237** (1962) 587.
40. Orrenius, S., Dallner, G. and Ernster, L., *Biochem. biophys. Res. Commun.* **14** (1964) 329.
41. Cooper, D. Y., Levin, S., Narasimhulu, S., Rosenthal, O. and Estabrook, R. W., *Science, N.Y.* **147** (1965) 400.

42. Orrenius, S. and Ernster, L., *Biochem. J.* **103** (1967) 3-4P.
43. Conney, A. H., Ikeda, M., Levin, W., Cooper, D. Y., Rosenthal, O. and Estabrook, R. W., *Fedn Proc. Fedn Am. Socs exp. Biol.* **26** (1967) 462.
44. Das, M. L., Orrenius, S., Ernster, L. and Gnosspelius, Y., *FEBS Letters* **1** (1968) 89.
45. Juchau, M. R. and Fouts, J. R., *Biochem. Pharmac.* **15** (1966) 891.
46. Tephly, T. R. and Mannering, G. J., *Molec. Pharmac.* **4** (1968) 10.
47. Staudinger, Hj. and Zubrzycki, Z., *Hoppe-Seyler's Z. physiol. Chem.* **332** (1963) 109.
48. Staudinger, Hj. and Zubrzycki, Z., *Hoppe-Seyler's Z. physiol. Chem.* **340** (1965) 191.
49. Conney, A. H., *Pharmac. Rev.* **19** (1967) 317.
50. Orrenius, S., Ericsson, J. L. E. and Ernster, L., *J. Cell. Biol.* **25** (1965) 627.
51. von Bahr, C., Lisboa, B. P. and Orrenius, S., *in* "Abstracts, 5th Meeting of the European Biochemical Societies", Prague, 1968.
52. Stitzel, R. E., Tephly, T. R. and Mannering, G. J., *Molec. Pharmac.* **4** (1968) 15.
53. von Bahr, C., Sjöqvist, F. and Orrenius, S., *Eur. J. Pharmac.*, submitted for publication.

FEBS Symposium, Volume 16, 1969, pp. 161-181

The Action of Aromatic *N*-Hydroxylated Compounds on Metabolism of Red Blood Cells

J. WAGNER

*First Department of Medical Biochemistry, Charles University,
Prague, Czechoslovakia*

List of non-usual abbreviations and code numbers of enzymes

PHA,phenylhydroxylamine
Hb^{II}, $Fe^{II}Hb$, hemoglobin, ferro-hemoglobin
Hb^{III}, $Fe^{III}HbOH$, met-hemoglobin, ferri-hemoglobin
HbO_2, $Fe^{II}HbO_2$, oxyhemoglobin
GSH, reduced glutathione
GSSG, oxidized glutathione

Hexokinase, ATP: *D*-hexose 6-phosphotransferase (EC 2 . 7 . 1 . 1)
PFK, Phosphofructokinase, ATP: *D*-fructose-6-phosphate 1-phosphotransferase
(EC 2. 7 . 1 . 11)
Aldolase, Fructosediphosphate aldolase, Fructose-1,6-diphosphate *D*-glycer-
aldehyde-3-phosphate-lyase (EC 4 . 1 . 2 . 13)
GAPDH, Glyceraldehydephosphate dehydrogenase, *D*-Glyceraldehyde-3-
phosphate: NAD oxidoreductase (phosphorylating) (EC 1.2.1.12)
PK, Pyruvate kinase, ATP: pyruvate phosphotransferase (EC 2 . 7 . 1 . 40)
LDH, *D*-Lactate dehydrogenase, *D*-Lactate: NAD oxidoreductase (EC
1 . 1 . 1 . 28)
G-6-PDH, Glucose-6-phosphate dehydrogenase, *D*-Glucose-6-phosphate: NADP
oxidoreductase (EC 1 . 1 . 1 . 49)
6-PGDH, Phosphogluconate dehydrogenase, 6-Phospho-*D*-gluconate: NADP oxi-
doreductase (EC 1 . 1 . 1 . 43)
PGI, *D*-Glucose-6-phosphate ketol-isomerase, Glucosephosphate isomerase (EC
5 . 3 . 1 . 9)
GSSG reductase, Glutathione reductase, Reduced-NAD(P): oxidized-glutathione
oxidoreductase (EC 1 . 6 . 4 . 2)
NADPH dehydrogenase, NADPH-dependent met-hemoglobin reductase,
NADPH-diaphorase
NADH dehydrogenase, NADH-dependent met-hemoglobin reductase, NADH-
diaphorase

After *N*-hydroxylation in organism was discovered by Kiese [1] and Uehleke [2], the formation of *N*-hydroxylated products *in vivo* and *in vitro* was studied in considerable detail (for reviews, see ref. 3 and the paper of Dr. Uehleke in this volume). On the other hand, our knowledge concerning the toxic action of *N*-hydroxylated amines and *N*-oxides on the metabolism of cells is poor. *N*-hydroxylated products are reactive and unstable and may be converted into *ortho*- or *para*-aminophenols [4].

One of the most striking effects of *N*-hydroxylamines is their oxidative action in the cells. In erythrocytes the hemoglobin is oxidized to ferri-hemoglobin [5]. The changes in metabolism and structure of erythrocytes were determined. Arylhydroxylamines cause a change in redox state in the cell [5-11].

Arylhydroxylamines and *o*- and *p*-aminophenols bound to proteins acquire antigenic properties, and this is the source of allergic reactions following administration of aromatic amines and nitro compounds [3, 12-14]. The aryl-hydroxylamines seem to be the true cancerogenic metabolites of cancerogenic amines (for reviews, see ref. 3 and the papers of Professor Boyland, Dr. Magee and Dr. Arrhenius in this volume). Marroqin and Farber found that aryl-hydroxylamines are incorporated into both DNA and RNA of the liver [15]. The inhibition as well as the stimulation of protein synthesis were estimated after administration of cancerogenic amines [16-19].

Oxidation of hemoglobin by arylhydroxylamines

Aromatic amines are among the most frequent causes of ferri-hemoglobin formation *in vivo*, but, except for diamines and aminophenols, they do not oxidize hemoglobin unless they undergo certain biochemical changes. The study of these reactions led to the discovery that, among the biochemical derivatives of aromatic amines, the aminophenols are of lesser importance in ferri-hemoglobin formation *in vivo* than the *N*-hydroxy derivatives.

The experiments by Heubner *et al.* [20] had already shown that phenyl-hydroxylamine, hemoglobin and oxygen react in a "coupled oxidation". Nitro-sobenzene and ferri-hemoglobin are products of this reaction [21]:

$$C_6H_5NHOH + 2\ Fe^{II}Hb + O_2 \longrightarrow C_6H_5NO + 2\ Fe^{III}HbOH$$

Whereas hemoglobin and phenylhydroxylamine alone in aqueous solution are slowly oxidized by molecular oxygen, both react rapidly with oxygen if present in the same solution [22]. The kinetics of ferri-hemoglobin formation by phenylhydroxylamine and oxygen in hemoglobin solution [23] is different from that in erythrocyte suspensions [24]. The oxygen utilization and ferri-hemoglo-bin formation in erythrocyte suspension are parallel phenomena [25] (see Fig. 1).

Since neither phenylhydroxylamine nor nitrosobenzene oxidizes hemoglobin, a reactive intermediate must be formed. Using the luminol test, Rostorfer and

Cornier [26] observed a "hydrogen peroxide-like substance" appearing in the formation of ferri-hemoglobin by phenylhydroxylamine:

$$C_6H_5NHOH + Fe^{II}HbO_2 \longrightarrow C_6H_5NO + Fe^{II}HbH_2O_2$$

The determination of H_2O_2 formation in erythrocytes is very difficult. We were able to estimate the formation of H_2O_2 in this reaction using the reaction of H_2O_2 with catalase and 3-amino-1,2,4-triazole to form an inactive complex [27]. But we are unable to demonstrate if the hydrogen peroxide is an

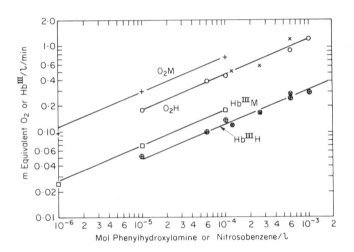

Figure 1. The utilization of O_2 and ferri-hemoglobin formation in erythrocytes as a function of phenylhydroxylamine or nitrosobenzene concentration. M: suspension of human erythrocytes in Ringer-phosphate-buffer solution pH 7·1; H: suspension of dog erythrocytes in Ringer-carbonate-buffer solution pH 7·4; Phenylhydroxylamine o and ⊗, Nitrosobenzene x and ⊕. Kiese and Waller, 1950 [25].

intermediate or end product of this reaction. One of two proposed mechanisms is possible:

$$C_6H_5NHOH + Fe^{II}HbO_2 \longrightarrow C_6H_5NO + Fe^{II}Hb + H_2O_2$$

The hydrogen peroxide produced oxidizes the hemoglobin also formed in this reaction. On the other hand, ferri-hemoglobin and $OH^\bullet$ radicals would be formed:

$$C_6H_5NHOH + Fe^{II}HbO_2 \longrightarrow C_6H_5NO + Fe^{III}HbOH + OH^\bullet$$

The hydrogen peroxide is formed by association of two $OH^\bullet$ radicals.

In erythrocytes, 1 molecule of arylhydroxylamine is able to oxidize several hundred molecules of hemoglobin when oxygen and carbohydrate substrates are available [5, 24]. This is achieved by a cyclic process in which the nitroso compound enzymatically reduces the arylhydroxylamine again [25, 28, 29] (see Fig. 2). The enzyme catalyzing the reduction of the nitroso compound is an

$$C_6H_5NHOH + 2\ FeHb + O_2 \rightarrow C_6H_5NO + 2\ Fe^{3+}HbOH$$

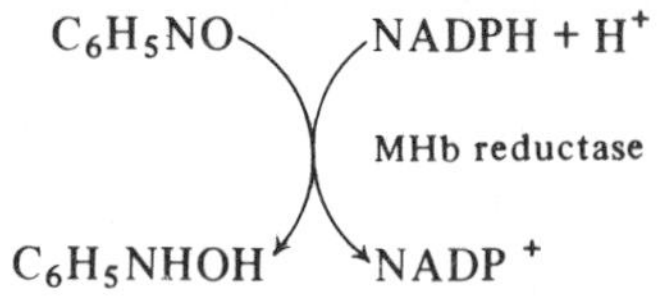

$$C_6H_5NO \diagdown \quad \diagup NADPH + H^+$$

$$\diagdown\diagup$$

MHb reductase

$$C_6H_5NHOH \diagup \quad \diagdown NADP^+$$

Figure 2. The reduction of nitrosobenzene to phenylhydroxylamine by $NADPH_2$ dehydrogenase ($NADPH_2$-met-hemoglobinreductase) in erythrocytes.

Table 1. Ferri-hemoglobin formation by different arylhydroxylamines in dog erythrocytes, Kiese, 1966 [5].

Hydroxylamine or nitroso analogue	Concentration (M)	Initial velocity of ferri-hemoglobin formation equivalent Hb^{III} $\times\ 1^{-1}\ \times\ s^{-1}$
Phenylhydroxylamine	10^{-4}	2×10^{-6}
Nitrosobenzene	3.7×10^{-4}	7×10^{-6}
p-Chloronitrosobenzene	3.7×10^{-4}	8×10^{-7}
m-Hydroxylaminopro-piophenone	10^{-4}	2×10^{-7}
p-Hydroxylaminoben-zenesulfonamide	10^{-4}	1.5×10^{-6}
4-(2-Methoxy-ethoxy)-3-acetylphenylhydroxyl-amine	10^{-3}	4×10^{-6}

Table 2. Ferri-hemoglobin formation by p-hydroxylaminebenzenesulfonamide (10^{-5} M) in human erythrocytes with hemoglobin A (Erw.-Erythr.) and hemoglobin F (NbS-Erythr.). Stoffler et. al., 1965 [30].

		$\dfrac{Hb^{III}}{Hb\ Ges.} \cdot 100$				
	n	5 min	10 min	20 min	30 min	60 min
NbS-Erythr.	15	0.46	2.19	6.80	11.26	19.95
Erw.-Erythr.	15	0.00	0.00	1.82	5.24	11.72

$p < 0.001$

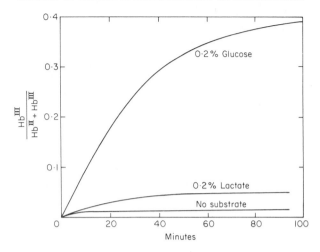

Figure 3. Formation of ferri-hemoglobin in washed red cells taken from dog blood. The cells were suspended in an equal volume of Ringer carbonate solution and kept at 37°C under a mixture of oxygen and 5% carbon dioxide. Phenylhydroxylamine was added to a concentration of 10^{-4} M. The substrates added are indicated beside the curves. Kiese et al., 1950 [24].

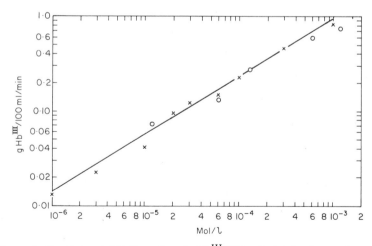

Figure 4. Ferri-hemoglobin formation (g Hb^{III}/100 ml/min) in dog erythrocytes as a function of phenylhydroxylamine (XX) or nitrosobenzene (OO) concentration. Kiese et al., 1950 [24].

NADPH dehydrogenase (diaphorase, met-hemoglobinreductase, hemi-globin-reductase) [29, 46]. This step is limiting in this cyclic process of ferri-hemoglobin formation, while the reaction of hemoglobin with phenylhydroxylamine and oxygen is very rapid and enzyme-independent. It is rather unusual for two physiological enzyme systems in the body (the N-hydroxylating and nitroso compound reduction system) to form a more toxic metabolite and potentiate its action.

Ferri-hemoglobin formation by arylhydroxylamines is dependent on:
(1) the structure of N-hydroxylated compounds;
(2) the properties of hemoglobin;
(3) the substrates employed;
(4) the metabolic activity of erythrocytes, e.g. on limiting factors of ferri-hemoglobin formation.

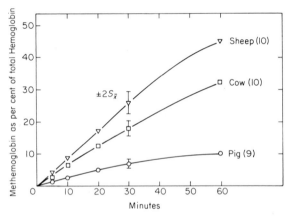

Figure 5. Ferri-hemoglobin formation in erythrocytes of pig, cow and sheep after addition of 10^{-5}M phenylhydroxylamine. Burger *et al.*, 1966 [31].

Ferri-hemoglobin formation was different in the same erythrocytes if different arylhydroxylamines were used [5] (see Table 1). The differences observed in erythrocytes of new-born and adult are caused by the different hemoglobin F and hemoglobin A. The oxidation of hemoglobin F is much more rapid than that of hemoglobin A [30] (see Table 2).

Ferri-hemoglobin formation in erythrocytes is dependent upon the substrate used. In red blood cells suspended in isotonic salt solution without substrate the phenylhydroxylamine (10^{-4}M) produced relatively little ferri-hemoglobin. Addition of glucose to the red cells led to a continuous production of ferri-hemoglobin [5, 24] (see Fig. 3). Lactate and malate are much less active than glucose in supporting this enzymatic cycle. Nitrosobenzene produced as much ferri-hemoglobin as phenylhydroxylamine [24] (see Fig. 4).

Using the same oxidative agent (e.g. phenylhydroxylamine), different ferri-hemoglobin formation was observed in erythrocytes of different species [31] (see Fig. 5). This was explained by the varying metabolic activity and different limiting factors in these erythrocytes [32, 33].

Metabolic processes associated with the cycle nitroso compound, arylhydroxyl-amine, in the red blood cells

The cyclic process of ferri-hemoglobin formation by phenylhydroxylamine in erythrocytes is coupled with the oxidative degradation of glucose over NADPH [32] (see Fig. 6). This led Schneider and Wagner [34] and Ross and Desforges

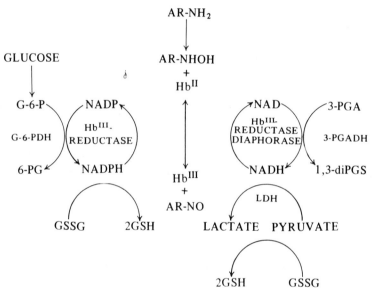

Figure 6. Red cell metabolism and ferri-hemoglobin formation by phenylhydroxyl-amine. Wagner and Burger, 1966 [32].

[35] to the conclusion that the regulative degree of ferri-hemoglobin formation is the glucose-6-phosphate dehydrogenase activity. Löhr and Waller [36] actually managed in 1961 to observe in erythrocytes of patients with a deficiency of G-6-PDH, that *in vitro* only negligible ferri-hemoglobin formation could be observed after erythrocyte incubation with nitrosobenzene (Fig. 7). We have been able to confirm this in our experiments. It is obvious that NADPH deficiency for the reduction of nitrosobenzene is the cause of this.

There are considerable species differences in G-6-PDH activity in erythrocytes [34, 37-39] and so we hoped to obtain a model of G-6-PDH deficiency in man. But we found that other factors were limiting in ferri-hemoglobin formation by

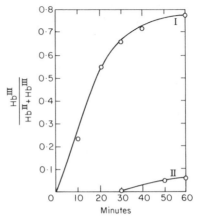

Figure 7. Ferri-hemoglobin formation after addition of nitrosobenzene (5×10^{-4} M) in normal erythrocytes (I) and in erythrocytes of patient with glucose-6-phosphate dehydrogenase deficiency (II). Suspension of erythrocytes in phosphate buffer solution pH 7·4, glucose 0·011M, hemoglobin 9·3 g/100 ml. Löhr and Waller, 1961 [36].

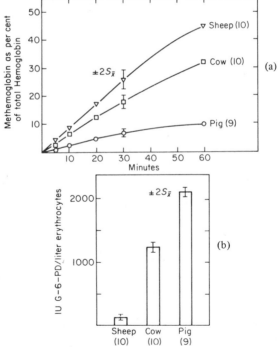

Figure 8. (a) Ferri-hemoglobin formation in erythrocytes of pig, cow and sheep after addition of 10^{-5} M phenylhydroxylamine.

(b) The activity of glucose-6-phosphate dehydrogenase. Numbers in brackets refer to numbers of experiments. Burger *et al.*, 1966 [31].

Table 3. The concentration of NAD, NADP, NADH and NADPH in erythrocytes of pig, cow and sheep. Wagner and Burger, 1966 [32].

10^{-9}Mol/ml erythr.	Pig	n	Cow	n	Sheep	n
NAD	40·7 $s_{\bar{x}} = \pm 3.5$	10	64·3 $s_{\bar{x}} = \pm 8.0$	10	171·6 $s_{\bar{x}} = \pm 8.1$	9
NADP	34·5 $s_{\bar{x}} = \pm 4.8$	10	21·9 $s_{\bar{x}} = \pm 1.2$	10	27·7 $s_{\bar{x}} = \pm 2.1$	9
NADH	2·5 $s_{\bar{x}} = \pm 0.2$	7	2·6 $s_{\bar{x}} = \pm 0.6$	7	4·4 $s_{\bar{x}} = \pm 0.9$	5
NADPH	9·2 $s_{\bar{x}} = \pm 0.8$	7	6·7 $s_{\bar{x}} = \pm 0.7$	6	10·3 $s_{\bar{x}} = \pm 0.8$	6
NADH/NAD	0·061		0·041		0·026	
NADPH/NADP	0·268		0·306		0·371	

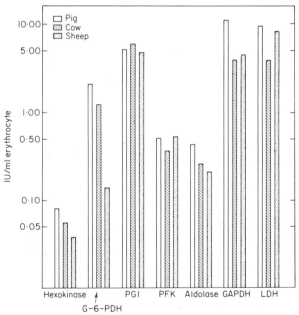

Figure 9. Enzyme activities of the glucose metabolism in erythrocytes of pig ☐, cow ▨ and sheep ▦. IU = International Units. Wagner and Burger, 1966 [32].

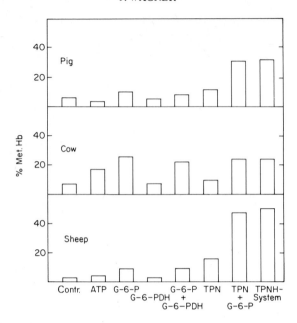

Figure 10. Ferri-hemoglobin formation in erythrocyte hemolysate after addition of some components participating in this reaction. TPNH-System: TPN, G-6-P, G-6-PDH, Phenyl-hydroxylamine 10^{-5} M, incubation 60 min, 37°C. Uehleke *et al.*, 1966 [33].

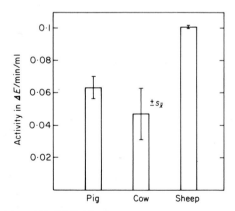

Figure 11. Activity of NADPH-dehydrogenase (diaphorase, met-hemoglobin reductase) in erythrocytes of pig, cow and sheep. Wagner and Burger, 1966 [32].

phenylhydroxylamine in these erythrocytes [31] (see Fig. 8). The rapid ferri-hemoglobin formation in sheep erythrocytes disclosed that, in spite of low G-6-PDH activity, sufficient NADPH must be formed. We were in a position to confirm this and found that ferri-hemoglobin formation in red cells increases parallel with the NADPH/NADP ratio [32] (see Table 3).

The study of the metabolism of erythrocytes provided evidence [32, 33] that the phosphorylation of glucose (the activity of hexokinase or ATP concentration) or the activity of NADPH dehydrogenase are the limiting factors for ferri-hemoglobin formation in erythrocytes by phenylhydroxylamine (Figs. 9, 10, 11).

Glucose metabolism during ferri-hemoglobin formation by phenylhydroxylamine

The metabolism of glucose in erythrocytes occurs both by the glycolytic and phosphogluconate oxidative pathways; the latter usually accounts for 10-12% of

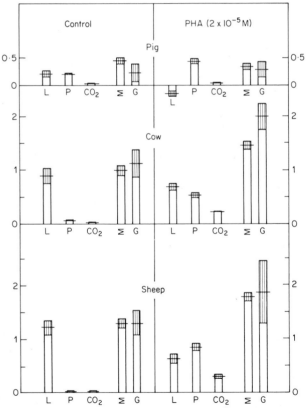

Figure 12. The effect of phenylhydroxylamine (2×10^{-5} M) on glucose utilization (G) and production of lactate (L), pyruvate (P) and CO_2 in μMol glucose/ml erythrocytes/2 h. Σ, sum of lactate, pyruvate and CO_2. Burger *et al.*, 1967 [9].

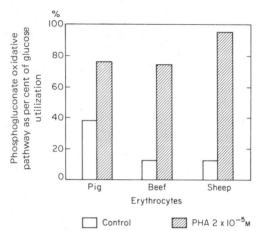

Figure 13. Stimulation of glucose utilization by the phosphogluconate oxidative pathway as per cent of total glucose utilization in erythrocytes after addition of phenylhydroxylamine. Burger *et al.*, 1967 [9].

Table 4. Correlation between ferri-hemoglobin formation by phenylhydroxylamine (10^{-5}M) and glucose utilization by the phosphogluconate oxidative pathway in erythrocytes after 2 h incubation. Wagner and Burger, 1968 [42].

	Pig	Cow	Sheep
$Fe^{III}Hb$ %	9·2	37·0	41·9
Glucose utilization by phosphogluconate oxidative pathway in μMol/ml erythrocytes/2 h	0·20	1·43	1·76

Table 5. Percentage energy produced by glucose metabolism between reduced pyridine nucleotides and ATP in erythrocytes after phenylhydroxylamine (2×10^{-5}M) addition. Burger *et al.*, 1967 [9].

		Controls		PHA 2×10^{-5}M		
Pig	NADH$_2$	43%		NADH$_2$	58%	
	NADPH$_2$	28%		NADPH$_2$	29%	
	NAD(P)H$_2$	71%	ATP 29%	NAD(P)H$_2$	87%	ATP 13%
Cow	NADH$_2$	13%		NADH$_2$	25%	
	NADPH$_2$	24%		NADPH$_2$	56%	
	NAD(P)H$_2$	37%	ATP 63%	NAD(P)H$_2$	81%	ATP 19%
Sheep	NADH$_2$	5%		NADH$_2$	27%	
	NADPH$_2$	24%		NADPH$_2$	57%	
	NAD(P)H$_2$	29%	ATP 71%	NAD(P)H$_2$	84%	ATP 16%

total utilized glucose. Because of the fact that erythrocytes do not possess a complete citric acid cycle [40-42], the CO_2 formed originates from the phosphogluconate oxidative pathway.

In ferri-hemoglobin formation by phenylhydroxylamine ($10^{-5}-10^{-3}$M) the glucose utilization in erythrocytes increases. Kiese and Waller [25] found glucose utilization increased by 90% in dog erythrocytes if phenylhydroxylamine was present at a concentration of 3 x 10^{-4}M. After addition of 2 x 10^{-5}M phenylhydroxylamine we found [9] an increase in glucose utilization of 45-75% in cow and sheep red cells. The sum of lactate and pyruvate is increased by 20-40%, which is smaller than that expected from glucose utilization. The change in lactate/pyruvate quotient in favour of pyruvate was simultaneously observed. On the other hand, much more CO_2 was formed if phenylhydroxylamine was present. The sum of the final products, CO_2 + lactate + pyruvate, corresponds to the consumed glucose; and the increased CO_2 formation points to an increased participation of phosphogluconate oxidative pathway in glucose utilization [9] (see Fig. 12).

The proportion of glucose metabolized by the phosphogluconate pathway during hemoglobin oxidation by phenylhydroxylamine is considerably stimulated. In this way, 70-90% of utilized glucose is then degraded, as compared to 10-12% under control conditions, where the total glucose utilization is considerably increased [9] (see Fig. 13).

Ferri-hemoglobin formation by phenylhydroxylamine in erythrocytes parallels the formation of glucose metabolized by the phosphogluconate pathway [42] (see Table 4).

In transformation of glucose in red cells to pyruvate and lactate, energy from glucose is transferred to ATP and reduced pyridinenucleotides. Under control conditions the predominant part of obtained energy is transferred to ATP and the remainder largely to NADPH. In the presence of phenylhydroxylamine and O_2 only about 20% of energy is transferred to ATP and 80% to reduced pyridinenucleotides. However, the absolute amount of ATP formed remains unchanged [9] (see Table 5).

The inhibition of glucose utilization by arylhydroxylamine

High concentrations of phenylhydroxylamine affect the metabolism of glucose in red cells somewhat differently than lower concentrations [7, 9, 42]. In the initial period of incubating rabbit erythrocytes with phenylhydroxylamine, 5 x 10^{-3} M, increased glucose utilization occurs similarly. After 2 h exposure of a suspension of erythrocytes to phenylhydroxylamine, the washed erythrocytes exhibited a 38% decrease in utilization of glucose upon further incubation with the latter (Table 6). This decrease was accompanied by a decrease in the amount of lactate and pyruvate by 30%. The large shift in the lactate/pyruvate ratio, observed to a lesser extent also at lower phenylhydroxylamine concentrations, is

Table 6. Glucose utilization and formation of pyruvate and lactate in rabbit erythrocytes after 2 h exposure to phenylhydroxylamine (5 x 10^{-3} M) in μMol/ml erythrocytes/2 h, x, s , n = 6. Wagner *et al.*, 1964 [7].

	Glucose	Lactate	Pyruvate
Control	3.60	8·25	0·26
	± 0·38	± 0·55	± 0·08
Phenylhydroxylamine	2·25	2·19	3·80
5 x 10^{-3} M	± 0·45	± 0·35	± 0·52

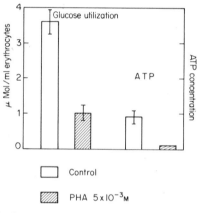

Utilization of glucose in μmol/ml erythrocytes
ATP concentration in μmol/ml erythrocytes
Suspension of rabbit erythrocytes in buffered
isotonic solution/NaCl 103 mM; TRIS - buffer
                    15 mM, pH 7·4; glucose 22·2 mM/
Incubation 240 min, 37°C, aerobic

Figure 14. Effect of phenylhydroxylamine (5 x 10^{-3}M) on glucose utilization and ATP concentration. Wagner and Burger, 1968 [42].

due to an NADH decrease in unchanged lactate dehydrogenase activity [8] (see Table 6).

The low rate of glycolysis, due to the effect of high phenylhydroxylamine concentration, is the reason for the decrease of ATP in red cells by 80% after 4 h incubation with phenylhydroxylamine (5 x 10^{-3}M) [42] (see Fig. 14). In the red cells the energy was produced exclusively by the glycolytic pathway. Probably such a decrease in energy formation then leads to hemolysis, which was appreciable after this period.

Arylhydroxylamines and the regulation of cell metabolism

Following dimethylaminoazobenzene administration in rats, Kunz [43] observed a decrease in the NADPH/NADP ratio in liver by approximately 50%. Various primary and secondary amines, formed in the body from dimethylaminoazobenzene, may be subjected to hydroxylation and lie at the source of this observation. Kamm and Gillette [44] found that phenylhydroxylamine or nitrosobenzene (3 x 10^{-5}M) were not reduced to aniline in the liver, but that they significantly stimulated NADPH oxidation by liver microsomes. Otsuka

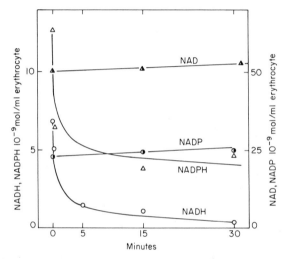

Figure 15. Effect of phenylhydroxylamine (5 x 10^{-4}M) on the NADH (O) and NADPH (△) concentration in erythrocytes. Wagner and Uehleke, 1966 [8].

[45], when studying nitrophenol reduction by soluble proteins of pig liver, also reported that NADPH is probably non-specifically oxidized by phenylhydroxylamine.

Wagner and Uehleke [8] demonstrated that phenylhydroxylamine decreases both NADH and NADPH concentrations. This means that phenylhydroxylamine affects both reduced pyridinenucleotides in red cells to the same extent (Fig. 15). The decrease of NADH concentration by 90% due to the effect of phenylhydroxylamine (5 x 10^{-3}M) corresponds to the observed 80% decrease of lactate formation from pyruvate. The reaction between phenylhydroxylamine and NADH is very rapid and parallels lactate formation. The fall in NADH concentration in red cells could lead to a slower reduction of formed ferri-hemoglobin, while the reduction of ferri-hemoglobin is catalyzed mainly by the NADH dehydrogenase (NADH-dependent diaphorase, NADH-dependent methemoglobin reductase) [46].

The decrease in the NADPH/NADP ratio affects regulatively the corresponding increase of glucose metabolism by the phosphogluconate pathway. This
explains the increase in oxidative degradation of glucose in erythrocytes by
phenylhydroxylamine, as already mentioned above.

Phenylhydroxylamine affects reduced pyridinenucleotides directly and indirectly. Mutual interactions of phenylhydroxylamine and pyridinenucleotides has
not as yet been fully interpreted. The indirect effect consists in increased
NADPH utilization for the reduction of nitrosobenzene in the cyclic process, as
for GSSG reduction, which occurs by GSH oxidation due to the phenylhydroxylamine effect (Fig. 18). When using a high concentration of phenylhydroxylamine (5×10^{-3}M), NAD and NADP concentrations also decreased by 25 and
50% respectively. It is not yet known why NAD and NADP also decreased in the
presence of phenylhydroxylamine. A direct reaction between phenylhydroxylamine and pyridinenucleotides is possible. Kaplan and Ciotti [48] found
formation of the complex from hydroxylamine, alcohol dehydrogenase and
NAD. It is possible that an analogue complex is formed from phenylhydroxylamine, lactate dehydrogenase and NAD. But the unchanged lactate dehydrogenase activity in red cells after phenylhydroxylamine action does not correspond
to this hypothesis.

The inhibition of glycolytic activity in red blood cells by phenylhydroxylamine (5×10^{-3}M) is combined with a decrease in production of energy
represented by ATP. This results in shortening the life of red cells. The fall in the
utilization of glucose is caused by the inhibition of some enzymes involved in
glucose metabolism. Wagner and Janata [47, 49] found that phenylhydroxylamine (5×10^{-3}M) inhibits the activity of hexokinase, phosphofructokinase,
pyruvate kinase, 3-phospho-glyceraldehyde dehydrogenase and glucose-6-phos-
phate dehydrogenase by 60-70%. Some enzymes, e.g. 6-phosphogluconate
dehydrogenase, lactate dehydrogenase and fructosediphosphate aldolase maintained their original activity (Table 7). The group of enzymes inhibited by
phenylhydroxylamine was made up mainly of enzymes containing SH groups
essential for their activity. The importance of free SH groups in the structure
and function of proteins is well known.

The reduced glutathione serves as a redox buffer system which protects SH
groups of proteins against oxidative denaturation by oxidant drugs [11, 47, 49].

Phenylhydroxylamine (5×10^{-3}M to 5×10^{-4}M) caused a fall in the GSH
level in erythrocytes within a few minutes [7, 10, 47] (see Table 8). Further
incubation of erythrocyte suspensions under anaerobic conditions led to a
reduction of oxidized glutathione or radicals [10]. A fall in the GSH concentration to zero by the action of phenylhydroxylamine leads to the partial
inhibition of SH enzyme activities; by contrast, GSH protects the activity of SH
enzymes against the oxidative effect of phenylhydroxylamine [47, 49]. The
oxidized glutathione was found to be an inhibitor of the activity of some SH
enzymes [50].

Table 7. Effect of phenylhydroxylamine on activity of some enzymes of glucose metabolism in erythrocytes. Incubation 30 min, 37°C, aerobic. Wagner *et al.*, 1967 [47].

Enzyme	Control	Phenylhydroxylamine	
		5×10^{-4}M	5×10^{-3}M
		IU/ml erythrocytes	
Hexokinase	0·120	0·084	0·034
Phosphofructokinase	3·50	2·90	1·11
Pyruvate kinase	2·70	1·80	1·00
Glyceraldehyde-3-phosphate dehydrogenase	4·30	4·40	1·60
Glucose-6-phosphate dehydrogenase	1·10	0·89	0·66
6-Phosphogluconate dehydrogenase	0·77	0·74	0·78
Fructose diphosphate aldolase	3·30	3·70	3·10
Lactate dehydrogenase	21·0	–	21·4

Allen and Jandl found a protective effect of reduced glutathione on the oxidative action of acetylphenylhydrazine on hemoglobin [11]. The same effect is presumed to exist for the action of phenylhydroxylamine. Phenylhydroxylamine, as a metabolite of aromatic amines and nitro compounds, causes Heinz bodies formation in erythrocytes. This fact is very important for clinical diagnostic purposes. Erythrocytes containing Heinz bodies are incapable of further existence, and the hemolysis and separation of such erythrocytes by the spleen occurs. The study of Allen and Jandl [11] provided evidence that Heinz bodies

Table 8. The effect of phenylhydroxylamine on reduced glutathione concentration in erythrocytes. Wagner and Janata, 1965 and 1967 [10, 47].

Control	Incubation with PHA				Conc. PHA in Mol/l
	10 min	30 min	60 min	120 min	
76·0	64·8	67·8	64·8	66·7	5×10^{-5}
74·8		15·7	30·3	38·2	5×10^{-4}
76·0	0·0	0·0	0·0	0·0	5×10^{-3}

Concentration of GSH in mg/100 ml erythrocytes suspension; incubation at 37°C, aerobic.

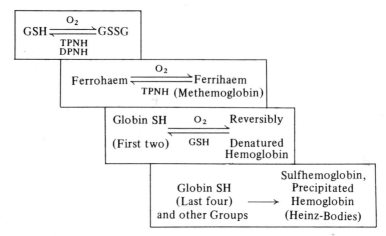

Figure 16. Mechanism of Heinz bodies formation. Allen and Jandl, 1961 [11].

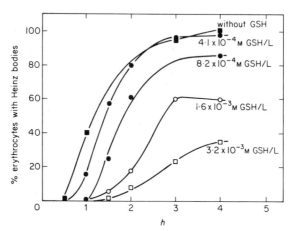

Figure 17. Protection of hemoglobin by reduced glutathione against oxidative denaturation by acetylphenylhydrazine. Waller and Löhr, 1963 [51].

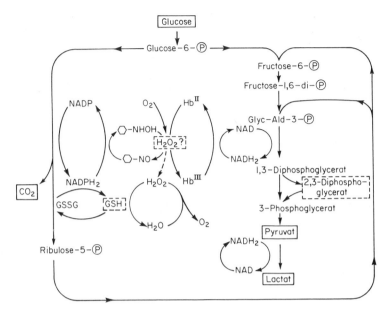

Figure 18. Metabolic processes associated with the formation of ferri-hemoglobin by phenylhydroxylamine and the reduction of ferri-hemoglobin in erythrocytes. Burger *et al.*, 1967 [9].

are formed by oxidative denatured globin. In this process hemoglobin is transformed to ferri-hemoglobin, following which the SH groups of globin are oxidized successively. If all SH groups of globin are oxidized, the irreversible oxidative denaturation of globin takes place and is followed by the precipitation of this protein (Fig. 16). The reduced glutathione protects the hemoglobin against the oxidative denaturation effects of such agents (Fig. 17). The metabolic pathways coupled with the action of *N*-arylhydroxylamines in erythrocytes are shown in Fig. 18.

The action of *N*-arylhydroxylamines on metabolism was studied chiefly in red cells because this was where the most striking toxic effects were observed. These cells have a limited metabolism and therefore it was easier to study it there. The changes in metabolism mentioned above explain disturbances in function and structure of these cells caused by the effect of arylhydroxylamines. Similar effects could be expected even in other tissues or cells. Probably some interference could also be manifest in the lipid and protein metabolism. The problem of arylhydroxylamines in the metabolism and effect of cancerogenic amines is the object of intense research and is discussed in other papers of this volume.

REFERENCES

1. Kiese, M., *Arch. exp. Path. Pharmak.* **235** (1959) 354.
2. Uehleke, H., *Arch. exp. Path. Pharmak.* **241** (1961) 150.
3. Uehleke, H., *Fortschr. Arzneimitt-Forsch.* **8** (1964) 197.
4. Booth, J. and Boyland, E., *Biochem. J.* **91** (1964) 362.
5. Kiese, M., *Pharmac. Rev.* **18** (1966) 1091.
6. Wagner, J., Janata, V., Hykes, P. and Kacl, K., *Sixth Int. Congr. Biochem.* New York, 1964, Abstr. Vol. 392 [1964].
7. Wagner, J., Hykes, P., Janata, V. and Kacl, K., *Acta biol. med. germ.* Suppl. 3 (1964) 312.
8. Wagner, J. and Uehleke, H., *Arch. Pharmak. exp. Path.* **254** (1966) 381.
9. Burger, A., Wagner, J., Uehleke, H. and Götz, E., *Arch. Pharmak. exp. Path.* **256** (1967) 333.
10. Janata, V. and Wagner, J., *Folia haemat.* Sonderheft des IV. Inter. Erythrozytensymposiums (1965) 420.
11. Allen, D. W. and Jandl, J. H., *J. clin. Invest.* **40** (1961) 454.
12. Mayer, R. L., *Klin. Wschr.* **36** (1958) 885.
13. Schulz, H., "Chemische Struktur und allergene Wirkung" (edited by Cantor), Anlendorf, 1962.
14. Schwarz-Speck, K. and M., *Int. Archs Allergy appl. Immun.* **16** (1960) 163.
15. Marroqin, F. and Farber, E., *Cancer Res.* **25** (1965) 1262.
16. Von der Decken, A. and Hultin, T., *Expl Cell Res.* **19** (1960) 591.
17. Arrhenius, E. and Hultin, T., *Expl Cell Res.* **22** (1961) 476.
18. Hawtrey, A. O. and Schirren, V., *Biochim. biophys. Acta* **55** (1962) 785.
19. Arrhenius, E. and Hultin, T., *Cancer Res.* **22** (1962) 823.
20. Heubner, W., Meier, R. and Rhode, H., *Arch. exp. Path. Pharmak.* **100** (1923) 149.
21. Dannenberg, H. and Kiese, M., *Arch. exp. Path. Pharmak.* **211** (1950) 102.
22. Kiese, H. and von Ruckteschell, A., *Arch. exp. Path. Pharmak.* **213** (1951) 128.
23. Kiese, M. and Reinwein, D., *Arch. exp. Path. Pharmak.* **211** (1950) 392.
24. Kiese, M., Reinwein, D. and Waller, H.-D., *Arch. exp. Path. Pharmak.* **210** (1950) 393.
25. Kiese, M. and Waller, H.-D., *Arch. exp. Path. Pharmak.* **211** (1950) 345.
26. Rostorfer, H. H. and Cornier, M. J., *Archs Biochem. Biophys.* **71** (1957) 235.
27. Ellederova, D. and Wagner, J., *Arch. Pharmak. exp. Path.* **260** (1968) 109.
28. Dannenberg, H. and Kiese, M., *Arch. exp. Path. Pharmak.* **211** (1950) 410.
29. Kiese, M., Schneider, C. and Waller, H.-D., *Arch. exp. Path. Pharmak.* **231** (1957) 158.
30. Stöffler, G., Thauer, R. K. and Uehleke, H., *Arch. exp. Path. Pharmak.* **251** (1965) 196.
31. Burger, A., Stöffler, G., Uehleke, H. and Wagner, J., *Med. Pharmacol. exp.* 15 (1966) 525.
32. Wagner, J. and Burger, A., *Arch. Pharmak. exp. Path.* **254** (1966) 138.
33. Uehleke, H., Burger, A. and Wagner, J., *Arch. Pharmak. exp. Path.* **254** (1966) 152.
34. Schneider, C. and Wagner, H. H., *Arch. exp. Path. Pharmak.* **231** (1957) 179.

35. Ross, J. and Desforges, J., *J. Lab. clin. Med.* **54** (1959) 450.
36. Löhr, G. W. and Waller, H.-D., *Dt. Med. Wschr.* **86** (1961) 27.
37. Khanolkar, V. R., Naik, S. N., Baxi, A. J. and Bhatia, H. M., *Experientia* **19** (1963) 472.
38. Smith, J., Barnes, J. K., Kaneko, J. J. and Freedland, R. A., *Nature, Lond.* **205** (1965) 298.
39. Salvidio, E., Pannacciulli, L. and Tizianello, A., *Nature, Lond.* **200** (1963) 372.
40. Prankerd, T. A. J., *Br. J. Haemat.* **1** (1955) 131.
41. Murphy, J. R., *J. Lab. clin. Med.* **55** (1960) 286.
42. Wagner, J. and Burger, A., *Folia haemat.*, Lpz. (1968) in press.
43. Kunz, J., *Arch. exp. Path. Pharmak.* **238** (1960) 52.
44. Kamm, J. J. and Gillette, J. R., *Fedn Proc. Fedn Am. Socs exp. Biol.* **22** (1963) 366.
45. Otsuka, S., *J. Biochem., Tokyo* **50** (1961) 87.
46. Scott, E., Duncan, I. W. and Ekstrand, V., *J. biol. Chem.* **240** (1965) 481.
47. Wagner, J., Janata, V., Manova, I. and Kacl, K., Abstracts, 4th Meeting of the FEBS, Oslo 1967, p. 26.
48. Kaplan, N. O. and Ciotti, M. M., *J. biol. Chem.* **211** (1954) 431.
49. Wagner, J., Janata, V. and Manova, I., *Arch. Pharmak. exp. Path.* **260** (1968) 217.
50. Scheuch, D., Kahrig, C., Ockel, E., Wagenknecht, C. and Rapoport, S. M., *Nature, Lond.* **190** (1961) 631.
51. Waller, H.-D. and Löhr, G. W., *Folia haemat., Frankf.* **8** (1963) 360.

FEBS Symposium, Volume 16, 1969, pp. 183-204

The Carcinogenic Action of Oxidation Products of Aromatic Compounds

E. BOYLAND

The Chester Beatty Research Institute,
Institute of Cancer Research, Royal Cancer Hospital,
London, England

From a teleological standpoint the metabolism of foreign compounds is directed towards the inactivation or detoxication of foreign substances. Sometimes, however, the metabolic processes increase the biological activity of the administered compound. In the field of chemotherapy, knowledge of the metabolic changes that Paludrine and Prontosil undergo led to more active therapeutic agents. All carcinogenic substances are metabolized in the sense that they undergo chemical change in the body. Some substances are probably themselves proximate carcinogens so that any metabolic processes which they undergo cause reduction in their biological activity. Carcinogenic alkylating agents such as mustard gas and dimethylsulphate are examples of direct carcinogens of this kind. On the other hand, some carcinogens that act at sites remote from those of application, such as dimethyl nitrosamine and 2-naphthylamine, require metabolic change to produce proximate carcinogens. The nature of these changes is still not completely understood in spite of the many investigations that have been carried out.

In considering pharmacological action in general, and carcinogenic action in particular, one is impressed by the fact that in many cases only a small fraction of the applied compound actually reaches the site of action. The situation is reminiscent of the parable of the sower [1] : "Some seed fell by the wayside and the fowls came and devoured them up"; this is equivalent to the drug that is administered but not absorbed. "Some fell upon stony places where they had not much earth . . . they withered away"; this is comparable to the drug that is quickly metabolized and excreted. "And some fell among thorns"; these might be considered to act like the portion of the compound reacting with sites in the cell that are not concerned with the carcinogenic action, or alternatively the plants choked with thorns might be similar to cancer cells that are suppressed or destroyed by the defence processes of the body. The seed that "fell into good ground and brought forth fruit some an hundredfold" is like the molecules of the proximate carcinogen that react or change the essential site or target material in the cell.

In explaining the biochemical mechanisms of action of carcinogens (cf. [2]) and mutagens [3] it has often been assumed that the target material in the cell is nucleic acid. Some of the known direct carcinogens such as mustard gas and β-propiolactone react with the guanine residues of deoxyribonucleic acid (DNA) (cf. [4]). These compounds and other carcinogens also react with protein, but if nucleic acids are the essential targets, then the carcinogen combining with other materials is equivalent to the seed falling among thorns.

These alkylating agents are themselves chemically reactive compounds. On the other hand, the aromatic carcinogenic agents, particularly the polycyclic hydrocarbons such as benzopyrene and the amines such as 2-naphthylamine, are stable substances that withstand strong acid or alkali. Benzopyrene is formed on the combustion of carbohydrates and 2-naphthylamine is formed on pyrolysis of amino acids [5] and probably on burning of protein. Man must therefore have been exposed to these two carcinogens since the discovery or invention of fire. It is probable that 3,4-benzopyrene plays some part in the induction of cancer of the lung, skin and other sites in man and it is certain that 2-naphthylamine is a cause of human bladder cancer.

At the present time it is not possible to define with certainty the nature of the active metabolic intermediates of aromatic carcinogenic compounds that are responsible for the biochemical lesions that finally result in cancer. We do not know whether the aromatic hydrocarbons such as 3,4-benzopyrene or 1,2-5,6-dibenzanthracene act with or without metabolic change, but the evidence that some aromatic amines, including 2-acetamidofluorene and 2-naphthylamine, act after metabolic activation is reasonably convincing.

Polycyclic hydrocarbons

The first polycyclic hydrocarbons which were found to be carcinogenic were the synthetic 1,2-5,6-dibenzanthracene (also called dibenz[a, h]anthracene) [6], and 3,4-benzopyrene (or benzo[a]pyrene) which was isolated from coal tar [7]. Following these discoveries, many polycyclic hydrocarbons were tested for carcinogenic activity mainly in London and Boston.

When the results of biological tests of many polycyclic hydrocarbons were known, Hewett [8] and also Robinson [9] pointed out that the active compounds were phenanthrene derivatives (see Fig. 1). Before this, Cook and Haslewood [10] had stressed the similarity between the ring structures of some carcinogens and of some sterols, which were hydrogenated cyclopentenophenanthrene derivatives. The carcinogenic 20-methylcholanthrene was prepared from a bile acid and is a cyclopentenylbenzanthracene and also a cyclopentenobenzophenanthrene. The French theoretical chemists, Dr. and Mrs. Pullman, Dr. and Mrs. Daudel and their colleagues made important studies of the relation between structure and activity of polycyclic hydrocarbons. Daudel and Pullman [11] showed that the active compounds contained a region of high electron density named the "K-region", which in many cases was a phenanthrene double bond (see Fig. 1). Many workers have developed the idea that the activity of carcinogenic hydrocarbons is dependent upon the chemical activity as indicated by the electron density of the K-region.

Carcinogenic hydrocarbons

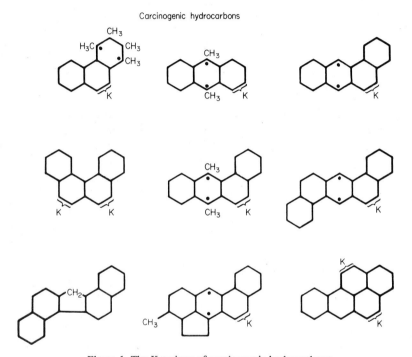

Figure 1. The K-regions of carcinogenic hydrocarbons.

Metabolism of polycyclic hydrocarbons

Study of the metabolic processes which aromatic hydrocarbons undergo has been facilitated by new techniques, particularly of paper chromatography, thin-layer chromatography, and the use of labelled compounds. The main metabolic pathways of hydrocarbons involve oxidation by addition of the elements of hydrogen peroxide by reaction of oxygen atoms with active double bonds.

Phenanthrene itself is not carcinogenic, but the metabolism of this compound is of interest because so many of the active hydrocarbons are derivatives of phenanthrene and the metabolic processes that phenanthrene undergoes are similar to those of some carcinogenic compounds. Although phenanthrene

186   E. BOYLAND

contains five double bonds, two, the 1,2 and 3,4 bonds, are equivalent to the 7,8 and 5,6 bonds, so that there are only three different types of bonds. Studies of the metabolism of phenanthrene by Boyland and Wolf [12] and Boyland and Sims [13-15] has shown that all the available double bonds react *in vivo* (Fig. 2).

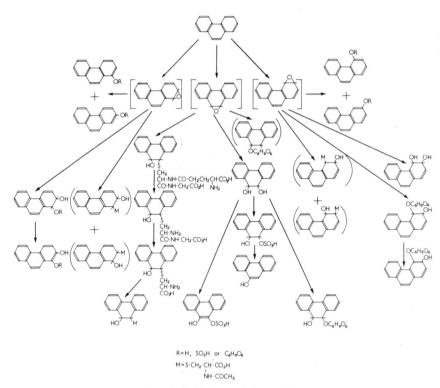

Figure 2. Metabolites of phenanthrene.

All the metabolites can be considered as derived from the three hypothetical epoxides–1,2 and 3,4 and 9,10 (cf. Fig. 4). The epoxides:

1. React with water to give the dihydrodihydroxy derivatives (diols) which may be conjugated with glucuronic acid or sulphuric acid. This type of metabolite was first described by Boyland and Levi [16] as a metabolite of anthracene.
2. Rearrange to give the monophenols, which may also be conjugated with glucuronic or sulphuric acid.
3. React with glutathione to give products that are 1,2-dihydro-1-hydroxy-S aryl derivatives, which are converted through three stages to the mercapturic acids.

4. After addition of water the diols first formed may be dehydrogenated to dihydric phenols or catechol derivatives.

Most of the hydrocarbon is converted to 9,10 derivatives, as a mixture of 9,10-dihydro-9,10-dihydroxyphenanthrene and 9,10-dihydro-9,10-hydroxyphenanthryl 10-mercapturic acid. The next most abundant group of metabolites is derived from the phenanthrene 3,4-epoxide and the least abundant from phenanthrene 1,2-epoxide. The amounts of the different groups of metabolites follow the bond orders of the different bonds of the molecule as calculated by Pullman and Pullman [17].

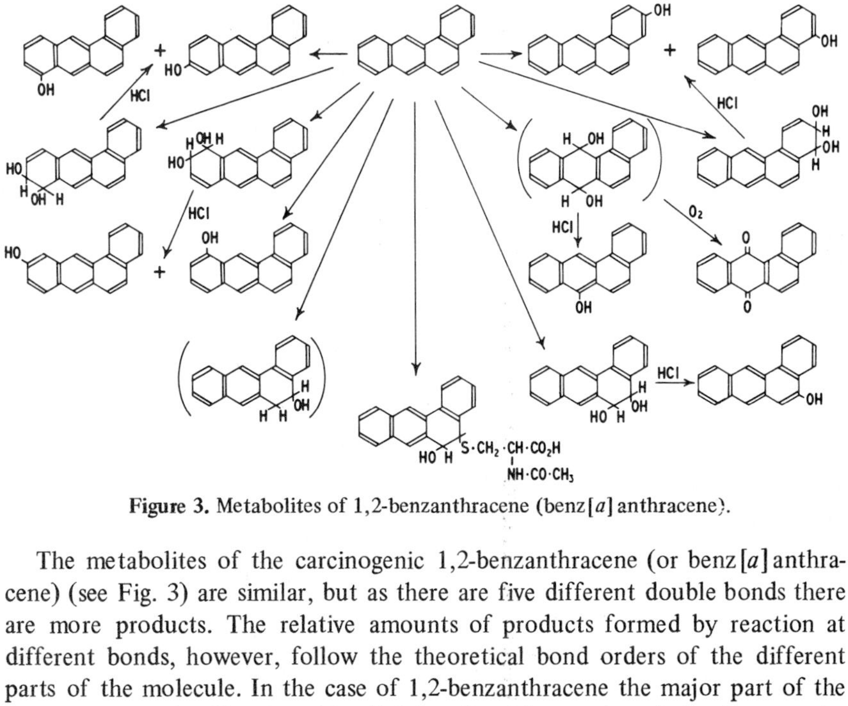

Figure 3. Metabolites of 1,2-benzanthracene (benz[a]anthracene).

The metabolites of the carcinogenic 1,2-benzanthracene (or benz[a]anthracene) (see Fig. 3) are similar, but as there are five different double bonds there are more products. The relative amounts of products formed by reaction at different bonds, however, follow the theoretical bond orders of the different parts of the molecule. In the case of 1,2-benzanthracene the major part of the reaction is at the K-region (the 5,6 bond) with cysteine derivatives to give mercapturic acids.

Older work on metabolism of carcinogenic hydrocarbons indicated that metabolic processes took place in regions of the molecule other than the K-region, e.g. the metabolic or M-region (see Fig. 5 from [18]). It was thought that this was because the K-region was protected by combination with some enzyme centre or other tissue constituent. The failure of earlier workers to detect or isolate the metabolic products in which the K-region has reacted was due to the instability of these products in acid. When the 1,2-dihydro-2-hydroxynaphthyl mercapturic acid (Fig. 6), which is a metabolite of naphthalene,

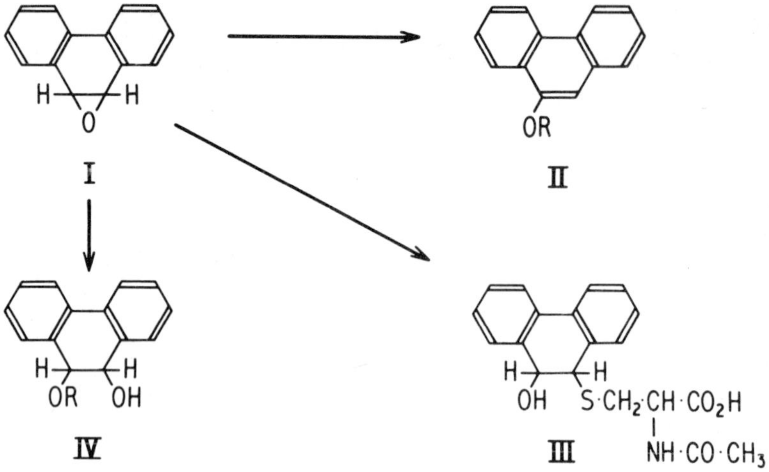

Figure 4. The metabolites formed from phenanthrene epoxide.

is treated with cold dilute acid, it loses water to yield mainly the 1-naphthyl mercapturic acid. The corresponding mercapturic acid derivatives of phenanthrene and 1,2-benzanthracene decomposed in acid to yield mainly the parent hydrocarbons and diacetyl cystine (see Fig. 6). In early work on hydrocarbon metabolism, the urine was acidified so that these mercapturic acid derivatives in which the K-region had reacted were decomposed.

The K-region therefore reacts in a different way from the other double bonds of the molecule. The reaction between epoxides and glutathione, which is an essential stage in mercapturic acid synthesis, is catalysed by the enzyme epoxide glutathione transferase [19]. The phenanthrene 9,10-epoxide and the 1,2-benzanthracene-3,4-epoxide may be better substrates than the other isomeric epoxides for such enzymes, which would explain the observed differences in type of products.

The biochemical changes which phenanthrene and 1,2-benzanthracene undergo are different from the chemical reactions which occur in the absence of

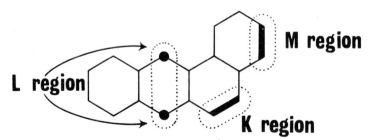

Figure 5. K-, L- and M-regions of 1,2-benzanthracene.

enzymes. The reactions of phenanthrene and 1,2-benzanthracene with osmium tetroxide or diazoacetic acid are almost entirely with the double bond with the highest chemical reactivity, which is the K-region. The biological oxidations, however, also give products in which the double bonds with less chemical reactivity are involved. The biological oxidations are in closer agreement with theoretical predictions of bond order than are the non-enzymic chemical reactions.

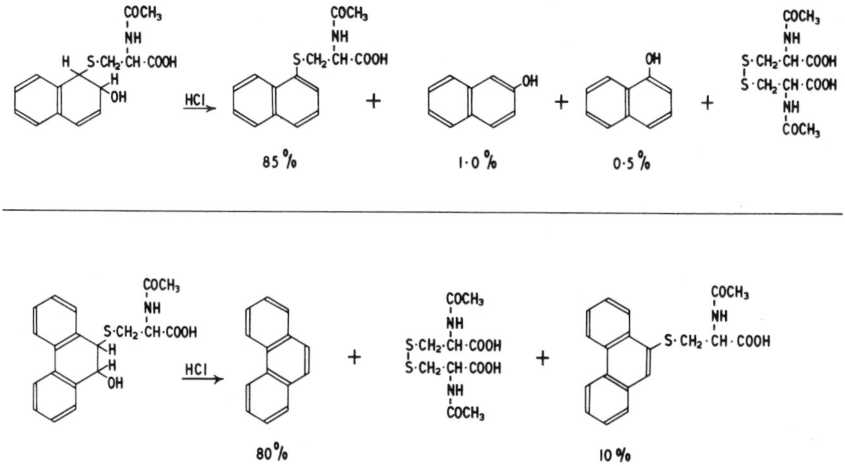

Figure 6. Acid decomposition of mercapturic acids.

The metabolic reactions as inactivation processes

Most of the metabolic processes by which cells metabolize carcinogenic poly-cyclic hydrocarbons facilitate excretion and so act in the defence of the body against carcinogens, although some may be involved with carcinogenicity. The oxidation processes carried out by microsomes convert lipid-soluble toxic materials of the environment into water-soluble ionized products which can be excreted by the kidneys. Although microsomes convert some carcinogenic aromatic amines (e.g. 2-acetamidofluorene) into active proximate carcinogenic agents, activation processes seem to be less likely to occur with the polycyclic hydrocarbons for a number of reasons.

The polycyclic hydrocarbons are generally local in their action—when applied to the skin they give papillomata, epitheliomata, and on injection induce sarcomata. On the other hand, the carcinogenic aromatic amines often produce tumours in tissues remote from the site of application, e.g. 2-acetamidofluorene on feeding or injection induces tumours of the liver, acoustic duct and other organs.

Polycyclic hydrocarbons are particularly active in young animals which metabolize hydrocarbons less actively than do more mature animals [20]. Many enzymes are absent in newborn mice [21] but newborn mice are sensitive to carcinogenic hydrocarbons [22].

None of the known metabolites of carcinogenic hydrocarbons has been found to be as carcinogenic as the parent hydrocarbon. The introduction of hydroxyl or other polar groups into the molecule reduces the activity. These arguments, however, are not conclusive.

Possible active metabolites of aromatic hydrocarbons

Metabolites which might be proximate carcinogens are the epoxides which are presumably intermediates in the metabolism of polycyclic hydrocarbons. Thus the 1,2-benzanthracene-3,4-epoxide (Fig. 7) is an alkylating agent like some other epoxides, as the mercapturic acid derivative is probably formed by the epoxide alkylating glutathione or some other cysteine derivative. A number of epoxides have been shown to be carcinogenic (see [23]).

The epoxy derivatives of some carcinogenic hydrocarbons have been synthesized by the method of Newman and Blum [24] and tested for carcinogenic action in mice by Miller and Miller [25] and Boyland and Sims [26]. Although the epoxides were not inactive, their carcinogenic activity was always less than that of the hydrocarbon from which they were derived (Table 1). It is therefore unlikely that the epoxide intermediates of hydrocarbons are the proximate carcinogens. The active proximate carcinogens might be reactive forms such as

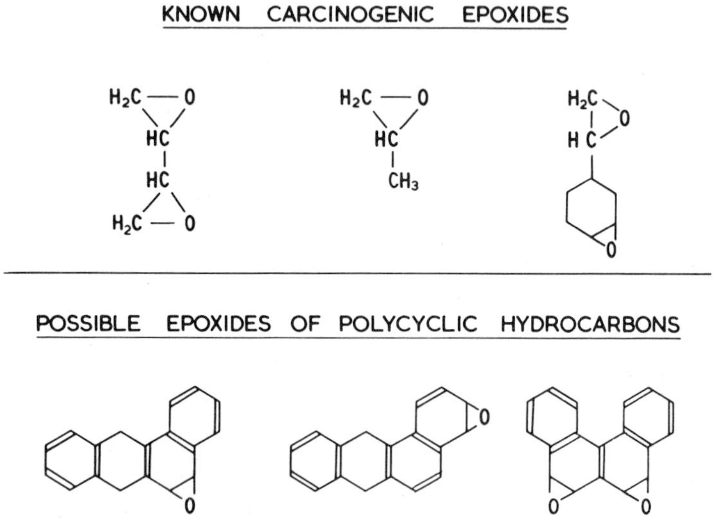

Figure 7. Known carcinogenic epoxides and the possible metabolic epoxide intermediates of carcinogenic hydrocarbons.

radicals or ions of the hydrocarbons that are the precursors of epoxides. It is possible that if the reactive form combines with the essential site in the cell the carcinogenic process proceeds, but that reaction with oxygen to form an epoxide is a competing reaction on an inactivation pathway.

Table 1.

INDUCTION OF SARCOMA BY K-REGION EPOXIDES DERIVED FROM AROMATIC HYDROCARBONS

Tested by subcutaneous injection (10 x 1 mg.) into C57 mice

K-REGION EPOXIDE OF	No. OF ANIMALS	SEX	No. OF ANIMALS WITH TUMOURS	MEAN LATENT PERIOD (days)
(structure, CH_3)	10	M	6	280
	10	F	7	242
(structure, CH_3)	10	M	9	130
	10	F	10	162
(structure)	20	M	5	320
	16	F	14	254
(structure)	10	M	5	226
	11	F	6	232
(structure)	20	M	3	252
(structure)	10	M	0	–
	10	F	0	–

Other work (e.g. [27]) has shown that the unsubstituted polycyclic carcinogenic hydrocarbons, which are planar molecules such as 1,2-benzanthracene and 3,4-benzopyrene, form complexes with DNA and the carcinogenic action may be exerted through the formation of such complexes that cause deformation of DNA (see Fig. 8). A mechanism of this kind would not necessarily involve metabolism of the hydrocarbons.

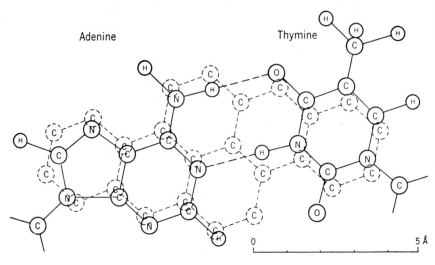

3 : 4 : 8 : 9-Dibenzpyrene

Figure 8. The superimposed structures of the carcinogenic dibenzopyrene and the adenine-thymine pair in DNA.

Hydrocarbons with methyl groups

The introduction of methyl groups into the ring structure of aromatic hydrocarbons has marked effects on biological activity. Phenanthrene is not carcinogenic but trimethyl [28] and tetramethyl phenanthrenes are carcinogenic. Benz[a]anthracene is a weak carcinogen but 7,12-dimethylbenzanthracene is

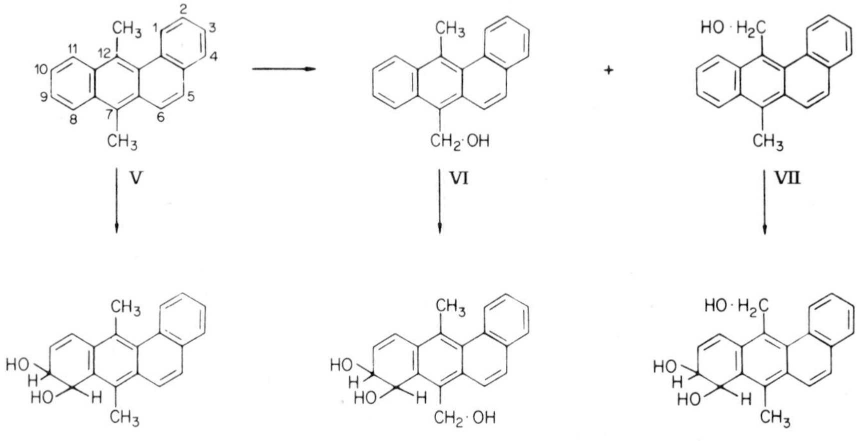

V   →   VI   +   VII

XIII   IX   X

Figure 9. Metabolism of 7,12-dimethylbenz[a]anthracene.

active and one of the most rapidly acting carcinogens known. The methyl groups in these compounds repel electrons and increase the activity of the K-region but the effects of methyl groups on carcinogenic activity are greater than would be expected from the increase in electron density caused by the methyl groups. Because of this, it was suggested [2] that these essential methyl groups "may react directly with some cell constituent".

In studying the metabolism of 7,12-benz[a]anthracene by liver homogenates from normal rats, Boyland and Sims [29] were suprised to find that the main metabolites were the isomeric hydroxymethyl derivatives and that no oxidation occurred on the K-region (Fig. 9). One of these metabolites, 7-hydroxymethyl-12-methylbenz[a]anthracene, appeared to be the active metabolite of 7,12-dimethylbenz[a]anthracene that causes adrenal damage in rats [30]. Liver homogenates from rats pretreated with carcinogens or other substances that induce microsomal enzymes converted 7,12-dimethylbenz[a]anthracene, 7-hydroxymethyl-12-methylbenz[a]anthracene or 12-hydroxymethyl-7-methyl-benz[a]anthracene to the corresponding 8,9-dihydro-8,9-dihydroxy derivatives. In these ring hydroxylations the reaction is at a site remote from the K-region.

The two hydroxymethyl methylbenz[a]anthracenes and 7-acetoxymethyl-12-methylbenz[a]anthracene, when tested for carcinogenic activity by injection

Table 2.

INDUCTION OF SARCOMA IN C57 MICE BY DERIVATIVES OF
7, 12-DIMETHYLBENZ [a] ANTHRACENE

COMPOUND	DOSE (mg.)	No. OF ANIMALS	SEX	No. OF ANIMALS WITH TUMOURS	MEAN INDUCTION TIME (days)
CH₃ / CH₃	1 x 1	7	M	7	108
CH₃ / CH₂OH	10 x 1	20	M	18	154
		20	F	18	188
CH₂OH / CH₃	10 x 1	10	M	9	152
		10	F	7	203
CH₃ / CHO	3 x 1	20	M	6	155

in mice, were less active than the parent hydrocarbon 7,12-dimethylbenz[a] an-thracene (Table 2). These metabolites therefore are unlikely to be the proximate carcinogens. It is possible that the active compounds and proximate carcinogens are radicals or ions that are intermediates in the oxidation of the methyl groups of the hydrocarbon.

Reaction of carcinogenic hydrocarbons with cell constituents

If labelled hydrocarbons are applied to the skin of mice the amount of carcinogen that is bound to the different cell components can be measured. Brookes and Lawley [31], using tritium-labelled compounds, found that the carcinogenic hydrocarbons 1,2-5,6-dibenzanthracene, 3,4-benzopyrene, 20-methylcholanthrene and 7,12-dimethylbenz[a]anthracene were all bound to the total protein of the skin to about the same extent. The carcinogenic hydrocar-bons were also bound to skin DNA, but in amounts increasing with the increase in carcinogenic activity of the compounds; naphthalene was not bound and the non-carcinogenic 1,2-3,4-dibenzanthracene to only a slight extent.

Goshman and Heidelberger [32], in a more extensive series of experiments with tritiated hydrocarbons on mouse skin, found that the compounds with methyl groups, 20-methylcholanthrene and 7,12-dimethylbenz[a]anthracene, were bound to DNA more quickly and at higher concentrations than either of two isomers of dibenzanthracene (see Fig. 10). The non-carcinogenic 1,2-3,4-

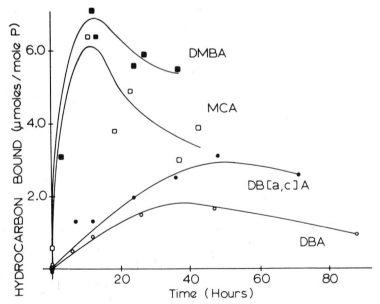

Figure 10. Binding of labelled hydrocarbons to DNA of mouse skin (from Goshman and Heidelberger [32]).

Table 3. Complex formation of aromatic hydrocarbons and amines in DNA solution (from Dannenberg [33]).

Compound	μMol/l in KHPO$_4$ (1)	μMol/l in DNA (2)	μMol/l Complexed (2)-(1)	Ratio of complex (2)/(1)
Coronene	1·54	2·1	0·56	1·4
Pyrene	0·13	0·5	0·37	3·8
1,2-Benzopyrene	0·35	0·9	0·55	2·6
1,2-Benzanthracene	0·03	0·5	0·47	17
1,2-5,6-Dibenzanthracene	1·2	0·7	5·5	5·5
3,4-Benzopyrene	0·05	0·77	0·72	16
7,12-Dimethyl-benzanthracene	0·05	0·13	0·08	2·6
20-Methylcholanthrene	0·9	10·7	9·8	12

dibenzanthracene was bound to a greater extent than the active 1,2-5,6-dibenzanthracene.

My interpretation of the results of Goshman and Heidelberger [32] and of Brookes and Lawley [31] is that the carcinogens with methyl groups are metabolized so that they combine with DNA through covalent links to a greater extent than the unsubstituted hydrocarbons 3,4-benzopyrene and 1,2-5,6-dibenzanthracene. On the other hand, the latter hydrocarbons form complexes with DNA as described by Boyland and Green [27] to a greater extent than does 7,12-dimethylbenz[a]anthracene (see Table 3 from [33]). 20-Methylcholanthrene combines with DNA to the same extent as 7,12-dimethylbenz[a]-anthracene. It also appears to dissolve in DNA by complex formation like 3,4-benzopyrene. Polycyclic hydrocarbons might exert their action either by:

1. Chemical combination with DNA, that occurs to a greater extent *in vivo* with compounds containing methyl groups, e.g. 7,12-dimethylbenz[a]-anthracene and 20-methylcholanthrene.
2. Complex formation with DNA, probably by intercalation, as occurs with planar compounds, e.g. 3,4-benzopyrene and 20-methylcholanthrene (cf. [34]). This takes place to a lesser extent with non-planar compounds such as 7,12-dimethylbenz[a]anthracene.

If carcinogenic hydrocarbons operate by these two different mechanisms, 20-methylcholanthrene and other compounds could also exert their effects by both mechanisms.

Aromatic amines

Aromatic amines have been suspected as causes of bladder cancer in man since Rehn [35] saw three cases of the disease in a German dyestuffs intermediates factory. Case [36] has shown that exposure of men to 1-naphthylamine, 2-naphthylamine or benzidine is associated with an increased risk of bladder cancer; 2-naphthylamine and 4-aminobiphenyl also cause bladder cancer in dogs (see Fig. 11). In mice, 2-naphthylamine induces liver tumours, and 4-aminobiphenyl produces intestinal and liver cancer in rats [37].

2-Acetamidofluorene (or 2-fluorenylacetamide) appeared to be a useful insecticide, but in chronic toxicity tests it was found to be a potent carcinogen [38] which has been widely investigated in many laboratories. It induces cancer of the liver, mammary gland, acoustic sebaceous gland and other sites in rats. It causes bladder cancer in dogs [39] and also in rats if the diet is supplemented with tryptophan [40, 41] or indole [42].

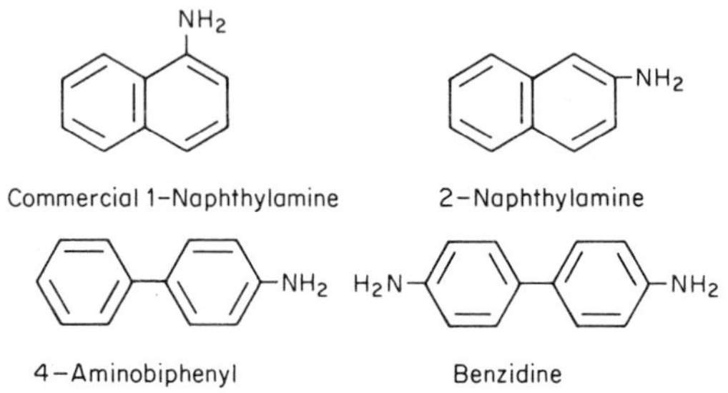

Figure 11. Aromatic amines that cause bladder cancer in man.

As the site of action of these amines is remote from that of application, it seems probable that some metabolite is the proximate carcinogen. Indications of activity of direct carcinogenic action can be obtained by injection tests or by bladder implantation. Injection of 2-acetamidofluorene does not induce tumours at the injection site whereas the metabolite N-hydroxy 2-acetamidofluorene produces tumours at the injection site [43]. That this injection test and the bladder implantation test are not reliable indicators of proximate carcinogens is illustrated by the fact that 20-methylcholanthrene, which may need metabolic activation, gives positive results with either test.

In the bladder implantation test, a pellet of inert material, usually cholesterol or paraffin wax in which the test substance is incorporated, is surgically implanted into the lumen of the bladder of a mouse [44]. This test requires some surgical skill; the tumours produced cannot be seen until the animals are killed, and the role of the "inert" pellet in the test is difficult to assess. In spite of these disadvantages the technique is of value in determining biochemical mechanisms of carcinogenesis.

Metabolism and mode of action of 2-acetamidofluorene

2-Acetamidofluorene is metabolized in rats so that phenolic compounds with hydroxyl groups in positions 1, 3, 5, 6, 7 and 8 are formed [45]; all these phenols are excreted as the corresponding glucuronides and the 7-hydroxy-2-acetamidofluorene is also excreted as the sulphate ester. The compounds are reversibly deacetylated so that the aminophenols are also formed. None of these phenolic metabolites has been found to be carcinogenic (cf. [46]).

Cramer *et al.* [47], however, identified *N*-hydroxy-2-acetamidofluorene in rats and mice but not in guinea pigs (Fig. 12).

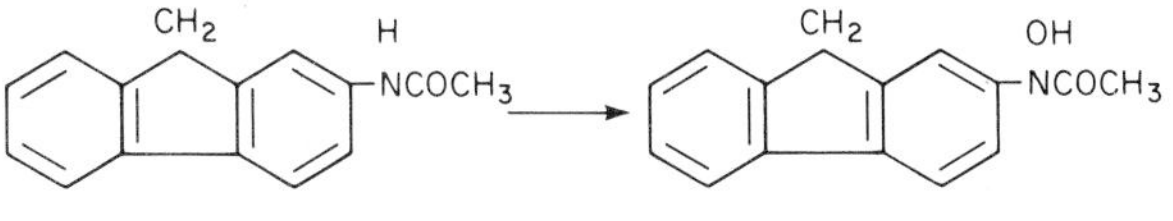

Figure 12. *N*-hydroxylation of 2-acetamidofluorene.

This metabolite was an active proximate carcinogen, inducing sarcomas at the site of injection of the compound itself, or of the less soluble copper chelate [48]. This discovery of the process of *N*-hydroxylation of carcinogenic amines opened a new avenue for the study of their biochemical mechanism of action.

Marroqin and Farber [49] showed that 2-acetamidofluorene or *N*-hydroxy-acetamidofluorene, labelled with ^{14}C in the 9 position, when administered to rats are incorporated into both DNA and RNA of the liver. Although neither 2-acetamidofluorene nor *N*-hydroxy-2-acetamidofluorene react with nucleic acid *in vitro* under neutral conditions [50], Kriek [51] found that *N*-hydroxy-2-acetamidofluorene reacted *in vitro* with the guanine residues of RNA and DNA at pH 5·6. On the other hand, Kriek *et al.* [52] showed that *N*-acetoxy-2-

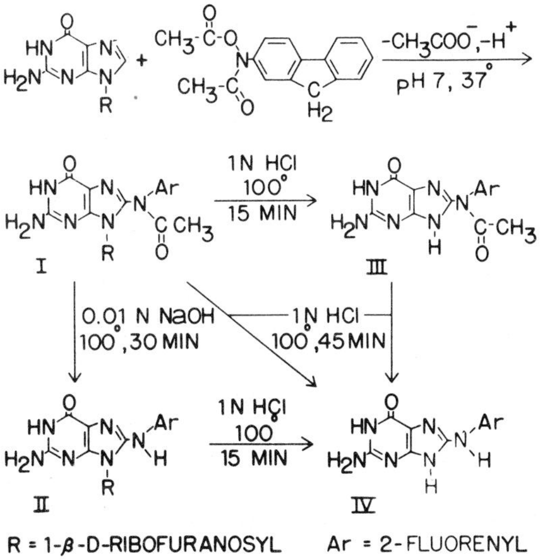

R = 1-β-D-RIBOFURANOSYL   Ar = 2-FLUORENYL

Figure 13. The reaction of *N*-acetoxy-2-acetamidofluorene with guanosine (from Kriek, Miller, Juhl and Miller [52]).

acetamidofluorene reacted with guanosine in neutral solution to give 8-(N-2-aceta-midofluorenyl)guanosine (Fig. 13). This was converted to 8-(N-2-acetamido-fluorenyl)guanosine with acid and to 8-(N-aminofluorenyl)guanosine with alkali. The acetoxy derivative also reacted with deoxyguanosine 5'-phosphate, with soluble RNA and with DNA in the same way to give 8-substituted guanine derivatives.

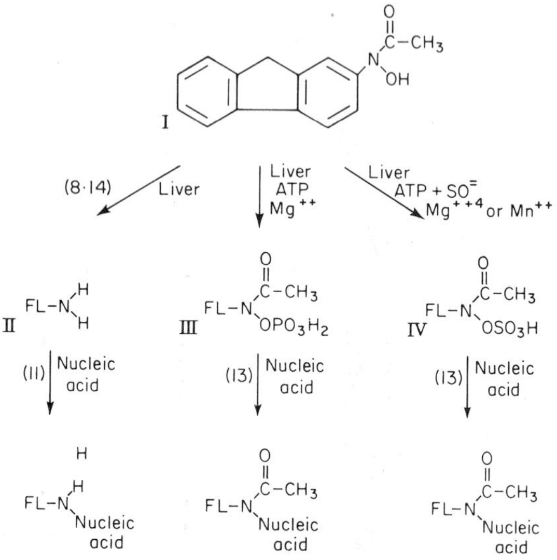

Figure 14. Metabolic incorporation of N-hydroxy-2-acetamidofluorene with nucleic acid.

These results indicate that N-hydroxy-2-acetamidofluorene, although a car-cinogenic metabolite of 2-acetamidofluorene, needs further activation before it can react with nucleic acid; substitution of the N-hydroxy group with an acetyl group provides this activation. In the cell, however, the function of the acetyl group may be taken by some other acid radical; thus, Lotlikar et al. [53] showed that N-sulphatoxy-2-acetamido-fluorene reacts very rapidly with guanosine and that the corresponding N-phosphatoxy is another possible active intermediate. King and Phillips [54] described a soluble rat liver fraction that catalyses the reaction of N-hydroxy-2-acetamidofluorene with sRNA. In the absence of activating factors the 2-aminofluorene moiety was bound but the acetyl group was not bound to the sRNA. If magnesium chloride, adenyltri-phosphate and sodium sulphate were added, the N-hydroxy-2-acetamidofluorene became bound to the nucleic acid (see Fig. 14).

These investigations indicate a mechanism by which 2-acetamidofluorene reacts with nucleic acid and could modify the inherited characters of the cell. Other carcinogenic aromatic amines may act by similar reactions, but they must be investigated.

2-Naphthylamine

Men are exposed to 2-naphthylamine because it is still manufactured in some countries and is formed in small quantities on burning protein. It is present in the air near the retorts of gas works in concentrations that can be measured [55]. As the carcinogenic action on the bladder of men and dogs is probably

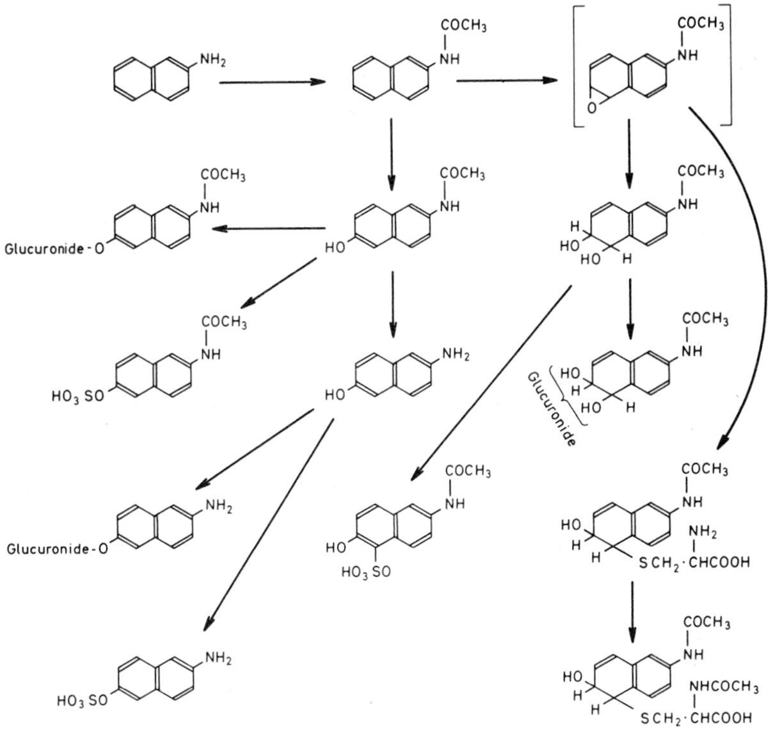

Figure 15. Metabolites of 2-naphthylamine and 2-acetamidonaphthalene in which the unsubstituted ring is involved.

exerted through metabolites, the metabolism of this amine has been studied extensively (for review of earlier work see [56]). The metabolites are shown in Figs. 15 and 16. The metabolites in Fig. 15 in which the reactions occur in the ring remote from the amino group are similar and analogous to the metabolites of naphthalene—a hydrocarbon that is not carcinogenic. Some of these metabolites have been tested by the bladder implantation test and found inactive; it is thought that all these metabolites are true detoxication products.

Of the metabolites shown in Fig. 16, 5 have been found to be locally carcinogenic by mouse bladder implantation tests. These are 2-amino-1-naphthyl glucuronide, bis(2-amino-1-naphthyl) phosphate, 2-formamido-1-naphthyl sulphate, 2-naphthyl hydroxylamine and 2-nitrosonaphthalene. Of these active compounds, 2-naphthylhydroxylamine and 2-nitrosonaphthalene are analogous to the *N*-hydroxy derivatives of 2-acetamidofluorene and may react with nucleic acid in the same way or by a different route. Aryl hydroxylamines in general, and 2-naphthylhydroxylamine in particular, are readily converted to *ortho* aminophenols by treatment with acid or by an enzyme present in rat liver [57]. *N*-Acetoxy 2-naphthylamine is converted to 2-acetamido-1-naphthol by the Udenfriend reagent. They react with thiols both *in vitro* and *in vivo* and the

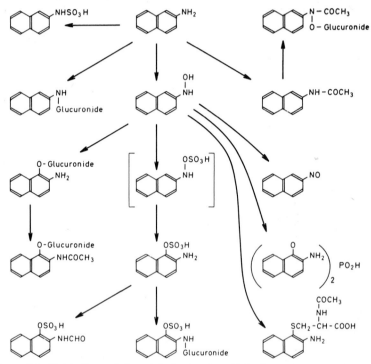

Figure 16. Metabolites of 2-naphthylamine in which the amino group is probably involved.

ortho amino aryl mercapturic acids that are excreted [58] are formed at least partly through this reaction. This reaction, which is analogous to the reaction of epoxides with glutathione, is almost certainly a detoxication process. The carcinogenic 2-nitrosonaphthalene also reacts with glutathione, but it may be reduced to 2-naphthylhydroxylamine before reacting.

Two of the three carcinogenic *ortho* amino naphthol derivatives also react with thiols to give the same products as does naphthylhydroxylamine (see Fig. 17). 2-Amino-1-naphthyl glucuronide, however, reacts only with acetylcysteine whereas bis(2-amino-1-naphthyl)phosphate reacts with glutathione also. Although the carcinogenic 2-formamido-1-naphthyl sulphate does not react with thiol compounds, the more common but non-carcinogenic 2-amino-1-naphthyl sulphate reacts spontaneously with glutathione (Manson, personal communication).

Although both 2-naphthylhydroxylamine and bis(2-amino-naphthyl) phosphate react with glutathione, only 2-naphthylhydroxylamine in acid solution and with 2-nitrosonaphthalene (in the presence of a reducing agent in neutral solution), of the known carcinogenic metabolites, react with guanylic

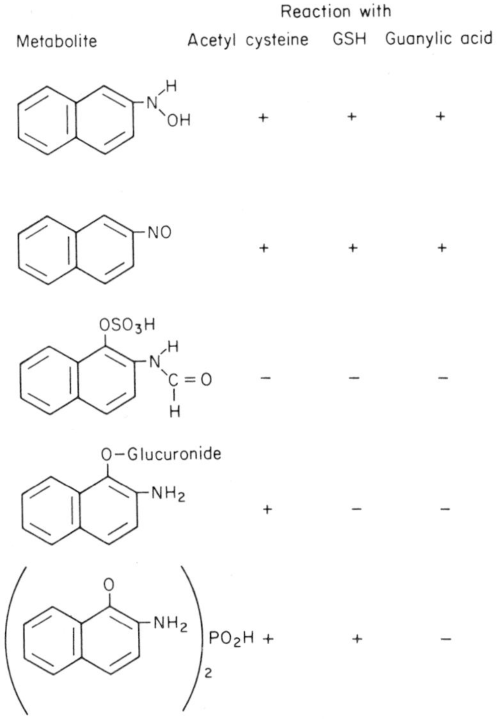

Figure 17. Reactions of carcinogenic metabolites of 2-naphthylamine.

acid. Although the reaction with 2-naphthylhydroxylamine only takes place in acid solution, N-formylsulphatoxy-2-naphthylhydroxylamine (a compound that could be a precursor of the carcinogenic metabolite, 2-formamido-1-naphthyl sulphate) reacts with guanylic acid in neutral solution to give the corresponding N-formyl derivative. This reaction is analogous to that found with 2-N-sulpha-toxyacetamidofluorene by Lotlikar et al. [53].

It is probable that in the reaction between 2-naphthylhydroxylamine and guanylic acid, the 8-position of guanine is substituted as the product formed from deoxyguanylic acid does not easily lose the deoxyribose group (see Fig. 18). A similar product is formed if a mixture of 2-naphthylamine and guanylic acid is oxidized with peracetic acid (Manson, personal communication). Thus the reaction of naphthylamine with nucleic acid might occur through the radical or ion formed in the oxidation of naphthylamine. Such a reaction would not account for the induction of cancer of the bladder rather than of other sites in men and dogs. The localized effect on the bladder might be due to slow release of an active carcinogen from an inactive excreted metabolite while the urine remains in the bladder (cf. [56]),

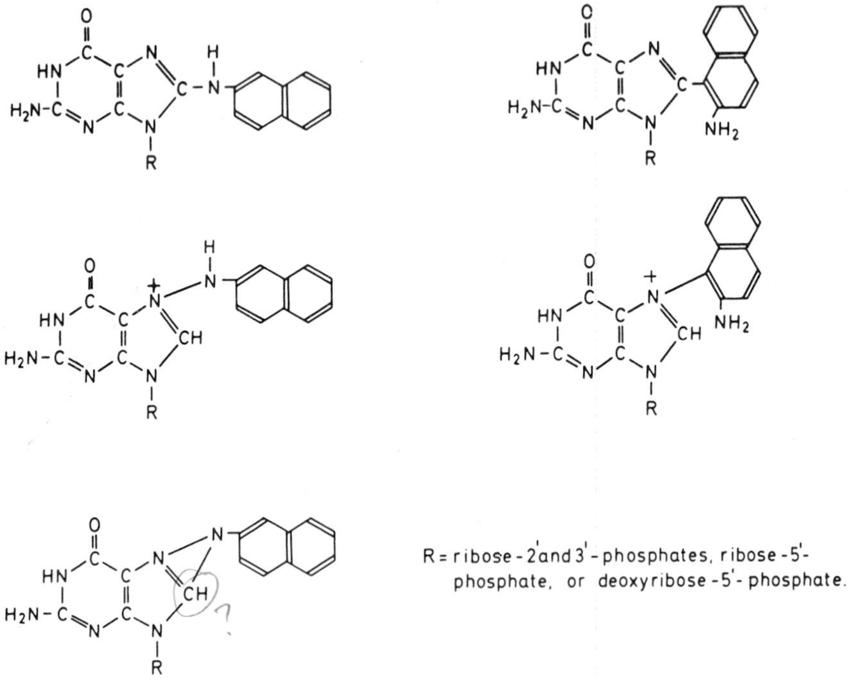

R = ribose - 2′ and 3′ - phosphates, ribose - 5′- phosphate, or deoxyribose - 5′- phosphate.

Figure 18. Possible products of reaction of the carcinogenic metabolites of 2-naphthylamine with guanine residues of nucleic acid.

With 2-naphthylamine there are clearly two types of carcinogenic metabolites, arylhydroxylamines and *ortho* amino phenols. The hypothesis that *ortho* amino phenols were the proximate carcinogens led to the idea that tryptophan metabolites of this structure, e.g. 3-hydroxyanthranilic acid and 3-hydroxykynurenine might be endogenous carcinogens. The findings that these substances were carcinogens [44, 59] are in agreement with the hypothesis.

If the effect were due to 2-amino-1-naphthyl glucuronide or bis(2-amino-1-naphthyl)phosphate, such a mechanism would explain the localized action. If the important carcinogens are 2-naphthylhydroxylamine or 2-nitrosonaphthalene, then other processes must operate to cause observed action on the bladder.

Induction of bladder cancer with 2-naphthylamine occurs in man, in dogs [60] and in hamsters given large doses of the amine [61], but not in mice or rats. All the five known carcinogenic metabolites are present in dog urine but only 2-amino-1-naphthyl glucuronide and 2-formamido-1-naphthyl sulphate are excreted by rats [62].

It is hoped that further work will clarify the mechanism of action of the aromatic hydrocarbons and amines, but it is unlikely that means of preventing cancer by application of this knowledge will be found. For this reason the exposure of mankind to the carcinogenic hydrocarbons and amines should be avoided.

REFERENCES

1. Matthew, Authorised Version XIII, 4-9.
2. Boyland, E., *Cancer Res.* **12** (1952) 77.
3. Boyland, E., *Pharmac. Rev.* **6** (1954) 345.
4. Brookes, P. and Lawley, P. D., *Br. med. Bull.* **20** (1964) 91.
5. Masuda, Y., Mori, K. and Kuratsune, M., *Int. J. Cancer* **2** (1967) 489.
6. Kennaway, E. L., *Biochem. J.* **24** (1930) 497.
7. Cook, J. W., Hewett, C. L. and Heiger, I., *J. chem. Soc.* (1933) 395.
8. Hewett, C. L., *J. chem. Soc.* (1940) 293.
9. Robinson, R., *Br. med. J.* i (1946) 946.
10. Cook, J. W. and Haslewood, G. A. D., *J. chem. Soc.* (1934) 248.
11. Daudel, R. and Pullman, A., *C. r. hebd. Séanc. Acad. Sci., Paris* **220** (1945) 599.
12. Boyland, E. and Wolf, G., *Biochem. J.* **47** (1950) 64.
13. Boyland, E. and Sims, P., *Biochem. J.* **84** (1962) 564.
14. Boyland, E. and Sims, P., *Biochem. J.* **84** (1962) 571.
15. Boyland, E. and Sims, P., *Biochem. J.* **84** (1962) 583.
16. Boyland, E. and Levi, A. A., *Biochem. J.* **29** (1935) 2679.
17. Pullman, B. and Pullman, A., "Les théories électroniques de la chimie organique", Masson, Paris, 1952.
18. Pullman, A. and Pullman, B., "Cancérisation par les substances chimiques et structure moléculaire", Masson, Paris, 1955.
19. Boyland, E. and Williams, J., *Biochem. J.* **94** (1964) 190.
20. Cramer, J. W., Miller, E. C. and Miller, J. A., *J. biol. Chem.* **235** (1960) 250.
21. Brodie, B. B. and Maickel, R. P., in "Proceedings 1st International Pharmacological Meeting" (Stockholm, August 1961), Vol. 6: Metabolic factors controlling duration of drug action, p. 299. Pergamon Press, Oxford, 1962.
22. Roe, F. J. C., Rowson, K. E. K. and Salaman, M. H., *Br. J. Cancer* **15** (1961) 515.
23. Van Duuren, B. L., Nelson, N., Orris, L., Palmer, E. D. and Schmitt, F. L., *J. natn Cancer Inst.* **31** (1963) 41.
24. Newman, M. S. and Blum, S., *J. Am. chem. Soc.* **86** (1964) 5598.
25. Miller, E. C. and Miller, J. A., *Proc. Soc. exp. Biol. Med.* **124** (1967) 915.
26. Boyland, E. and Sims, P., *Int. J. Cancer* **2** (1967) 500.
27. Boyland, E. and Green, B., *Br. J. Cancer* **16** (1962) 507.

28. Butenandt, A. and Dannenberg, H., *Arch. Geschwulstforsch.* **6** (1953) 1.
29. Boyland, E. and Sims, P., *Biochem. J.* **95** (1965) 780.
30. Boyland, E., Sims, P. and Huggins, C., *Nature, Lond.* **207** (1966) 816.
31. Brookes, P. and Lawley, P. D., *Nature, Lond.* **202** (1964) 781.
32. Goshman, L. M. and Heidelberger, C., *Cancer Res.* **27** (1967) 1678.
33. Dannenberg, H., *in* "17 Colloquium der Gesellschaft für physiologische Chemie" (21/23 April 1966) in Mosbach/Baden. Springer-Verlag, 1967.
34. Iball, J. and MacDonald, S. G. G., *Kristallographie* **114** (1960) 439.
35. Rehn, L., *Arch. klin. Chir.* **50** (1895) 588.
36. Case, R. A. M., *Ann. R. Coll. Surg.* **39** (1966) 213.
37. Walpole, A. L. and Williams, M. H. C., *Br. med. Bull.* **14** (1958) 141.
38. Wilson, R. M., De Eds, F. and Cox, A. J., *Cancer Res.* **1** (1941) 595.
39. Morris, H. P. and Eyestone, W. H., *J. natn Cancer Inst.* **13** (1953) 1139.
40. Dunning, W. F., Curtis, M. R. and Maun, M. E., *Cancer Res.* **10** (1950) 454.
41. Boyland, E., Harris, J. and Horning, E. S., *Br. J. Cancer* **8** (1954) 647.
42. Dunning, W. F. and Curtis, M. R., *Proc. Am. Ass. Cancer Res.* **2** (1957) 197.
43. Miller, J. A., Cramer, J. W. and Miller, E. C., *Cancer Res.* **20** (1960) 950.
44. Allen, M. J., Boyland, E., Dukes, C. E., Horning, E. S. and Watson, J. G., *Br. J. Cancer* **11** (1957) 212.
45. Weisburger, E. K. and Weisburger, J. H., *Adv. Cancer Res.* **5** (1958) 331.
46. Bonser, G. M., Boyland, E., Busby, E. R., Clayson, D. B., Grover, P. L. and Jull, J. W., *Br. J. Cancer* **17** (1963) 127.
47. Cramer, J. W., Miller, J. A. and Miller, E. C., *J. biol. Chem.* **235** (1960) 885.
48. Miller, J. A., Enomoto, M. and Miller, E. C., *Cancer Res.* **22** (1962) 1381.
49. Marroqin, F. and Farber E., *Cancer Res.* **25** (1965) 1262.
50. Miller, E. C., Juhl, U. and Miller, J. A., *Science, N.Y.* **153** (1966) 1125.
51. Kriek, E., *Biochem. biophys. Res. Commun.* **20** (1965) 793.
52. Kriek, E., Miller, J. A., Juhl, U. and Miller, E. C., *Biochemistry, N.Y.* **6** (1967) 177.
53. Lotlikar, P. D., Irving, C. C., Miller, E. C. and Miller, J. A., *Proc. Am. Ass. Cancer Res.* **8** (1967) 42.
54. King, C. M. and Phillips, B., *Science, N.Y.* **159** (1968) 1351.
55. Battye, R., *in* "Transactions of the 15th International Congress on Industrial Medicine", **3** (1966) 156.
56. Boyland, E., "The Biochemistry of Bladder Cancer", Charles C. Thomas, Springfield, Ill., 1963.
57. Booth, J. and Boyland, E., *Biochem. J.* **91** (1964) 362.
58. Boyland, E., Manson, D. and Nery, R., *Biochem. J.* **86** (1963) 263.
59. Bryan, G. T., Brown, R. R. and Price, J. M., *Cancer Res.* **24** (1964) 596.
60. Hueper, W. C., *Archs. Path.* **25** (1938) 856.
61. Saffiotti, U., Cefis, F., Montesano, R. and Sellakumar, A. R., *Ind. Med. Surg.* **35** (1966) 564.
62. Boyland, E. and Manson, D., *Biochem. J.* **101** (1966) 84.

FEBS Symposium, Volume 16, 1969, pp. 205-207

The Metabolism of Carcinogenic Nitrosamines and the Metabolic Fate of their Alkyl Groups

P. N. MAGEE

Courtauld Institute of Biochemistry,
Middlesex Hospital Medical School,
London, England

Many alkyl *N*-nitroso compounds are powerfully carcinogenic and can cause acute cellular injury to the liver and other organs. Some of these compounds are also strongly mutagenic and teratogenic [1-3]. The dialkylnitrosamines, as exemplified by dimethylnitrosamine (*N*-nitrosodimethylamine) are relatively stable chemically, while the nitrosamides, for example, *N*-nitrosomethylurea, may be chemically unstable and decompose quite rapidly at neutral pH. The balance of the available evidence suggests that the nitrosamines only become biologically active after metabolic decomposition in the cells of affected organs, while the nitrosamides probably decompose in the tissues without metabolic activation, although, in some cases, their decomposition may be accelerated by sulphydryl compounds [1, 2]. Both types of nitroso compound have been shown to alkylate cellular constituents of the tissues of treated animals [2] and it has been concluded that an active alkylating compound must be formed by the decomposition of the nitroso compounds in the body. The nature of the alkylating intermediate is not known and various suggestions have been made including the corresponding diazoalkane and the carbonium ion. Recent work by Lijinsky *et al.*, using fully deuterated dimethylnitrosamine, has shown that the alkyl group reacts as -CH$_3$, which suggests that the diazoalkane is not involved [4]. The formation of an active methylating agent from dimethylnitrosamine *in vivo* was inferred from the evidence of methylation of RNA and DNA in the livers of rats treated with dimethylnitrosamine [5]. As with alkylation of nucleic acids *in vitro* by chemical alkylating agents, the main site of alkylation was on the 7-position of guanine [5], but recent work has shown that reaction may also occur on adenine and cytosine [6]. The biological significance of the cellular alkylations following exposure of animals to carcinogenic nitroso compounds is not clear, nor is the role of possible alkylations in mutagenesis and teratogenesis by these compounds. The formation of other biologically active metabolites from nitroso compounds cannot be excluded and a number of potent mutagens might be formed, including nitrous acid and derivatives of hydroxylamine and hydrazine.

Each nitroso carcinogen tends to show a characteristic distribution of tumour induction in the different organs [3]. The factors determining the tumour distribution are not well understood but there is some correlation between the extent of reaction with cellular components as measured by alkylation of nucleic acids in the different organs and the incidence of tumours. This is evident with dimethylnitrosamine in the rat [7, 8], where methylation of DNA and RNA occurs mainly in the liver and to a lesser extent in the kidney and lungs, which are organs in which tumours are induced in this species. Methylation is extremely low in the small intestine and dimethylnitrosamine has never been reported to induce tumours of this organ in the rat. Metabolism of dimethyl-nitrosamine occurs relatively rapidly with rat liver slices *in vitro* [9] and at a lower rate with kidney slices. Rat small intestine slices with oxygen uptake about equal to that of liver slices showed no detectable metabolism of dimethylnitrosamine as measured by production of radioactive CO_2 from [^{14}C] dimethylnitrosamine (P. N. Magee, unpublished results). These findings suggest that organ specificity of the nitrosamines may be determined to some extent by the level of activity of the enzymes involved in their decomposition.

Following the administration of dimethylnitrosamine to rats, the level of methylation of the DNA and RNA, as measured by formation of 7-methyl-guanine in the liver and kidney rises to a maximum during the first 24 hours and then falls [10]. The presence of 7-methylguanine with the methyl group derived from dimethylnitrosamine was still detectable 12 days after treatment with the carcinogen but could not be detected at 61 days (J. Frei and P. N. Magee, unpublished results).

Radioactive 7-methylguanine is present in the urine of rats 5 hours after administration of ^{14}C- or ^{3}H-labelled dimethylnitrosamine (30 mg per kg body wt.) and, following this dose, the excretion of 7-methylguanine is raised above the normal urinary level by a factor of about 2 to 3 [11].

Treatment of rats with diethylnitrosamine is followed by ethylation of liver RNA with the formation of 7-ethylguanine [12]. Subsequent work has shown that DNA is also ethylated and that 7-ethylguanine, with the ethyl group derived from the diethylnitrosamine, is excreted in the urine (P. N. Magee, unpublished results). There is some evidence that some of the labelled 7-methylguanine appearing in the urine after treatment with [^{14}C] dimethylnitrosamine may have been derived from methylated nucleic acids [11].

The function of nucleic acids might be affected in at least two ways in organs of animals treated with nitroso carcinogens. The presence of foreign or excessive alkyl groups on guanine, adenine and cytosine might lead to impairment of template function, and the possible excision of alkylated guanines, and perhaps other bases, from DNA might be followed by chain breakage and deletion of genetic material, as suggested by Brookes and Lawley [13].

REFERENCES

1. Magee, P. N. and Schoental, R., *Br. med. Bull.* **20** (1964) 102.
2. Magee, P. N. and Barnes, J. M., *Adv. Cancer Res.* **10** (1967) 163.
3. Druckrey, H., Preussmann, R., Ivankovic, S. and Schmähl, D., *Z. Krebsforsch.* **69** (1967) 103.
4. Lijinsky, W., Loo, J. and Ross, A. E., *Nature, Lond.* **218** (1968) 1174.
5. Magee, P. N. and Farber, E., *Biochem. J.* **83** (1962) 114.
6. Lawley, P. D., Brookes, P., Magee, P. N., Craddock, V. M. and Swann, P. F., *Biochim. biophys. Acta* **157** (1968) 646.
7. Lee, K. Y., Lijinsky, W. and Magee, P. N., *J. natn. Cancer Inst.* **32** (1964) 65.
8. Swann, P. F. and Magee, P. N., *Biochem. J.* **110** (1968) 39-47.
9. Magee, P. N. and Vandekar, M., *Biochem J.* **70** (1958) 600.
10. Craddock, V. M. and Magee, P. N., *Biochem. J.* **89** (1963) 32.
11. Craddock, V. M. and Magee, P. N., *Biochem. J.* **104** (1967) 435.
12. Magee, P. N. and Lee, K. Y., *Biochem. J.* **91** (1964) 35.
13. Brookes, P. and Lawley, P. D., *Br. med. Bull.* **20** (1964) 91.

FEBS Symposium, Volume 16, 1969, pp. 209-225

Correlation of N- and C-Oxygenation of Aromatic Amines with Conditions which Increase the Carcinogenicity of these Compounds*

E. ARRHENIUS

The Wenner-Gren Institute, University of Stockholm, Stockholm, Sweden

It has been known for almost 200 years that cancer can be induced by chemical agents [1]. However, the experimental study of chemical carcinogenesis has developed almost entirely during this century [2, 3]. With the orbitant development of the chemical industry in this century a wide variety of chemically well-defined substances became available, which had high enough carcinogenic potency to induce high frequencies of neoplasms even in such short-lived species as laboratory rodents [4-6]. This introduced rich possibilities for experimental studies; attention could be extended to physiological and histological alterations during early neoplastic and pre-neoplastic stages in the tumour-inducing process. With the development of biochemistry and molecular biology in the last decades it finally became feasible to study the effects of carcinogenic agents on specific functions of cells and subcellular units.

From present knowledge of hereditary functions it seems evident that the neoplastic transformation of somatic cells implies an inheritable loss of response to the growth-regulating mechanisms of the organism [7]. Thus, either the genome itself or the cellular differentiation mechanism by which the expression of the genome is governed must be irreversibly changed by the action of the carcinogen.

In contrast to virus-induced neoplasms, where tumours produced by a particular virus exhibit identical specific antigens, individual neoplasms induced by a given chemical carcinogen vary in their antigenic properties [8, 9]. This suggests that the primary event in chemical carcinogenesis is a random interaction of the carcinogens or their metabolities with macromolecules capable of storing and regulating the expression of cellular information, i.e. nucleic acids and proteins.

Such a possible interaction of carcinogens with the genetic mechanism was provided by the demonstration by Miller and Miller [10] of a covalent binding

* Supported by grants from the Swedish Cancer Society.

of the carcinogen N,N-dimethyl-4-aminoazobenzene to liver protein in rats and mice. Similar effects were soon demonstrated for a wide variety of carcinogens *in vivo* and *in vitro* and a certain correlation of binding capacity with carcinogenic potency was obtained. Binding to RNA* and DNA has also been demonstrated for several carcinogens, thus offering further possible mechanisms for interaction with hereditary functions [11].

CARCINOGENIC AMINES

The carcinogenic amines include a variety of aromatic members, e.g. AF, AAF, 2-AN, methylated amino-azo dyes, etc. and the aliphatic dialkylnitrosamines [4]. Unlike the majority of tumour-inducing agents, these compounds do not exert their carcinogenic action at the site of application, but rather in distal organs. This has been regarded as evidence that metabolic activation of the amine molecules is needed for the manifestation of their tumour-inducing properties. Extensive studies of the metabolism of these compounds *in vivo* have been performed by analysis of the urinary products from animals fed the carcinogens. A variety of metabolites, free or conjugated to water-soluble carriers, have been reported [11-14]. The main metabolic conversions involve oxygenation at different ring positions to phenolic derivatives, oxygenation of the amine nitrogen to hydroxylamines, oxidative dealkylations and reductive cleavage of azo bonds. These reactions are not specific for carcinogenic amines but represent a general detoxication mechanism for amines [15, 16].

The dependence of these amines upon metabolic attack by the host cell for the induction of their carcinogenic properties is very useful in the exploration of the primary events in the carcinogenic process. A broad spectrum of exogenous and endogenous factors are known which influence the neoplasm-inducing potency of carcinogenic amines [13, 14, 17-19], and these various conditions have also been demonstrated to influence the metabolic pattern *in vivo* [20-22]. This enables a flexible experimental system to be devised for correlating effects of carcinogenic amines on the function of cells and subcellular fractions with carcinogenic effects *in vivo*. Also, by comparing the effects of carcinogenic amines *in vitro* on preparations obtained from normal animals, and from animals with modified responsiveness towards the carcinogenetic effect of these substances, it may be possible to evaluate which effects are relevant for the carcinogenic process.

In 1948 Mueller and Miller [23] demonstrated by *in vitro* experiments that the reductive cleavage of carcinogenic azo dyes was located in the liver. By

---

* The following abbreviations are used: AAF, 2-acetylaminofluorene; acetoxy-AAF, 2-acetoxyacetylaminofluorene; AF, 2-aminofluorene; 2-AN, 2-aminonaphthalene; DMA, dimethylaniline; DMA-N-oxide, dimethylaniline-N-oxide; DNA, deoxyribonucleic acid; Fp, flavoprotein; FpH_2, reduced flavoprotein; $NADH_2$, reduced nicotinamidadenine dinucleotide; $NADPH_2$, reduced nicotinamidadenine dinucleotide phosphate; RNA, ribonucleic acid.

differential centrifugation they also demonstrated that the enzymes responsible for this reaction were bound to the microsomal fraction and utilized reduced nicotinamidadenine dinucleotide phosphate (NADPH$_2$) as electron donor. Localization to microsomal structures and utilization of NADPH$_2$ as electron donor was later demonstrated by several groups for various oxygenation reactions [15, 16, 24].

The localization of these mixed function oxygenases [25] in the membranes of the endoplasmic reticulum of liver cells is of great interest to those studying the carcinogenic action of amines. Although these carcinogens produce tumours in several organs, their main target is the liver [4]. Also the binding of carcinogenic amines to macromolecules occurs mainly in this organ, indicating that the metabolic process which converts the originally harmless amines to noxious metabolites is localized to the liver [11].

The correlation between this binding of carcinogenic amines to macromolecules and their metabolism in the microsomal detoxifying enzyme systems is strengthened by the demonstration by Hultin [26-28] that the primary binding of carcinogenic amines in short-term experiments occurs in the microsomal fraction.

Besides detoxication the endoplasmic network in liver cells has another vital function. The ribosomal particles, which are attached to the surface of the membranes, play a key role in the synthesis of specific proteins according to the information coded by messenger-RNA. The ribosomes thus fulfil two prerequisites for consideration as one of the key sites in chemical carcinogenesis, viz. they have an essential function in the expression of the genome, and they are also very closely localized at the sites at which reactive metabolites of carcinogenic amines may be emitted during the detoxication process. As the endoplasmic reticulum is continuous with the perinuclear membrane [29, 30], these prerequisites are also fulfilled by the nucleus, i.e. the reactive metabolites of the carcinogens may exert their action on the genome itself. It has been shown that when animals were treated with carcinogenic amines, or when liver slices were incubated *in vitro* in the presence of these substances, disturbances of the functions of ribosomes in protein synthesis *in vitro* have been observed [31-38]. The above-mentioned exogenous and endogenous factors which affect the metabolic pattern *in vivo,* and the carcinogenic potency of the amines, also influence the effects exerted by these amines on ribosomal functions. There is a certain, although not complete, correlation between the manifestation of carcinogenic properties and the effects on protein synthesis *in vitro* [32-35, 38].

METABOLISM OF CARCINOGENIC AMINES BY LIVER MICROSOMES

A mechanism for the primary event in chemical carcinogenesis can thus be inferred, which implicates an effect of reactive metabolites of carcinogens on ribosomal anabolic functions. What is the nature and mode of formation of reactive metabolites required by this hypothesis?

The chemical nature of the reactive metabolites has been the subject of extensive discussion [11]. *In vivo* carcinogenic amines, like amines in general, are oxygenated on various carbon atoms (*C*-oxygenation), yielding ring-hydroxylated or dealkylated products, or on the nitrogen atom (*N*-oxygenation). These metabolites appear in the urine, both free and conjugated to form water-soluble products [12-14]. During the last decade considerable interest has been focused on the role of *N*-oxygenated metabolites in the carcinogenetic process. These compounds, in contrast to *C*-oxygenated metabolites, have a high carcinogenic potency, they are to a certain degree carcinogenic at sites other than the liver; and they are carcinogenic in the guinea pig, a species which is refractory towards the carcinogenic action of the parent amines. These *N*-oxygenated metabolites also exhibit a greater ability than the parent amines or *C*-oxygenated metabolites to bind to nucleic acids and proteins *in vivo* [11]. Furthermore, a progressive increase in the urinary output of *N*-oxygenated products becomes apparent after some weeks in animals given carcinogenic amines at tumour-inducing levels in the diet [39].

Influence of endogenous and exogenous factors on microsomal amine oxygenation

The effects of carcinogenic amines on ribosomal anabolic functions described above are influenced by a variety of genetic, hormonal and environmental factors. There is a certain, although not complete, correlation of the effects on ribosomes with the variations in tumour-inducing capacity of the carcinogens under these conditions. The formation of *N*-oxygenated urinary metabolites also exhibits a similar correlation [40].

Evidence has been presented indicating that a shift in the microsomal metabolic pattern from *C*- to *N*-oxygenation is a result of decreased functional intactness of the detoxication chain in the endoplasmic reticulum [41, 42]. It thus seemed pertinent to evaluate whether those *in vivo* conditions that quantitatively affect ribosomal function were correlated with a shift in the metabolic pattern of aromatic amines towards the proposedly pernicious *N*-oxygenation pathway. A variety of *in vivo* conditions, both known to alter the tumour-inducing capacities of aromatic amines, and to accentuate their effects on ribosomal anabolic activities, were tested for such an effect [40]. The monocyclic non-carcinogenic amine DMA was selected as a test substrate, rather than the carcinogens AF or AAF, to avoid *in vitro* interference with microsomal detoxication mechanisms observed with the carcinogenic amines [43]. Thus, the studies of *in vivo* effects on microsomal detoxication were not obscured by *in vitro* damage.

(a) Rats fed an AAF-containing tumour-inducing diet, within some weeks exhibited a several-fold increased urinary output of *N*-oxygenated AAF metabolites [39]. The increased accumulation of *N*-oxygenated DMA in microsomal systems from similarly treated rats [40] offered a good correlation between changed oxygenation pattern in *in vitro* systems and *N*-oxygenation of carcinogenic aromatic amines in tumour induction experiments. It thus seems evident that this changed metabolism during tumour induction was due to a decreased stability of the detoxication chain in the endoplasmic reticulum. In short term *in vivo* treatment with larger doses of AF or AAF, the shift towards *N*-oxygenation in *in vitro* systems was even more marked. As this *in vivo* treatment also affected ribosomal anabolic functions [33-35], it seems evident that malfunctions of ribosomes induced by carcinogenic aromatic amines were associated with disturbances of the detoxication mechanism in the endoplasmic reticulum.

(b) In this connection, the effects of vitamin E merit specific attention [35, 40]. This vitamin plays a role in the manifestation of various characteristics of carcinogenic aromatic amines; E-deficiency potentiates tumour induction by AAF [18, 44] and increases the output of urinary *N*-oxygenated metabolites in animals given AAF-containing tumour-inducing diets [22]. E-deficiency also potentiates the inhibition of ribosomal anabolic functions caused by large doses of AF or 2-AN in short-term experiments; administration of vitamin E to the deficient animals totally abolishes the inhibitory effect [35]. A marked shift in *in vitro* metabolism of DMA towards *N*-oxygenation has been demonstrated in response to a depression of the vitamin E level of the rats [40]. High doses of vitamin E *in vivo* completely abolished this effect. This *in vitro* change towards a pernicious detoxication pathway seems to be paralleled *in vivo* by an increased production of reactive metabolites from carcinogenic amines, as indicated by the synergistic effect of vitamin E-depletion together with short-term *in vivo* AF administration on the oxygenation pattern of DMA *in vitro* [40]. The physiological effects of vitamin E have been the object of extensive studies but are by no means exhaustively clarified [45]. The basic property, inherent in its phenolic structure, of acting as an antioxidant by transfer of an electron followed by a proton migration to electrophilic acceptors seems, however, to be well established [46, 47]. This implies an inhibitory action on lipid peroxidation by inactivation of propagating radicals [42]. The possibility that the effect of vitamin E-depletion described here is due to a labilization of the endoplasmic lipoprotein membranes by lipid peroxidation has therefore to be considered. However, it would seem to be ruled out because lipid peroxidation is strongly inhibited by the added substrate in *in vitro* oxygenation studies [40], as well as by large amounts of AF given *in vivo* [35]. Furthermore, it has not as yet been possible to demonstrate increased levels of peroxides or peroxide-dependent functional disturbances in vitamin E-deficient animals *in vivo* [48, 49]. Binding of the reactive metabolites of carcinogens, however, occurs mainly in nucleophilic sites [11]; Boyland *et al.* [50] and Haddow [51] also postulated that these reactive metabolites had electrophilic properties. Thus the protective effect of vitamin E against the effects of carcinogenic amines may be due to a quenching action on reactive metabolites of aromatic amines, leaking out from the endoplasmic reticulum, rather than a reinforcing effect on the membraneous structures themselves [40].

(c) The induction of liver tumours with aromatic amines is prevented by adrenalectomy or hypophysectomy, and is strongly stimulated by the administration of corticosteroids [17, 19]. Available experimental evidence [17] indicates that this effect is associated with the initiation phase of chemical carcinogenesis. The possibility has been considered [34, 38] that the action of corticoids could be related to the stimulation of a pattern of protein synthesis severely disturbed under the influence of reactive metabolites of the carcinogens. As an alternative, or as an additional explanation for the potentiating effect of corticosteroid treatment, possible effects of the hormone on the detoxication mechanism must, however, be considered. It has been shown [40] that the overall *in vitro* metabolism of DMA, i.e. both C-oxygenation and N-oxygenation, was stimulated by glucocorticoid treatment *in vivo*. However, this stimulation was preferential for N-oxygenation; a marked shift towards this noxious pathway was observed. Similar effects were obtained by stressing the animals with Celite [40].

Although a direct action of corticosteroids on the membranes of the endoplasmic reticulum cannot be excluded as the cause of this shift [40], it seems more probable that some microsomal enzymes may be among those proteins whose synthesis is stimulated by glucocorticoids [33]. Experiments on induction of drug-metabolizing enzymes indicate that newly-synthesized detoxicating enzymes are less tightly coupled [52] and that cytochrome P450, which takes part in C-oxygenation, but not in N-oxygenation [42, 53], may become rate-limiting [54]. Thus, the relevance of stimulation of protein synthesis by carcinogenic aromatic amines for tumour induction might be due to the induction of an enzyme pattern which favours production of reactive metabolites. This interpretation is consistent with the extreme histological damage obtained by simultaneous administration of carcinogenic aromatic amines and corticoids [55].

When the corticoid response was evoked by non-specific stress, i.e. intraperitoneal Celite injection, the increase in N-oxygenation was similar to that obtained with corticoid administration; there was, however, some difference in the effect on N-demethylation. As mentioned previously, the pituitary activity involved in the complex pattern of hormonal and neural mechanisms of a stress reaction [56] may directly affect the enzymic transformation of corticoids in the liver [57]. In stress induced by carcinogenic amines the further possibility of a direct action of reactive metabolites on the corticoid-transforming enzymes must also be considered [43].

(d) Upon feeding rats a protein-free diet for some days, oxygenation of amines by their liver microsomes is inhibited [40, 58]. This is entirely an effect on *C*-oxygenation; *N*-oxygenation is slightly stimulated and thus the metabolism is diverted towards this potentially harmful pathway [40].

The influence of dietary protein level on carcinogenicity of aromatic amines is a matter of some controversy [13, 14]. It should be emphasized, however, that the protein content of the diet must be decreased below 6% to obtain inhibited *C*-oxygenation [58]; most tumour-induction experiments have investigated effects of variations above this level [13, 14]. Measuring the effect of protein addition to a polished rice diet, Mori [59] obtained a decrease in tumour incidence from 44% to 20%. Thus protein-deficiency also seems to provide a positive correlation of increased tumour induction with a shift towards *N*-oxygenation in microsomal systems.

(e) The lack of response of guinea pigs towards the tumour-inducing properties of carcinogenic amines has been interpreted as due to more efficient metabolic conversion of these amines to harmless excretion products [60]. Indeed, these animals do not *N*-oxygenate AF or AAF to any appreciable extent *in vivo* [20, 39], although their overall metabolism of these compounds is much more rapid than that of rats [60]. Experiments on microsomal oxygenation of amines [40] are in agreement with these facts. Although total oxygenation of DMA is higher than in rat microsomes, this is essentially a *C*-oxygenation; the *N*-oxygenation/*C*-oxygenation quotient was only about one-third of that in rats.

These facts indicate that a variety of environmental, hormonal and genetic conditions, which favour tumour induction by aromatic amines, and potentiate the effect of these agents on ribosomal protein synthesis, are associated with a decreased intactness of the microsomal detoxication chain. In this way, *N*-oxygenation, which is favoured in vitiated systems [41. 42], is accentuated. *N*-oxygenation of the non-carcinogenic amine DMA, used as a test substrate in these systems, cannot, however, be demonstrated *in vivo* [61]. The acquirement of this pernicious oxygenation pathway in cell-free systems may indicate constitutional changes in the structure-bound enzyme systems, to favour a type of metabolism which, with carcinogenic amines as substrates, leads to the production of harmful metabolites, also *in vivo*. In this way the carcinogen-induced changes in cell macromolecules, proposed above as constituting a primary event in chemical carcinogenesis, are accentuated.

Nature of the reactive metabolites of carcinogenic amines

In the above discussion it has been shown that conditions which potentiate the tumour-inducing properties of carcinogenic amines [13, 14, 17-19], and the impairment of ribosomal function by these substances [32, 35, 38], are associated with a shift of *in vitro* amine oxygenation towards *N*-oxygenation [40]. This is in keeping with the increased urinary output of *N*-oxygenated metabolites of carcinogens under similar conditions [20-22]. It thus seems that this oxygenation pathway possesses pernicious properties. It does not, however, necessarily imply that the *N*-oxygenated metabolites are those reactive metabolites that manifest themselves by binding to macromolecules in the cell, thereby affecting microsomal anabolic functions, reactions which seem to be of central importance in the tumour-inducing process. On the contrary, there is some evidence presented by the Miller group disproving this possibility; the *N*-oxygenated derivatives lack the essential ability of the ultimate carcinogen to bind to proteins and nucleic acids when tested in model systems at physiological pH [62, 63], and they do not themselves affect microsomal protein synthesis when added *in vitro* [64]. It therefore seems pertinent to assume that an intermediate in the *N*-oxygenation process [40], or a product of further metabolic conversion of the *N*-oxygenated derivatives [64, 65], possesses the reactive properties of the ultimate carcinogenic metabolite. In order to further elucidate the nature and origin of these reactive metabolites of carcinogenic amines, an investigation of the mechanisms of microsomal *N*- and *C*-oxygenation of aromatic amines has been performed [66]. Again, the non-carcinogenic amine DMA was used as substrate to avoid the damage to microsomal detoxication of enzymes that is observed with low concentrations of carcinogenic amines *in vitro* [43]. The results obtained with this technique were further related to carcinogenesis by a study of the effects of small amounts of carcinogenic amines on DMA oxygenation *in vitro* [43].

The functional relationship between *N*-oxygenation and *C*-oxygenation is a question of central interest. *C*-oxygenation is catalysed by a mixed function oxygenase in liver microsomes, including a flavoprotein and cytochrome P450 as essential enzymic components. As in all mixed function oxygenations, molecular oxygen and an electron donor, usually $NADPH_2$, are utilized in this reaction [15, 24]. *N*-oxygenation takes place under similar conditions. This latter reaction is, however, not dependent on intact P450, as indicated in experiments where P450 has been inactivated by treatment with carbon monoxide [43, 53], or where the coupling between flavoprotein and P450 in the detoxication chain is disturbed by treatment with detergents [41, 42]. These findings have been taken by Ziegler *et al.* [41, 67] and Uehleke [16] as evidence that the *N*-oxygenated metabolites are intermediates in the *C*-oxygenation process. According to their hypothesis the flavoprotein would be the oxygenating enzyme. The function of P450 would then be to act as an intramolecular transoxygenase, conveying a Bamberger rearrangement [68] of the *N*-linked oxygen to a carbon atom. In support of this Ziegler *et al.* [67, 69] demonstrated that the transoxygenation of DMA-*N*-oxide was more rapid than the *C*-oxygenation of DMA; thus this step could not be rate-limiting. It was, however, demonstrated [66] that when both reactions were compared in the presence of $NADPH_2$, at substrate concentrations where both functions show time linearity, then *C*-oxygenation is several-fold more rapid than *N-C*-transoxygenation. Furthermore, *C*-oxygenation is totally inhibited by MeHgOH in concentrations which did not markedly affect the two postulated partial reactions (i.e. *N*-oxygenation and *N-C*-transoxygenation). Other evidence against the above hypothesis has been provided. Kämpffmeyer and Kiese demonstrated that the K_m value for oxygen is 40 times higher for *N*-oxygenation than *C*-oxygenation of aniline [70]. McMahon and Sullivan were unable to detect any radioactivity in an added pool of the proposed *N*-oxygenated intermediate during the *C*-oxygenation of labelled amine [71].

It thus seems well established that *N*-oxygenation, followed by a subsequent *N-C*-transoxygenation of the *N*-oxygenated metabolite, cannot represent more than a rather insignificant alternative pathway for *C*-oxygenation of aromatic amines. Thus, the previously discussed shift from *C*- to *N*-oxygenation under the influence of various *in vivo* conditions cannot be interpreted as the leaking out of an intermediary product caused by a dissociation of the enzymic components in the detoxication chain. Such a shift must rather imply a change of acceptor site for the oxygen from P450, which directs the oxygenation to a carbon atom, to the flavo-protein which guides this reaction to the amine nitrogen.

A more profound understanding of this process was obtained by a comparative study of the substrate inhibition of *C*-oxygenation and the effect of electrophilic agents on the oxygenation reactions [66].

Microsomal *C*-oxygenation of DMA exhibited a marked substrate optimum followed by a progressive decline with increasing substrate concentration; on the other hand, *N*-oxygenation as well as *N-C*-transoxygenation showed a continuously increased activity with increasing substrate concentration. Progressively manifesting itself during incubation, the inhibitory effect was deduced to be due to the production of an inhibitory metabolite. The inhibition was evident before abnormally high *N*-oxide levels were reached, and excess of *N*-oxide added to incubations with optimal *C*-oxygenation had no effect; thus this metabolite was not identical with the *N*-oxygenated product. As the *C*-oxygenation activity of the microsomes could not be restored by washing, this inhibition was obviously due to irreversible damage of an essential component in the *C*-oxygenation mechanism, which is not common to *N*-oxygenation.

The *C*-oxygenation of DMA was much more sensitive than the *N*-oxygenation towards the inhibitory action of electrophilic agents such as organic mercurials. In fact these agents show a pattern of inhibition of amine oxygenation which is very similar to that of high substrate concentrations of the amine. This points to an electrophilic intermediate in the *N*-oxygenation of aromatic amines as the metabolite which inhibits the *C*-oxygenation reaction. It is appropriate to this hypothesis that aromatic amines have electron donor properties [72]. The demonstration by Evans of a labile adduct of DMA and oxygen [73] implicating "less then one electron transfer" [74] is a sign of this property. With more efficient electron acceptors, complexes involving ammonium cation radicals could be demonstrated [75]; these radicals, by hydrogen atom release and a subsequent intramolecular electron redistribution from a carbon atom to the

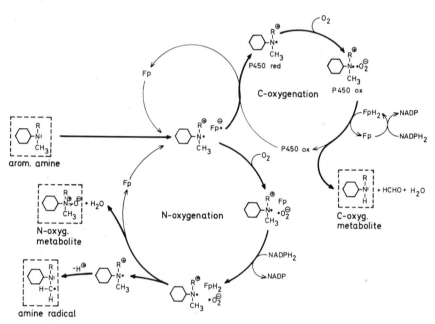

Figure 1. Tentative scheme for *C*- and *N*-oxygenation of aromatic amines and formation of carbon radicals.

nitrogen, assume the character of electrophilic carbon radicals [75]. Considering the electron acceptor properties of oxidized flavin [76, 77], and the experimental results obtained by the author [66], tentative schemes were constructed which offered an explanation of the mechanism of *C*-oxygenation, *N*-oxygenation, *N*-*C*-transoxygenation and radical formation [66].

According to these schemes, presented in simplified form in Fig. 1, the primary event in all oxygenation of amines involves the above-mentioned electron donor properties of these substances. The common step in *N*- and *C*-oxygenation is the transfer of an electron from the amine nitrogen to an oxidized flavoprotein in the microsomal detoxication enzyme system, resulting in a complex between an ammonium radical cation and a flavoprotein free radical, or semiquinone. In the intact electron transport chain an electron, and thereby the adduced ammonium radical cation, are transferred to P450; this enzyme is by this reduction activated to adduce molecular oxygen. The site of adduction of the radical to the P450 is shifted from the nitrogen to a carbon by loss of a labilized proton in α-*ortho*- or *para*-position and an electron rearrangement yielding a carbon radical. The ternary complex is labilized by a further electron transfer from $NADPH_2$ mediated by the flavoprotein, probably by means of a second prosthetic group of this enzyme. The *C*-oxygenated (ring-hydroxylated or dealkylated) metabolite is thus released from the enzyme.

In *N*-oxygenation, which proceeds in the absence of functional P450 [42, 53], the flavoprotein alone is responsible for the oxygen activation. The ternary complex formed is reduced by electrons accepted from a pyridine nucleotide, $NADPH_2$ of $NADH_2$. The amine-peroxy-FpH_2 adduct which results then cleaves into *N*-oxygenated amine, water and oxidized flavoprotein. However, amine-peroxy adducts are liable to form carbon radicals [75]. The formation of these noxious metabolites is dependent on the electronic structure of the components of the complex; the affinity of the nitrogen for electrons from the ring or alkyl groups of the amine must be high enough to enable the radical to split from the complex.

The K_m value for oxygen is, however, several-fold larger in *N*-oxygenation than in *C*-oxygenation [70]. This may be interpreted as a competition for electrons from pyridine nucleotide between the oxygen adduction site of the flavoprotein and the flavin mediating an electron flow to P450, in favour of the latter. Thus, when the $NADPH_2$-P450 electron transfer mediated by this second prosthetic group of the flavoprotein is inhibited by electrophilic agents, the inhibition of *C*-oxygenation is associated with an increased *N*-oxygenation evoked by the lost competition for electrons. This also promotes further formation of electrophilic radicals and an autocatalytically-increasing production of these noxious metabolites occurs.

This scheme was based mainly on experiments *in vitro* with the non-carcinogenic amine DMA. Obviously in such a system this amine fulfils the prerequisites for formation of electrophilic radicals. *In vivo*, however, no *N*-oxygenation of this substrate can be demonstrated [61] and thus it presumably does not manifest these pernicious properties in intact animals. As mentioned previously the polycyclic carcinogenic aromatic amines are *N*-oxygenated and form reactive metabolites *in vivo* under conditions which eventually lead to tumour induction [21, 22, 39]. There is also a close correlation between the increased *N*-oxygenation/*C*-oxygenation ratio of DMA *in vitro* with conditions which favour *N*-oxygenation and tumour induction with carcinogenic amines *in vivo* [40]. This suggests that the mechanism for production of reactive radicals proposed above is also functional *in vivo*. In the living animal, however, the intactness of the detoxication system efficiently counteracts the tendency to form electrophilic radicals. But if the substrates for detoxication *in vivo* are amines, which have inherent in the electronic configuration of their molecules a much stronger tendency than DMA to form electrophilic radicals, they may do so even in the intact animal. Such a hypothesis is supported by the demonstration [43] of a several hundred times higher efficiency of the carcinogen AF, when added *in vitro,* than the non-carcinogenic DMA, to divert the microsomal detoxication of aromatic amines from *C-* to *N-*oxygenation.

Further support for the relevance of *in vitro* carbon radical formation for the *in vivo* condition is obtained from experiments with acetoxy-AAF [43]. Amine derivatives of this type may spontaneously form carbon radicals [75] as is also indicated by the binding of acetoxy-AAF to nucleophilic sites in RNA and protein independent of metabolic conversions [62, 63]. The inhibitory pattern of this compound on microsomal *C-*oxygenation of aromatic amines is almost identical with that of AF [43]. The binding pattern of this and other *N-*acyloxy derivatives to protein and RNA shows marked similarities with that of corresponding amines *in vivo* with regard to attacked nucleophilic site as well as bonding position on the amine molecule [62, 63, 78].

Effects of environmental, genetic and hormonal factors on carbon radical formation

The nature of the effects of environmental, genetic and hormonal factors on the manifestation of the pernicious properties of carcinogenic amines may now be more closely scrutinized in the light of the above-detailed discussion of oxygenation mechanisms (Fig. 2). These effects all seem to be intimately connected with the autocatalytic increase in the production of carbon radicals. In tumour-inducing experiments, with animals fed low levels of AF or AAF, the originally low rate of *N-*oxygenation increases progressively within a few weeks [39]. This effect could be explained by the inhibitory action of the electrophilic metabolites on the electron transport from pyridine nucleotide to P450; as mentioned above, this effect, in addition to an inhibition of *C-*oxygenation, also gives rise to an increased *N-*oxygenation evoked by the decreased competition for electrons. However, the author's experiments [43] on combined effects of Celite *in vivo* and mercurials *in vitro,* indicate that such a mechanism is not the sole cause of increased *N-*oxygenation and carbon radical production. It is clearly demonstrated in this experiment that an adrenal-dependent stress amplifies the shift towards the pernicious *N-*oxygenation induced by electrophilic agents in microsomal systems. Applying these findings to conditions in living animals, the effect of prolonged AF treatment could be interpreted as a combined result of two effects: (a) attack by carbon radicals on the vulnerable flavin which mediates electron transfer from $NADPH_2$ to P450, thus causing autocatalytically-magnified leakage of these radicals, and (b) a stress response induced by the noxious electrophilic radicals, involving preferential stimulation of amine *N-*oxygenation, thus further reinforcing the outflow of carbon radicals.

As mentioned previously, this latter effect of aromatic amines does not necessarily act via the normal neural-hormonal stress circuit; it could be the outcome of a direct attack of carbon radicals on microsomal enzymes responsible for cortical steroid biotransformation, thereby sensitizing the liver cells to the action of the prevailing level of corticosteroids [40, 43].

It should be noted in this context that tumour induction with AF can be potentiated and accelerated by administration of extraneous corticosteroids.

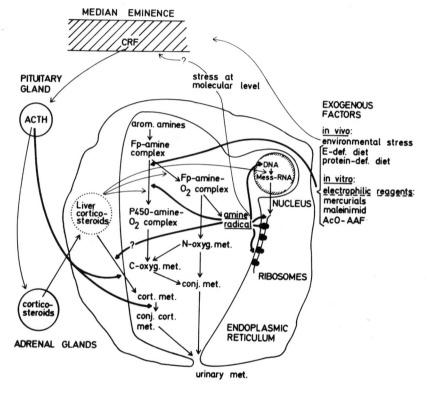

Figure 2. Schematic representation of factors influencing the metabolism of aromatic amines in liver cells.
Straight arrows: Metabolic pathways
Curvilinear thin arrows: Stimulatory effects
Curvilinear thick arrows: Inhibitory effects

Similar synergistic effects by environmental stress inducers may, although not yet demonstrated, be considered a serious possibility [79].

The effect of electrophilic agents *in vitro* also merits some consideration, in that they can inhibit the electron flow from $NADPH_2$ to P450 in a fashion similar to that of the carbon radicals [43, 66]. This implies that these agents act as synergists to carcinogens by initiating the autocatalytic increase in carbon radical formation. Whether this effect can be achieved *in vivo* depends on the ability of the electrophilic agents to reach the microsomal detoxication enzymes in the liver cells of intact animals. This has as yet not been shown, but the marked and early accumulation of the organic mercurial compounds in the livers of rats and men exposed to these substances [80, 81] indicates that possible synergistic effect of these substances on carcinogenetic processes, alone or in combination with environmental stress, should be investigated [79].

Finally, the relevance of the difference in response pattern of the guinea pig microsomal oxygenation of DMA towards the effects of aromatic amines and electrophilic agents will be considered. The guinea pig is refractory towards the carcinogenic action of aromatic amines [13, 14] and N-oxygenate these substances only to a limited extent [20, 39]. In microsomal preparations from these animals neither aromatic amines nor electrophilic agents can divert the amine metabolism from C- to N-oxygenation [43]. This is not because of a resistance to the inhibitory effect of electrophilic metabolites on $NADPH_2$-P450 electron flow, but rather to a concomitant inhibition of a function involved in N-oxygenation. Paradoxically, therefore, due to this greater susceptibility towards the deleterious effects of carbon radicals, the guinea pigs do not show the preferential inhibition of $NADPH_2$-P450 electron transport which is a prerequisite for the autocatalytically-magnified production of these noxious metabolites. This protective effect does not seem to be obligate; under certain conditions a preferential inhibition may occur, as indicated by the marked effects of aromatic amines on ribosomal function in guinea pig liver slices [32].

CONCLUDING REMARKS

From the above discussion some salient conclusions can be drawn concerning the carcinogenic nature of amines:

(1) Primarily the carcinogenic property of amines resides in their molecular configuration. Thus, they must possess sufficiently strong electron donor properties to allow formation of a complex with the flavoprotein of the microsomal detoxication chain, involving an electron transfer to P450 or oxygen. This prerequisite allows them to enter the metabolic pathway leading to C-oxygenation or N-oxygenation. On the other hand, the nitrogen of the ammonium radical cation must have high enough attraction for electrons in the ring or alkyl groups of the amine to split off from the ternary complex with reduced flavoprotein-peroxide and form an electrophilic carbon radical.

(2) Whether these properties result in production of high levels of electrophilic carbon radicals is dependent on a variety of genetic, environmental, dietary and hormonal factors. These may induce or accentuate a progressively increasing change in acceptor site for the oxygen in the microsomal detoxication enzymes from P450 to flavoprotein. The metabolism of the amines is thus

diverted from the harmless *C*-oxygenation to *N*-oxygenation and the associated autocatalytically-increased production of carbon radicals.

(3) The site of nascense of the carbon radicals in close proximity to the ribosome-messenger-RNA entities, as well as perhaps in functional proximity to the nucleus, is of essential importance. The attack of the electrophilic radicals on nucleophilic sites in proteins and nucleic acids of these structures gives rise to irreversible changes of the anabolic functions of the ribosomes. In this way inheritable anomalies in intracellular information expression are obtained which, eventually, by a series of secondary events, may give rise to autonomously-growing cell populations.

Hence, the question whether an amine exhibits carcinogenic properties cannot be answered without specifying the endogenous and extraneous environmental conditions under which the carcinogenetic process takes place. By evaluation of the functional disturbances to subcellular organelles which are caused by a given amine it might, however, be possible to predict under which circumstances that substance could be expected to give rise to an increased incidence of tumours.

REFERENCES

1. Pott, P., London, 1775. Reprinted in *Natn. Cancer Inst. Monogr.* **10** (1963) 7.
2. Yamagiwa, K. and Ichikawa, K., *Mitt. med. K. jap. Univ.* **15** (1916) 295.
3. Tsutsui, H., *Gann* **12** (1918) 17.
4. Clayson, D. B., "Chemical Carcinogenesis", Little, Brown and Company, Boston, Mass., 1962.
5. Hartwell, J. L., *Pub. Hlth Serv. Publs., Wash.* **149** (1951).
6. Shubik, P. and Hartwell, J. L., *Publ. Hlth Serv. Publs., Wash.* **149** (1957) Suppl. 1.
7. Miller, J. A. and Miller, E. C., *Lab. Invest.* **15** (1966) 217.
8. Klein, G. and Klein, E., *Symp. quant. Biol.* **27** (1962) 463.
9. Old, L. J., Boyse, E. A., Clarke, D. A. and Carswell, E. A., *Ann. N.Y. Acad. Sci.* **101** (1962) 80.
10. Miller, E. C. and Miller, J. A., *Cancer Res.* **7** (1947) 468.
11. Miller, E. C. and Miller, J. A., *Pharmac. Rev.* **18** (1966) 805.
12. Cramer, J. W., Miller, J. A. and Miller, E. C., *J. biol. Chem.* **235** (1960) 885.
13. Miller, J. A. and Miller, E. C., *Adv. Cancer Res.* **1** (1953) 339.
14. Weisburger, E. K. and Weisburger, J. H., *Adv. Cancer Res.* **5** (1958) 331.
15. Brodie, B. B., Gillette, J. R. and La Du, B. N., *A. Rev. Biochem.* **27** (1958) 427.
16. Uehleke, H., *Prog. Drug Res.* **8** (1964) 195.
17. Goodall, C. M., *N.Z. med. J.* **67** (1968) 32.
18. Sugai, M., Witting, L. A., Tsuchiyama, H. and Kummerow, F. A., *Cancer Res.* **22** (1962) 510.
19. Weisburger, J. H. and Weisburger, E. K., *Clin. Pharmac. Ther.* **4** (1963) 110.
20. Kiese, M., Renner, G. and Wiedemann, I., *Naunyn-Schmiedebergs Arch. exp. Path. Pharmak.* **252** (1966) 418.

21. Lotlikar, P. D., Enomoto, M., Miller, E. C. and Miller, J. A., *Cancer Res.* **24** (1964) 1835.
22. Margreth, A., Lotlikar, P. D., Miller, E. C. and Miller, J. A., *Cancer Res.* **24** (1964) 920.
23. Mueller, G. C. and Miller, J. A., *J. biol. Chem.* **180** (1949) 1125.
24. McMahon, R. E., *J. Pharm. Sci.* **55** (1966) 457.
25. Hayaishi, O., *Proc. Fourth Int. Congr. Biochem., I.U.B.,* **33** (1964) 31.
26. Hultin, T., *Expl. Cell Res.* **10** (1956) 697.
27. Hultin, T., *Expl. Cell Res.* **13** (1957) 47.
28. Hultin, T., *Expl. Cell Res.* **18** (1959) 112.
29. Goldfischer, S., Essner, E. and Novikoff, A. B., *J. Histochem. Cytochem.* **12** (1964) 72.
30. Watson, M. L., *J. biophys. biochem. Cytol.* **6** (1959) 147.
31. Arrhenius, E. and Hultin, T., *Acta chem. scand.* **13** (1959) 2130.
32. Arrhenius, E. and Hultin, T., *Expl. Cell Res.* **22** (1961) 476.
33. Arrhenius, E. and Hultin, T., *Cancer Res.* **22** (1962) 823.
34. Hultin, T. and Arrhenius, E., *Adv. Enzyme Regul.* **3** (1965) 389.
35. Hultin, T. and Arrhenius, E., *Cancer Res.* **25** (1965) 124.
36. Hultin, T., Arrhenius, E., Löw, H. and Magee, P. N., *Biochem. J.* **76** (1960) 109.
37. Mukherjee, T., Gustafsson, R. G., Afzelius, B. A. and Arrhenius, E., *Cancer Res.* **23** (1963) 944.
38. Arrhenius, E., "Carcinogenic Amines. Some Aspects of their Metabolism and Interaction with Microsomal Functions of Liver Cells". Stockholm, 1968.
39. Miller, J. A., Cramer, J. W. and Miller, E. C., *Cancer Res.* **20** (1960) 950.
40. Arrhenius, E., *Cancer Res.* **28** (1968) 264.
41. Ziegler, D. M. and Pettit, F. H., *Biochem. biophys. Res. Commun.* **15** (1964) 188.
42. Ziegler, D. M. and Pettit, F. H., *Biochemistry, N.Y.* **5** (1966) 2932.
43. Arrhenius, E., *Chem. Biol. Interaction*, submitted for publication.
44. Kummerow, F. A., *in* "Symposium on Foods: Lipids and their Oxidation" (edited by H. W. Schultz, E. A. Day and R. O. Sinnhuber), Avi Publ. Comp. Inc., Westport, Conn., 1962, pp. 294-330.
45. Karrer, E. (chairman). "Symposium on Vitamin E and Metabolism in Honor of Professor H. M. Evans". *Vitams Horm.* **20** (1962) 374.
46. Fueno, T., Ree, T. and Eyring, H., *J. phys. Chem., Ithaca* **63** (1959) 1940.
47. Bolland, J. L. and ten Have, P., *Discuss. Faraday Soc.* **2** (1947) 252.
48. El Khatib, S., Chenau, V. A., Carpenter, M. P., Trucco, R. E. and Caputto, R., *Nature, Lond.* **201** (1964) 188.
49. Green, J., Diplock, A. T., Bunyan, J., Edwin, E. E. and McHale, D., *Nature, Lond.* **190** (1961) 318.
50. Boyland, E., Manson, D. and Nery, R., *J. chem. Soc.* (1962) 606.
51. Haddow, A., *Br. med. Bull.* **14** (1958) 79.
52. McMahon, R. E. and Sullivan, H. R., *Life Sci.* **5** (1966) 921.
53. Kampffmeyer, H. and Kiese, M., *Naunyn-Schmiedebergs Arch. exp. Path. Pharmak.* **250** (1965) 1.
54. Silverman, D. A. and Talalay, P., *Molec. Pharmac.* **1** (1967) 90.
55. Goodall, C. M., personal communication.
56. Vernikos-Danellis, J., *Endocrinology* **76** (1965) 122.

57. Berliner, D. L. and Dougherty, T. F., *Pharmac. Rev.* **13** (1961) 329.
58. McLean, A. E. M. and McLean, E. K., *Biochem. J.* **100** (1966) 564.
59. Mori, K., *Gann* **45** (1954) 23.
60. Weisburger, J. H., Weisburger, E. K. and Morris, H. P., *Cancer Res.* **18** (1958) 1039.
61. Horn, F., *Hoppe-Seyler's Z. physiol. Chem.* **242** (1936) 23.
62. Lotlikar, P. D., Scribner, J. D., Miller, J. A. and Miller, E. C., *Life Sci.* **5** (1966) 1263.
63. Miller, E. C., Juhl, U. and Miller, J. A., *Science, N.Y.* **153** (1966) 1125.
64. Miller, E. C., McKechnie, D., Poirier, M. M. and Miller, J. A., *Proc. Soc. exp. Biol. Med.* **120** (1965) 538.
65. Grantham, P. H., Weisburger, E. K. and Weisburger, J. H., *Biochim. biophys. Acta* **107** (1965) 414.
66. Arrhenius, E., *Chem. Biol. Interaction,* submitted for publication.
67. Machinist, J. M., Orme-Johnson, W. H. and Ziegler, D. M., *Biochemistry N.Y.* **5** (1966) 2939.
68. Bamberger, E. and Tchirner, F., *Ber. dt. chem. Ges.* **32** (1899) 1882.
69. Pettit, F. H. and Ziegler, D. M., *Biochem. biophys. Res. Commun.* **13** (1963) 193.
70. Kampffmeyer, H. and Kiese, M., *Biochem. Z.* **339** (1964) 454.
71. McMahon, R. E. and Sullivan, H. R., *Life Sci.* **3** (1964) 1167.
72. Stuckey, B. N., *in* "Symposium on Foods: Lipids and Their Oxidation" (edited by A. W. Schultz, E. A. Day and R. O. Sinnhuber), Avi Publ. Comp. Inc., Westport, Conn., 1962, pp. 139-150.
73. Evans, D. F., *J. chem. Soc.* **1957** (1957) 1351.
74. Tsubomura, H. and Mulliken, R. S., *J. Am. chem. Soc.* **82** (1960) 5966.
75. Horner, L., *in* "Autooxidation and Antioxidants, Vol. I" (edited by W. O. Lundberg), Interscience Publ., New York, 1961, pp. 171-232.
76. Ehrenberg, A., *in* "Electronic Aspects of Biochemistry" (edited by B. Pullman), Academic Press, New York, 1964, pp. 379-96.
77. Pullman, B. and Pullman, A., "Quantum Biochemistry", Interscience Publ. New York, 1963, pp. 508-563.
78. Scribner, J. D., Miller, J. A. and Miller, E. C., *Biochem. biophys. Res. Commun.* **20** (1965) 560.
79. Arrhenius, E., *Oikos* Suppl. 9 (1967) 32.
80. Berlin, M., *Acta med. scand.* Suppl. 396 (1963).
81. Ekman, L., Greitz, U., Magi, A., Snihs, J.-O. and Åberg, B., *Nord. Med.* **79** (1968) 456.

FEBS Symposium, Volume 16, 1969, pp. 227-232

The Role of Hydroxylation Products in Hypersensitivity to Salicylates and Amidopyrine

M. LEDVINA

*First Department of Medical Chemistry, Charles University,
Prague, Czechoslovakia*

For a drug or low molecular weight compound to induce an immune response, it must first be bound strongly by covalent bonding to tissue macromolecules, presumably proteins, to form hapten-protein conjugates[1].

For most drugs, however, a direct chemical reaction with proteins appears improbable on the basis of their structural formulae. In these cases it is believed that degradation products, metabolites or impurities, react chemically with tissue proteins to form immunogenic hapten-protein conjugates[2, 3].

Although the assumption has been generally accepted that metabolites have an important role in drug sensitization, the experimental evidence is very

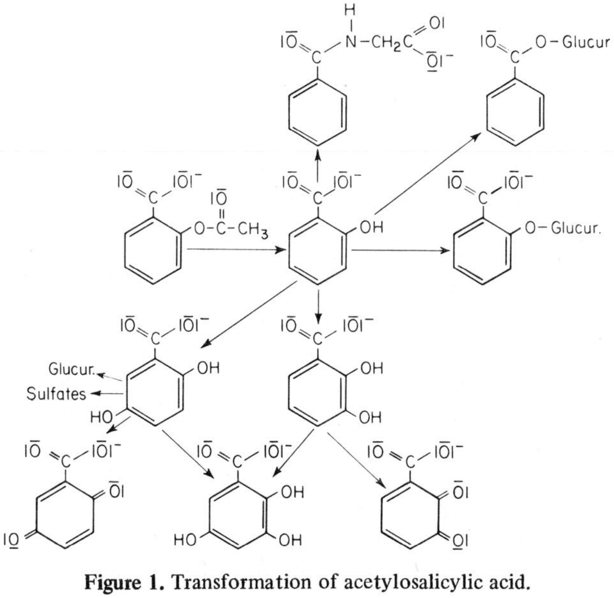

Figure 1. Transformation of acetylosalicylic acid.

meagre. The chemical structure of protein-bound derivatives is available only in penicillin hypersensitivity. There is suggestive evidence for antibody formation to several penicillin derivatives [2]. Every haptenic group induces the formation of antibodies with different specificity. However, antibodies to the same

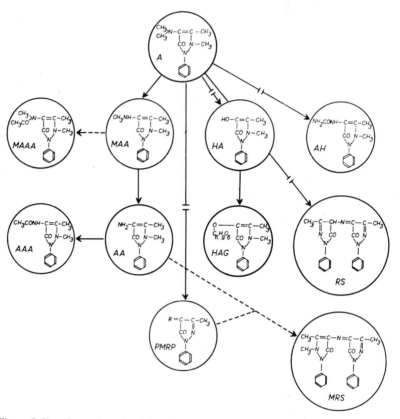

Figure 2. Transformation of amidopyrine. A-amidopyrine, MAA-methylaminoantipyrine, AA-aminoantipyrine, AAA-acetylaminoantipyrine, HA-hydroxyantipyrine HAG-glucuronide of HA, RS-rubazonic acid, MRS-methylrubazonic acid.

haptenic group of the same specificity also have different physical and biological properties. This explains the variability of allergic reactions evoked by penicillin.

It is reasonable to suppose that in sensitization to other drugs as well, several haptenic groups may be present. Therefore a detailed knowledge of drug metabolism and degradation products is essential for the study of drug allergy. This paper reports a study on the role of salicylic acid and amidopyrine metabolites in drug sensitization (Figs. 1 and 2).

Skin sensitivity to metabolites of both drugs was tested in the Department of

Allergology of Vinohrady Hospital in cooperation with our laboratory. Skin tests to salicylic acid, 2,3-dihydroxybenzoic acid, 2,5-dihydroxybenzoic acid and 2,4-dihydroxybenzoic acid (10 μg in 0·1 ml) were performed on 31 patients with a history of salicylate allergy. The tests with 2,5- and 2,3-dihydroxybenzoic acids were positive in four patients while the tests to 2,4-dihydroxybenzoic acid and salicylic acid were negative.

Four patients with a history of amidopyrine hypersensitivity were tested in the same way with amidopyrine, N-methylaminoantipyrine, aminoantipyrine. One patient gave a positive test to N-methylaminoantipyrine. The tests with other metabolites were negative.

Delayed hypersensitivity to metabolite-protein conjugates was tested in experiments in guinea pigs. The question at issue was whether autologous proteins must be used to simulate the situation in drug allergy.

Benacerraf, Gell and Silverstein [4, 5] suggested that the specificity of the delayed hypersensitivity reaction was to a considerable degree influenced by a protein carrier.

In our experiments, guinea pig albumin and γ-globulin were isolated from serum chromatographically on DEAE Sephadex. After conjugation with commercial dinitrofluorobenzene, the conjugate was separated on a Sephadex G-25 column. The autologous protein conjugates (50 μg in 0·2 ml of complete Freud adjuvant) were injected into the foot pads of six white guinea pigs. Ten days after sensitization the guinea pigs were tested in the flanks. The test doses were 0·1 ml volumes containing 10 μg autologous and homologous protein conjugates. The responses were recorded 24 hours later. The average diameters of the erythema for autologous and homologous γ-globulin conjugates were 12·2 and 8·7 mm. There was no difference between reactions to autologous and homologous albumin conjugates.

Autologous proteins were used in the experiments with drug metabolites. Autologous guinea pig γ-globulins and red cell stromata were incubated overnight with 1% solutions of 2,5- and 2,3-dihydroxybenzoic acids and with 2,3,5-trihydroxybenzoic acid.

The method of Horii et al. [6] was used for the preparation of 2,3,5-trihydroxybenzoic acid. The compound was contaminated by black oxidation products. The dihydroxybenzoic acids were recrystallized, chromatographically pure preparations.

After separation on Sephadex G-25 the autologous proteins were used for immunization. The immunization and testing was performed as described for dinitrophenyl-protein conjugates. The 2,3,5-trihydroxybenzoic acid conjugate elicited positive reactions. The experiments were repeated with autologous erythrocyte stromata. The results were similar (Table 1). The metabolite of amidopyrine, N-methylaminoantipyrine, gave positive results by similar testing (Table 2).

Table 1. Delayed hypersensitivity reaction to autologous and homologous protein conjugates of 2,3,5-trihydroxybenzoic acid in guinea pigs.

Test antigen	Guinea pig no.					
	I γ-235	II γ-235	III str-235	IV str-235	V	VI
GI γ-235	– ++	– ++			–	–
GII γ-235	– +	– ++			–	–
GIII str-235			± ++	– ++	–	–
GIV str-235			– +	– ++	–	–
235	– ±	– ±	– ±	– –	±	–
25	– ±	– –	– ±	– ±	±	–
Autolog str			±	–	–	–
Autolog γ	–	–	–	–		

GI
γ-235 } –guinea pig No. I γ-globulin preincubated with 2,3,5-trihydroxybenzoic acid.

GIV
str-235 } –guinea pig No. IV stromata preincubated with 2,3,5-trihydroxybenzoic acid.

235 – 2,3,5-trihydroxybenzoic acid.
25 – 2,5-dihydroxybenzoic acid.
Animals Nos. I, II, III, IV sensitized with 50µg of autologous γ-globulin or stromata preincubated with 2,3,5-trihydroxybenzoic acid.
The reactions were read at 10 and 24 hours.

Both metabolites giving positive tests were unstable to air, especially in water solution. The possibility was investigated that intermediary oxidation products become bound to proteins. The 2,5-dihydroxybenzoic acid (0·1 mol) was oxidized with an equivalent solution of ferricyanide in the presence of 1% bovine serum albumin. After 1 h incubation, the protein was separated on a column of Sephadex G-25 and the UV spectrum of the protein recorded (Fig. 3).

The results indicate that intermediary oxidation products of gentisic acid are bound to protein. The oxidation of 2,3-dihydroxybenzoic acid and N-methylaminoantipyrine in protein solutions also enhanced the binding of oxidation products to protein. Gamma globulin had a lower binding capacity.

Table 2. Delayed hypersensitivity reaction to autologous and homologous protein conjugates of methylaminoantipyrine in guinea pigs.

Test antigen	Guinea pig no.					
	I γ-MAAP	II γ-MAAP	III str-MAAP	IV str-MAAP	V	VI
I γ-MAAP	++ +	+ ±			−	−
II γ-MAAP	++ ±	++ +				
III str-MAAP			+ ±	++ +	−	−
IV str-MAAP			+ ±	++ +	±	−
MAAP	± −	− −	− −	− −	−	−
DAAP	− −	− −	− −	− −	−	−
Autolog			− −	± −		
Autolog γ	− −	− −				

Animals Nos. I, II, III and IV sensitized with $50\mu g$ of autologous γ-globulin or stromata preincubated with N-methylaminoantipyrine.
γ-MAAP–guinea pig γ-globulin preincubated with N-methylaminoantipyrine.
str-MAAP–guinea pig stromata preincubated with N-methylaminoantipyrine.
The reactions were read at 24 and 48 hours.
+: 5 to 10 mm. ++: larger than 10 mm.

It is known that the oxidation of phenolic compounds is connected with their binding to proteins. This reaction takes place in tanning and in the hardening of insect cuticles[7, 8]. Allergens from poison ivy are also pentadecylcatechols and may be bound to protein in a similar way[9].

232 M. LEDVINA

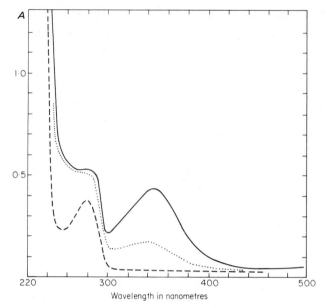

Figure 3. Binding of 2,5-dihydroxybenzoic acid by bovine serum albumin.
—— albumin preincubated with 0·1N 2,5-dihydroxybenzoic acid and 0·1N ferricyanide.
----- albumin preincubated with 0·1N ferricyanide.
...... albumin added 15 min later to a mixture of 0·1N solutions of dihydroxybenzoic acid and ferricyanide.

From this experiment it can be concluded that N-methylaminoantipyrine and 2,3,5-trihydroxybenzoic acid are bound to protein and can induce the immunological reaction. Reactive oxidation intermediary products may be involved in the binding of metabolites to protein.

REFERENCES

1. Landsteiner, K., "The Specificity of Serological Reactions", 2nd Ed., Harvard Univ. Press, Cambridge (1946).
2. Levine, B. B., *A. Rev. Med.* **17** (1966) 23-38.
3. Davies, G. E., *R. Soc. Med.* **55** (1962) 11-14.
4. Gell, P. G. H. and Benacerraf, B., *J. exp. Med.* **108** (1958) 891,
5. Gell, P. G. H. and Silverstein, A. M., *J. exp. Med.* **115** (1962) 1037-51.
6. Horii, Z., Komiyama, Y., Otsuki, K. and Yamamura, Y., *J. pharm. Soc. Japan* **72** (1952) 1520-22.
7. Karlson, P., *Nature, Lond.* **195** (1962) 183-4.
8. Dennelle, R., *Biol. Rev.* **33** (1958) 176-96.
9. Baer, H., Watkins, R. C. and Bowser, R. T., *Immunochemistry* **3** (1966) 479.

FEBS Symposium, Volume 16, 1969, pp. 233-238

Hydroxylation of 4-Hydroxyphenylpyruvate in Relation to the Formation of 3, 4-Dihydroxyphenylalanine

K. F. GEY

*Department of Experimental Medicine, F. Hoffmann-La Roche & Co. Ltd.,
Basle, and Department of Medical Chemistry, University of Berne, Switzerland*

The catecholamine precursor DOPA (3,4-dihydroxyphenylalanine) is believed to be synthesized by hydroxylation of L-tyrosine [1, 2], but since DOPA can also derive from transamination of 3,4-dihydroxyphenylpyruvate [3-5], it remains to be investigated whether 3,4-dihydroxyphenylpyruvate can be formed from 4-hydroxyphenylpyruvate. Hydroxylation in the *meta-position* of other *para*-hydroxyphenylcarbonic acids has already been described [6-9] and 4-hydroxy-phenylpyruvate is a normal and quantitatively important metabolite of tyrosine [10]. In the present study, therefore, the transformation of ^{14}C-labelled tyrosine and 4-hydroxyphenylpyruvate into DOPA and catecholamines was compared *in vitro* and *in vivo*. Whereas previous authors absorbed the total catechol derivatives derived from L-[^{14}C]tyrosine on Al_2O_3 [1, 2], in the present study the levels of ^{14}C-labelled tyrosine, DOPA and catecholamines were measured separately by means of a fractionation procedure comprising the passage through two cation exchange columns and subsequent paper chromatography.

METHODS

In vitro

Guinea pig hearts were homogenized by a tight all-glass Potter-homogenizer in 3 vol. ice-cold 0·1M potassium phosphate buffer, pH = 6·0, and centrifuged at 20,000 x g for 30 min. The supernatant (2 ml in a final incubation volume of 4 ml) was supplemented by 2×10^{-3}M 2-amino-4-hydroxy-5,6,7,8-tetrahydro-6,7-dimethyl-4-pteridine hydrochloride, 1×10^{-2}M mercaptoethanol and 1×10^{-5}M of L-2-[^{14}C]tyrosine [1] or 2-[^{14}C]hydroxyphenylpyruvate as substrate (100 and 96 μC/mg respectively),* incubated under air at $37°$C for 1 h and deproteinized by 3·6N $HClO_4$. After neutralization with KOH to pH = 6·0, $KClO_4$ was removed by centrifugation. For blanks the enzyme preparation was boiled, supplemented and incubated as described above.

---

* The labelled substances were synthesized by Dr. J. Würsch, F. Hoffmann-La Roche & Co. Ltd., Basle, and finally purified by paper chromatography.

In vivo

Groups of three normally fed female albino rats of 100-200 g body weight received by s.c. injection 5 mg/kg body weight of either L-2-[^{14}C] tyrosine (100 μC/mg; dissolved in water) or 2-[^{14}C] hydroxyphenylpyruvate (96 μC/mg; dissolved in acetate buffer, pH = 5·6) 30 min before decapitation. Blood was collected in 1 vol. 0·7N HClO$_4$ and the organs were frozen in heptane at $-70°$C, pooled and homogenized under N$_2$ in 4 vol. 0·4N HClO$_4$. After centrifugation the supernatant was brought to pH = 5·0 by KOH and crystals of KClO$_4$ were removed. Aliquots were incubated anaerobically at 37°C for 2 h with 16,000 and 2,000 units/ml respectively of an enzyme mixture containing sulphatase and β-glucuronidase ("Glusulase" of Endo Lab.) which was subsequently inactivated by treatment with HClO$_4$ and KOH (as above).

Fractionation

The tissue extracts (of pH = 6·0) were passed over a column of 500 mg Dowex 50-K$^+$ (X-4, 200-400 mesh) which absorbed the catecholamines. The effluent containing amino acids and metabolic end products was brought to pH = 2·0 and passed over a second column of Dowex 50-H$^+$ which retained the amino acids [11]. The amines were eluted from the first column with 2N HCl (after washing with 20 ml 0·09N HCl), the amino acids from the second column with potassium acetate, pH = 6·0. The radioactivity of the main fractions was counted by liquid scintillation spectrometry [11].

Paper chromatography

The eluate containing the amines was evaporated in a rotary evaporator at 35°C for paper chromatography in n-butanol/0·5N HCl which separated norepinephrine, dopamine and 3-0-methyldopamine [11]. The fraction of amino acids was supplemented by 50 μg each of unlabelled L-DOPA and L-tyrosine, desalted by being passed through amberlite CG 50-H$^+$ (100-200 mesh), concentrated in a rotating vacuum evaporator at 35°C, spotted on strips of No. 3 MM Whatman paper and chromatographed in n-butanol/0·5N HCl for 24 h. This permitted a clear separation of all phenolic amino acids that might be present, i.e. 3,4-dihydroxyphenylserine (R_f = 0·14), DOPA (R_f = 0·28), 3-0-methyl-DOPA (R_f = 0·38) and tyrosine (R_f = 0·48). The radioactivity present on the paper strip in the position of DOPA and dopamine was assayed by liquid scintillation spectrometry. At present no labelled metabolite of tyrosine, hydroxyphenylpyruvate and DOPA is conceivable that might behave like DOPA on two cation exchange columns and paper chromatography. Nevertheless, the [^{14}C] DOPA isolated in this way should be finally identified by further procedures, e.g. enzymatic decarboxylation.

Overall recovery

If L-2-[^{14}C]DOPA was added to the HClO$_4$ extract, 98 ± 1% could be recovered on the paper chromatogram in the position of DOPA. The recovery of added L-2-[^{14}C] tyrosine or 2-[^{14}C] norepinephrine exceeded 95%.

RESULTS

In vitro

Supernatant of the guinea pig heart, known to be rich in tyrosine hydroxylase [12], was incubated with either L-2-[^{14}C] tyrosine or 2-[^{14}C]hydroxyphenyl-pyruvate under the conditions optimal for tyrosine hydroxylation [1]. The DOPA formation from L-[^{14}C] tyrosine (Table 1) corresponded to the formation of total catechol derivatives as measured by previous investigators [1]. Amazingly, about 3 times more DOPA was derived from 2-[^{14}C] hydroxyphenylpyruvate than from L-2-[^{14}C] tyrosine (Table 1). The formation of tyrosine from 2-[^{14}C] hydroxyphenylpyruvate, however, was relatively small (final level of tyrosine approximately 7 times lower than in samples incubated with L-2-[^{14}C] tyrosine) and thus in samples incubated with 2-[^{14}C] hydroxyphenyl-pyruvate, the ratio DOPA x 100/tyrosine was about 20 times higher than in samples incubated with L-2-[^{14}C] tyrosine. Little dopamine was formed from L-2-[^{14}C] tyrosine and even less from 2-[^{14}C] hydroxyphenylpyruvate (Table 1).

Table 1. Transformation of L-2-[^{14}C] tyrosine (TYR) and 2-[^{14}C] p-hydroxy-phenylpyruvate (HOPP) into dihydroxyphenylalanine (DOPA) and dopamine *in vitro*

Precursor (1 x 10^{-5}M)	α-Methyl-tyrosine	Recovered			DOPA x 100 / TYR
		TYR	DOPA	DOPAMINE	
		mμmole/g wet guinea pig heart/h			
L-2-[^{14}C] TYR	—	74·7 ± ·7	·56 ± ·19	·08 ± ·009	·8 ± ·3
2-[^{14}C] HOPP	—	10·7 ± ·9	1·59 ± ·36	·01 ± ·002	16·5 ± 5·2
Significant difference		p < 0·01	p < 0·025	p < 0·01	p < 0·01
L-2-[^{14}C] TYR	+	76·7 ± 1·2	< ·01*	·02 ± ·003	< ·7
2-[^{14}C] HOPP	+	23·3 ± 8·3*	1·95 ± ·59	·01 ± ·002	23·3 ± 8·3
Significant difference		p < 0·01	p < 0·01		p < 0·01

* p   0·01 in comparison to samples without α-methyltyrosine.
  Supernatant of guinea pig heart was incubated at pH = 6 (as described in "Methods") in the presence and absence of 10 M DL-α-methyltyrosine. N = 8.

Table 2. Transformation of L-2-[^{14}C]tyrosine (TYR) and 2-[^{14}C]p-hydroxyphenylpyruvate (HOPP) into dihydroxyphenyl-alanine (DOPA) in vivo.

Injected 5 µg/g body wt. s.c.	Fraction	Recovered after 30 min				
		BLOOD	BRAIN		HEART	
			absolute	corrected	absolute	corrected
		^{14}C-recovered/g wet tissue in % of ^{14}C-injected/g body weight				
L-2-[^{14}C]TYR	TYR	25·55 ± ·94	14·10 ± ·57	8·69 ± ·55	18·42 ± 1·33	12·94 ± 1·30
2-[^{14}C]HOPP		10·69 ± ·87	6·89 ± ·27	4·65 ± ·14	11·14 ± ·71	9·05 ± ·62
L-2-[^{14}C]TYR	DOPA	<·01	·27 ± ·06	·27 ± ·06	·59 ± ·17	·59 ± ·17
2-[^{14}C]HOPP		<·01	·36 ± ·06	·36 ± ·04	1·27 ± ·28	1·27 ± ·28
L-2-[^{14}C]TYR	DOPA x 100 / TYR	—	2·01 ± ·40	3·22 ± ·69	3·72 ± 1·40	5·82 ± 2·62
2-[^{14}C]HOPP		—	5·34 ± 1·02	7·84 ± 1·29	11·49 ± 2·76	14·15 ± 3·40
Significant increase of DOPA x 100 / TYR			p < 0·01	p < 0·01	p < 0·05	—

Correction for the extracellular space was attempted by subtraction of 20% of the blood values. N = 7 (each experiment with a pool of three rats).

The relatively smaller formation of dopamine from 2-[^{14}C] hydroxyphenylpyruvate may be attributed to an inhibition of DOPA decarboxylase by phenolic α-keto acids [13]. The tyrosine hydroxylase inhibitor α-methyltyrosine at 10^{-3}M suppressed the synthesis of DOPA from L-2-[^{14}C] tyrosine as described [1]. In contrast, α-methyltyrosine did not significantly interfere with the transformation of [^{14}C] hydroxyphenylpyruvate into DOPA and dopamine (Table 1).

In vivo

Thirty min after s.c. injection of L-2-[^{14}C] tyrosine the level of tyrosine in brain and heart was higher than that in animals injected with [^{14}C] hydroxyphenylpyruvate. In contrast, [^{14}C] hydroxyphenylpyruvate yielded more radioactivity in the DOPA position of the chromatogram than [^{14}C] tyrosine (Table 2). Consequently, the ratio DOPA x 100/tyrosine in the brain and heart of rats given [^{14}C] hydroxyphenylpyruvate was about 2-3 times higher than in animals injected with [^{14}C] tyrosine. This was true for the measured values as well as for those corrected for the extracellular space (Table 2).

DISCUSSION

Provided that DOPA is specifically assayed, the present study indicates that *in vitro* the production of DOPA from 2-[^{14}C] hydroxyphenylpyruvate exceeds that from L-2-[^{14}C] tyrosine. In contrast to the latter, the formation of DOPA from 2-[^{14}C] hydroxyphenylpyruvate seems not to be suppressed by α-methyltyrosine, an inhibitor of tyrosine hydroxylase (Table 1). *In vivo* 5 mg/kg of 2-[^{14}C] hydroxyphenylpyruvate yields at least as much radioactivity in the DOPA position as equal amounts of L-2-[^{14}C] tyrosine although 2-[^{14}C] hydroxyphenylpyruvate is only partly transaminated into tyrosine (Table 2). Therefore, *in vitro* and *in vivo* 2-[^{14}C] hydroxyphenylpyruvate might, at least in part, be transformed into DOPA via 3,4-dihydroxyphenylpyruvate, i.e. without intermediary formation of tyrosine. *In vitro* the conversion of hydroxyphenylpyruvate into DOPA could even be independent of tyrosine hydroxylase. In conclusion, the present results favour the hypothesis of a hitherto unknown route by-passing tyrosine hydroxylase according to the following scheme:

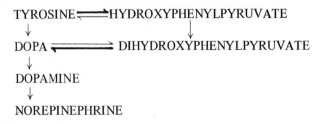

For two reasons the present *in vivo* experiments do not, however, permit an evaluation of the quantitative importance of this by-pass:

(a) The absorption as well as the distribution of exogenous L-2-[^{14}C]tyrosine and 2-[^{14}C]hydroxyphenylpyruvate in the tissue might differ.

(b) Labelled tyrosine (5 mg/kg) is diluted by a large pool of endogenous tyrosine (about 10^{-5}M), whereas 2-[^{14}C]hydroxyphenylpyruvate is presumably mixed with a relatively smaller pool of endogenous hydroxyphenylpyruvate.

REFERENCES

1. Nagatsu, T., Levitt, M. and Udenfriend, S., *J. biol. Chem.* **239** (1964) 2910.
2. Udenfriend, S., *Pharmac. Rev.* **18** (1966) 43.
3. Pogrund, R. S., Drell, W. and Clark, W. G., *J. Pharmac. exp. Ther.* **131** (1961) 294.
4. Gey, K. F., *Helv. physiol. pharmac. Acta* **23** (1965) C 89.
5. Gey, K. F., *Helv. physiol. pharmac. Acta* **25** (1967) CR 187.
6. Inamori, K., Nasu, H., Sakamoto, Y. and Ischihara, K., *Proc. Japan Acad.* **34** (1958) 645; *Chem. Abstr.* **53** (1959) 11'457 g.
7. Bertolani, F. and Bergamini, A., *G. Biochim.* **2** (1953) 310; *Chem. Abstr.* **49** (1955) 13'351 c.
8. Bray, H. G., Ryman, B. E. and Thorpe, W. V., *Biochem. J.* **41** (1947) 212.
9. Smith, J. N., *in* "Biological Oxidation of Aromatic Rings", Biochemical Society Symposium No. 5, Cambridge University Press, 1950, p. 15.
10. Meister, A., "Biochemistry of the Amino Acids", Vol. 2, Academic Press, New York, 1965, p. 887.
11. Gey, K. F. and Pletscher, A., *Biochem. J.* **92** (1964) 300.
12. Levitt, M., Gibb, J. W., Daly, J. W., Lipton, M. and Udenfriend, S., *Biochem. Pharmac.* **16** (1967) 1313.
13. Gey, K. F. and Messiha, F., *Experientia* **20** (1964) 498.

FEBS Symposium, Volume 16, 1969, pp. 239-247

The Formation of Hydroxy Derivatives of Cinchophen in Man and Rat

Z. ŠÍPAL and A. JINDRA

Department of Biochemistry, Charles University,
Prague, Czechoslovakia

2-Phenylcinchoninic acid, known under the names "Cinchophen" or "Atophan" is pictured by its classical formula as follows:

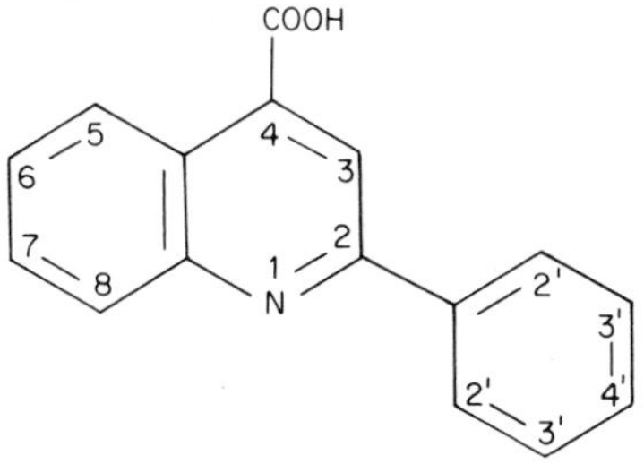

The pK_{a_2} value for the dissociation of the proton from cinchophen is 4·43 and thus, at physiological pH, more than 99·5% of it is in the form of an anion.

The drug was known to be hydroxylated in the body, various authors having found different hydroxy derivatives in human urine after oral doses of cinchophen [1-3]. Only 2% of the unchanged compound was excreted in this way [4]. We attempted to separate all the derivatives from urine by paper chromatography, but without success. This method permits a separation of some groups of cinchophen derivatives only, and is worthless when the amounts of various components are very different, as in the case of the urinary metabolites studied. We have succeeded in isolating and identifying the biotransformation products using partition chromatography on Sephadex.

The method represented schematically in Fig. 1 was adopted for the isolation of the mixture of cinchophen derivatives from the urine. It consisted in repeated extraction with ether at pH 4 and purification through consecutive transfer to Na_2CO_3 solution, conc. HCl, and finally to ether after neutralization to pH 4. In model experiments, we showed that triple shaking with ether is sufficient for quantitative extraction of the compounds studied; yet by repetition of the extraction process with the urine which has been shaken with ether seven times

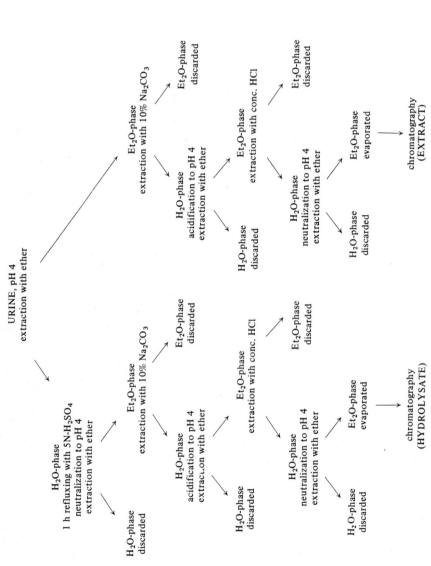

Figure 1. Scheme of the extraction procedure used for isolation of cinchophen derivatives from the urine.

and then refluxed with sulphuric acid, we obtained an additional mixture of cinchophen derivatives, which was chromatographed separately.

The samples were chromatographed on a Sephadex G-25 column (length 650 mm) in n-butyl alcohol: 0·5N ammonia; 2 ml fractions were collected, acidified

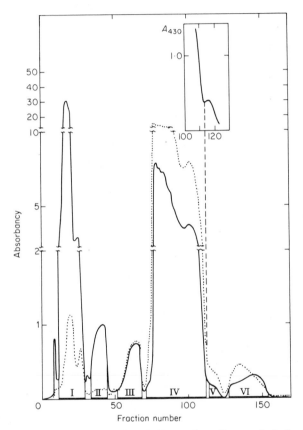

Figure 2. Partition chromatography of 65 mg of a mixture of cinchophen derivatives from ether extract of human urine on a 9 × 650 mm Sephadex G-25 (Fine) column. System: n-butylalcohol: 0·5N ammonia 1:1. Sample volume 0·5 ml, fraction volume 2 ml, temperature 20°C. For analysis, fractions were diluted with 2 ml EtOH and acidified with 1 ml 1N HCl. Solid line—A_{345}, dotted line—A_{390}.

with HCl and their optical density was determined at 345, 390 and 430 nm, respectively. Figure 2 shows the result of chromatography of the ether extract of human urine under the conditions specified. Compounds corresponding to the peaks of the elution curve were identified by paper chromatography and UV-spectra. Fractions containing the individual derivatives were combined, evaporated to dryness, dissolved in 0·1N HCl and the concentration of the components was determined by spectrophotometry. Sample I was a mixture of cinchophen and its 8-hydroxy derivative, samples III, IV and V contained 6-hydroxy-, 4′,hydroxy- and 3′-methoxy-4′-hydroxycinchophens, respectively, and sample VI was 4′-8-dihydroxy-cinchophen with traces of the 7-hydroxy derivative. Another compound, characterized by intensive violet fluorescence, remained on the column. It was isolated by chromatography of an equivalent sample of extract on a short column of Sephadex G-25 (length 140 mm) and

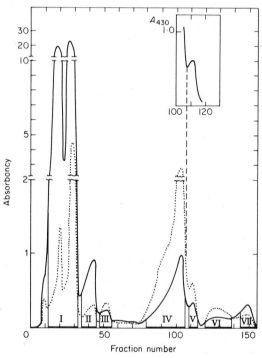

Figure 3. Partition chromatography of 37 mg of a mixture of cinchophen derivatives from acid hydrolysate of human urine, previously extracted with ether. Conditions as in Fig. 2.

identified as 4′,6-dihydroxycinchophen. Sample II from the long column gave no reaction for phenolic hydroxyl, but by standing overnight in an acid solution, the A_{345}/A_{390} ratio diminished and we were able to determine the 7-hydroxy-cinchophen in it, both by fluorescence and paper chromatography.

The composition of the mixture of cinchophen derivatives from hydrolysed urine is different both qualitatively and quantitatively, as can be seen from Fig. 3. Here sample I contains also cinchophen and 8-hydroxycinchophen, but their relative amounts differ from those in the first ether extract. Samples II, III, IV, V, VI and VII contain 3′-hydroxy-, 3′-hydroxy-4′-methoxy-, 4′-hydroxy-,

-->

Table 1. The amounts of derivatives of cinchophen (in mg) in human urine following an administration of 2 g of cinchophen per os.

Derivative found	Extract	Hydrolysate	Total
Cinchophen	56	32	88
6-Hydroxycinchophen	8	0	8
7-Hydroxycinchophen	12*	8	20
8-Hydroxycinchophen	20	34	54
3'-Hydroxycinchophen	0	6	6
4'-Hydroxycinchophen	220	8	228
4',6-Dihydroxycinchophen	7	0	7
4',8-Dihydroxycinchophen	7	8	15
3'-Hydroxy-4'-methoxycinchophen	0	1	1
3'-Methoxy-4'-hydroxycinchophen	8	4	12

* After acid hydrolysis of sample II.

3'-methoxy-4'-hydroxy-, 7-hydroxy- and 4',8-dihydroxycinchophens, respectively. Neither 6-hydroxy- nor 4',6-dihydroxycinchophens were found in this case.

Table 1 shows the distribution of cinchophen metabolites in human urine. The total represents about 20% of the original dose. The 4'-hydroxycinchophen is the principal metabolic product, excreted in the urine, from which it can be extracted with ether, as for all the compounds containing a hydroxyl group in the 6-position. All the other products can be detected after acid hydrolysis, either only in the hydrolysate like the 7-hydroxy and 3'-hydroxy derivatives, or, like cinchophen and 8-hydroxycinchophen, they are present both before and after hydrolysis. Hydroxy derivatives substituted in the 3-, 5- and 2'- positions were not found at all.

Table 2. The amounts of cinchophen derivatives (in mg) in rat urine following an administration of 37 mg of cinchophen intraperitoneally.

Derivative found	Extract	Hydrolysate	Total
Cinchophen	1·6	1·3	2·9
6-Hydroxycinchophen	0·2	—	0·2
7-Hydroxycinchophen	—	—	0
8-Hydroxycinchophen	0·2	0·1	0·3
3'-Hydroxycinchophen	0·1	0·4	0·5
4'-Hydroxycinchophen	7·7	1·3	9·0
4',6-Dihydroxycinchophen	0·2	—	0·2
4',8-Dihydroxycinchophen	—	—	0
3'-Hydroxy-4'-methoxycinchophen	—	0·3	0·3
3'-Methoxy-4'-hydroxycinchophen	0·4	0·2	0·6

Table 3. The amounts of derivatives of cinchophen (in mg) in rat urine following an administration of 24 mg of hydroxycinchophens intraperitoneally.

Derivative administered	Derivative found	Extract	Hydrolysate	Total
6-Hydroxycinchophen	6-Hydroxycinchophen	1.9	1.0	2.9
	4′,6-Dihydroxycinchophen	0.3	0.2	0.5
8-Hydroxycinchophen	8-Hydroxycinchophen	0.8	1.5	2.3
	4′,8-Dihydroxycinchophen	1.2	0.6	1.8
3′-Hydroxycinchophen	3′-Hydroxycinchophen	1.0	2.2	3.2
	3′-Hydroxy-4′-methoxycinchophen	—	0.8	0.8
4′-Hydroxycinchophen	4′-Hydroxycinchophen	5.6	0.3	5.9

Urinary metabolites of cinchophen of the rat are not fully identical with those from human urine. As can be seen from Table 2, 4'-hydroxycinchophen is here also the most important metabolite, but the amount of the 8-hydroxy derivative is diminished, the 7-hydroxy- and 4',8-dihydroxycinchophens being absent.

The substituents in the dihydroxy derivatives from urine are in the same positions as in the monohydroxy metabolites; consequently, the urinary dihydroxycinchophens can be derived by further hydroxylation of the primarily formed monohydroxy compounds. Upon administration of the principal monohydroxy derivatives to rats, their urine was found to contain the compounds listed in Table 3. As follows from the table, similar to the unsubstituted drug,

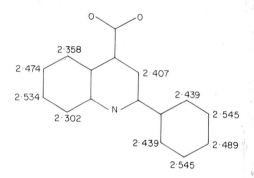

Figure 4. Carbon localization energies for an electrophilic substitution of the cinchophenate anion (in β-units), calculated by the simple HMO method. (Coefficients 0·5 and 1·0 were used for the Coulombic integrals for quinoline nitrogen and carboxylic oxygen, respectively; for all the resonance integrals, values for a C-C bond were used.)

the hydroxycinchophens are hydroxylated in the 4'-position, the 4'-hydroxycinchophen being practically metabolically inert and excreted as such.

The isomeric 3',4'-(hydroxymethoxy)cinchophens, formed from the unsubstituted drug and its 3'-hydroxy derivative, can be derived from a 3',4'-dihydroxy compound, which was not detected in the urine. This could be caused, as we have proved by model experiments, by the instability of the compound during the isolation procedure used. Both the isomers mentioned were formed from synthetic 3',4'-dihydroxycinchophen by rats *in vivo*, as well as by rat liver homogenate in the presence of S-adenosylmethionine *in vitro*. With regard to the catecholic character of this derivative, the reaction can be explained by the action of the S-adenosylmethionine: catechol-methyltransferase (EC 2.1.1.6.).

Considering the biological hydroxylation of aromatics as an electrophilic substitution by some oxygen species on the surface of an appropriate catalyst [5], we should examine the ability of different carbon atoms of cinchophen to act as objects of an electrophilic attack. From the corresponding localization energies, listed in Fig. 4, it follows that the 8-, 5-, 3- and 2'- positions are the most likely ones.

Thus, apparently, the results of experiments contradict the theory. This conflict can be resolved, we believe, by considering the role of the non-polar part of the hydroxylating enzyme in binding the substrate [6]. The highly polar carboxylate anion can hinder the contact of substrate with the oxidizing moiety, which may be mediated by a postulated lipid compound in the active centre of the enzyme. Thus, simple aromatic acids are slightly hydroxylated in the body [7] and a larger molecule, like cinchophen, can be hydroxylated only in the most distant parts, as can be seen from Fig. 5.

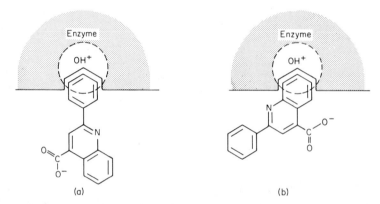

Figure 5. Scheme of the two possibilities of binding of the cinchophenate anion on the (non-polar) active centre of hydroxylating enzyme.

If the cinchophenate anion can react with an oxidizing agent only in either of the two positions shown, then, according to the theoretical considerations, the 4'-hydroxycinchophen should be the expected product in case (a), and 8- and (to a minor extent) 6-hydroxycinchophens in case (b), which agrees well with the experimental results in humans.

The small amount of 8-hydroxycinchophen in rat urine can be accounted for by the preference for type (a) binding of the substrate in this species, due to the nature of the active centre.

The formation of 7- and 3'-hydroxycinchophens, which cannot be interpreted in terms of electrophilic substitution, may be caused by a secondary reaction of the "NIH-shift"-type [5]. It is interesting that both the products can be isolated from the urine only after hydrolysis and, in accord with the small amount of 8-hydroxycinchophen in rat urine, the 7-hydroxy derivative is absent in this material.

ACKNOWLEDGMENT

We wish to thank Dr. M. Tichý for the quantum-mechanical calculations of the cinchophen molecule.

REFERENCES

1. Skorczewski, W. and Sohn, I., *Wien. klin. Wschr.* **25** (1912) 593.
2. Dohrn, M., *Biochem. Z.* **43** (1912) 240.
3. Šípal, Z. and Jindra, A., *Pharmazie* **20** (1965) 376.
4. Axelrod, J. and Chenkin, T., *Proc. Soc. exp. Biol. Med.* **26** (1954) 401.
5. Guroff, G., Daly, J. W., Jerina, D. M., Renson, J., Witkop, B. and Udenfriend, S., *Science, N.Y.* **157** (1967) 1524.
6. Mason, H. S., North, J. C. and Vanneste, M., *Fedn Proc. Fedn Am. Socs exp. Biol.* **24** (1965) 1172.
7. Williams, R. T., "Detoxication Mechanisms", 2nd Ed., Chapman & Hall, London, 1959, p. 348.

FEBS Symposium, Volume 16, 1969, pp. 249-260

Model Investigations on the Function of Tetrahydropteridines as Cofactors in Biological Hydroxylations

L. JAENICKE and A. W. WAHLEFELD

Institut für Biochemie der Universität,
Cologne, Germany

Several years ago Seymour Kaufman [1-3] showed that tetrahydrobiopterine is the natural cofactor for the hydroxylation in animal tissue of phenylalanine to tyrosine, and also of tyrosine to dihydroxyphenylalanine. A labile intermediate was formed and called "oxidized tetrahydropterine". It was postulated to be a dihydrobiopterine with quinonoid structure which is stabilized, finally, as 7,8-dihydrobiopterine; 6,7-dimethyl-2-amino-4-hydroxypteridine has qualitatively similar coenzyme activity, exhibits the same chemical behaviour, and can thus serve as a model for the cofactor. The mechanism of this aromatic hydroxylation is, however, not yet understood. It could either be a mixed-function-hydroxylation, as with phenolases or in aliphatic oxidations, in which

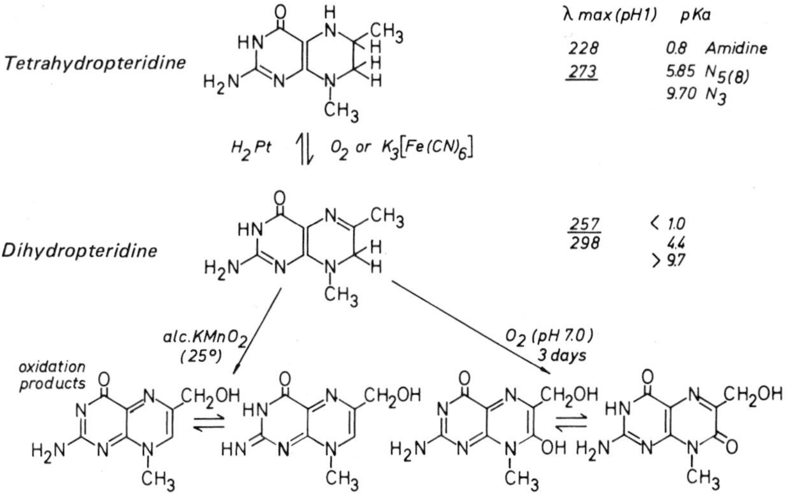

Figure 1. Transformations of 6,8-dimethyl-7,8-dihydropteridine and physical constants of compounds.

249

the tetrahydropteridine cofactor is reduced to the dihydro-stage and regenerated in each turn of the cycle; alternatively it might be a radical process, the cofactor acting only as electron shuttle in a purely catalytic way.

Recently, Viscontini [4-7] deduced from model experiments a radical reaction mechanism for the hydroxylation of phenylalanine by means of oxygen and a tetrahydropteridine cofactor. The trihydropteridine which lies on the way

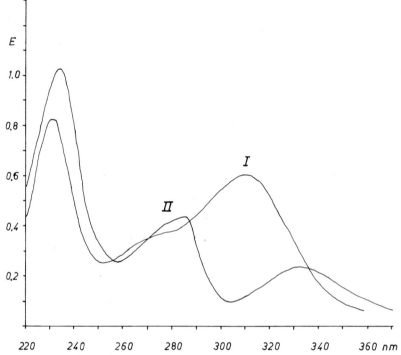

Figure 2. Spectra of 6,8-dimethyl-5,6,7,8-tetrahydropteridine and 6,8-dimethyl-7,8-dihydropteridine at pH 7·0; C = 0·046 nmoles/ml.

to the dihydropteridine—again formulated as a quinone—was isolated in the 5-methyl-6,7-diphenyl series and its structure identified [8].

In our studies of the course of oxidation of tetrahydropteridines [9] we have also demonstrated the occurrence of a trihydropteridine or its dimerization product. Furthermore, we have determined the metal affinities of the various reduced pteridines by spectrophotometry and polarography. In this paper evidence will be presented for a possible alternative mechanism of the oxygen activation in the aromatic hydroxylation reaction, catalysed by trihydropteridines as electron pumping devices.

To render oxidation of the tetrahydropteridines beyond the dihydro-level impossible, N-8 was blocked by methylation and 2-amino-4-hydroxy-6,8-di-

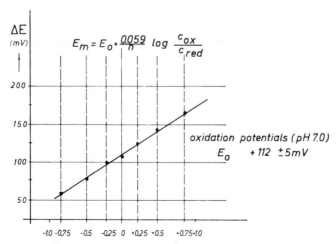

o-quininoid   p-quininoid

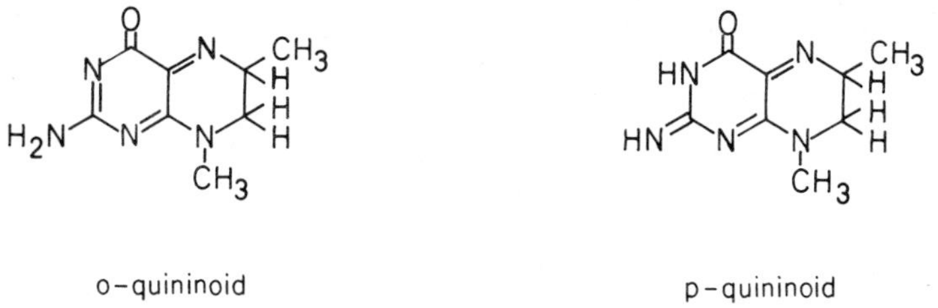

Figure 3. Quinonoid structures of 6,8-dimethyl-7,8-dihydropteridine.

methyl-5,6,7,8-tetrahydropteridine was used as a model [10]. This was synthesized by generally known procedures [11]. In these pteridines all hydrogens
relevant to the reaction, viz. those at C-6 and N-8, which would be removed in
7,8-dihydropteridines and 5,6-dihydropteridines respectively, are substituted by
methyl groups.

   The tetrahydro- and dihydro-compounds are presented in Fig. 1 together with
some of their physical parameters. The tetrahydro compound is very easily
autoxidized. Its UV-spectrum (Fig. 2) resembles that of 2,4,5-triamino-6-
hydroxy-pyrimidine with a strong bathochromic shift in the neutral molecule.

   The NMR measurements of the cation and the neutral molecule of the
dihydropteridine at least exclude the possibility of a pH-dependent transformation of the 7,8-dihydropteridine to an o- or p-quinonoid structure [10] since the
shift of the NMR signals is less than 0.2 p.p.m. and there is no splitting of the
methyl signal at C_6 to a doublet, which should occur in either of the quinonoid
dihydro-structures (Fig. 3).

$$E_m = E_0 + \frac{0.059}{n} \log \frac{c_{ox}}{c_{red}}$$

oxidation potentials (pH 7.0)

E_0 $+ 112 \pm 5mV$

Figure 4. Dependence of electromotive force on oxidation ratio of reduced pteridine
(oxidation with ferricyanide at pH 7.0).

The tetrahydropteridine can be oxidized quantitatively within 30 min at pH 7 to the dihydro-compound by means of air or under strictly anaerobic conditions by ferricyanide. This oxidation was followed spectrophotometrically or potentiometrically. As shown by the spectrum and the polarographic curves, the end product is clearly the dihydropteridine.

The electromotive force is related to the ratio of the oxidized to the reduced form according to the Nernst formula. Thus, plotting the measured electrode potential against the logarithm of the ratio of oxidized to reduced form, a straight line is obtained. Its slope gives the number of electrons taken up per molecule; 30 mV for a two-electron shift, or 60 mV for a one-electron reaction. As can be seen from Fig. 4 the experimentally found slope is about 60 mV, indicating a one electron transfer during the oxidation.

Table 1. Indicator potentials (E_i) of the system tetrahydropteridine/trihydropteridine and its dependence on concentration (c).

c (M $\times$ 10^{-3})	E_i (pH 7·0) (mV)	
	E_i (a)	E_i (b)
20	22·5	14
13	17	17
9·3	17	18
6·0	15	16
4·0	15	16

The same conclusion was reached by calculating the redox equivalent weight. According to Michaelis [12], the indicator potentials allow a more exact description of a redox reaction. These are summarized in Table 1, showing that they are dependent upon the concentration of the tetrahydropteridine. They increase with increasing concentration and, in addition, the titration curves become more and more asymmetric. This, again following Michaelis' interpretation, is taken to mean that the intermediate free radical dimerizes quickly (Fig. 5).

The equilibrium constant of the dimerization reaction is estimated to be $< 10^{-4}$ [13]. This strong tendency of the radical to dimerize, together with the poor solubility of our model pteridine, rendered unsuccessful attempts to prove the trihydropteridine-intermediate by ESR measurements.

The stability of the radical, however, could be determined by UV-spectrophotometry (Fig. 6); 2 to 3 min after mixing equivalent amounts of tetrahydropteridine with ferricyanide at pH 7·0, a new spectrum is found, showing a bathochromic shift of about 10 nm to 310 nm and a new low maximum at

290 nm. This spectrum is definitely not the mixed spectrum of tetrahydro-
and dihydropteridine, indicating that there is no formation of a semiquinone
between the two species. Comparison of the spectrum of the newly formed
radical with that of the "oxidized tetrahydropteridine", which was isolated by
Kaufman [3] as an intermediate in the phenylalanine hydroxylation reaction
(Fig. 7), shows that not only are the spectra quite similar, but so are the

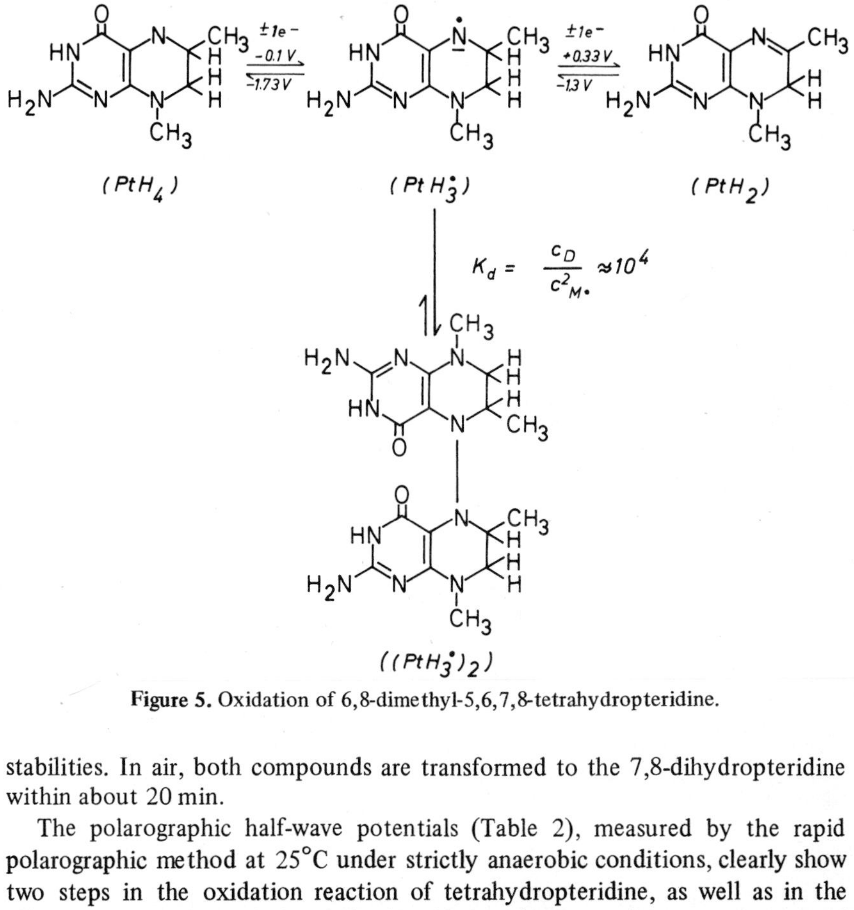

Figure 5. Oxidation of 6,8-dimethyl-5,6,7,8-tetrahydropteridine.

stabilities. In air, both compounds are transformed to the 7,8-dihydropteridine
within about 20 min.

The polarographic half-wave potentials (Table 2), measured by the rapid
polarographic method at 25°C under strictly anaerobic conditions, clearly show
two steps in the oxidation reaction of tetrahydropteridine, as well as in the
reduction of dihydropteridine. The dihydropteridine has a definite step at -1.36
V and a shoulder at -1.73 V. For the tetrahydropteridine the values are -0.09
and $+0.33$ V, respectively. The half-wave potentials of the shoulders are assumed
to be those of the free radical, which is present only in small concentration, as
discussed above. They represent the pair trihydro/tetrahydro in the case of the
dihydropteridine, and the pair trihydro/dihydro in the case of the tetrahydropteridine.

In the presence of metal ions such as Ag^+ and Cu^+, the half-wave potentials are changed considerably; the step decreases, the shoulder increases in height and is shifted to somewhat more positive values. It now becomes very distinct. From such measurements it is concluded that the concentration of the radical

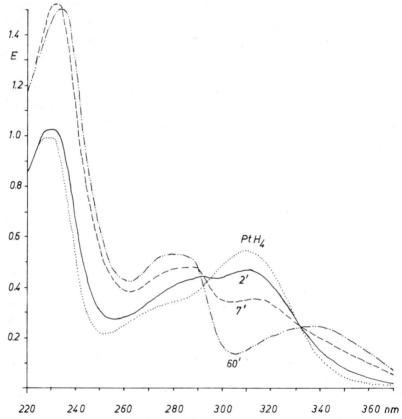

Figure 6. Time course of oxidation of 6,8-dimethyl-5,6,7,8-tetrahydropteridine with equimolar amounts of ferricyanide at pH 7·0.

$$c = 0·046 \text{ mM}; \, d = 1 \text{ cm}$$

The spectra were taken with a Bausch & Lomb Spectronic 505 at the times indicated.

increases, presumably due to stabilization by complex formation with the metal ion. The polarographic shifts may be similarly explained.

Hemmerich [14] recently showed coordination complex formation between flavins or pteroquinones with metal ions. Similar experiments were carried out with our reduced pteridines, and the metal affinity of the pteridines was followed by UV-spectrophotometry in the range pH 5 to pH 9, using increasing concentrations of metal. The data from the UV-spectra are presented in Table 3.

Only metal ions, easily interconvertible but existing in two stable oxidation states, coordinate with the reduced pteridines. Thus, bivalent ions, such as Mg^{2+}, Zn^{2+} or Cd^{2+} form complexes neither with the tetrahydropteridine nor with the dihydropteridine. However, the latter coordinates with Ag^+ or Cu^+, but it does

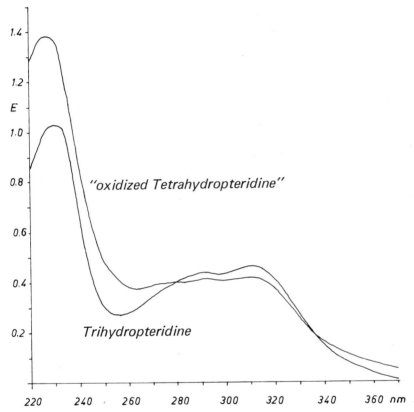

Figure 7. Comparison of spectra of the "oxidized tetrahydropteridine" (Kaufman [3]) and the trihydropteridine.

not complex with Cu^{2+} or Fe^{3+}. Some spectra of such complexes are shown in Fig. 8. As can be seen, there is a bathochromic shift of 20 to 25 nm and a general lowering of the extinction in the spectrum of the dihydropteridine.

Tetrahydropteridine has no affinity for Cu^+ and Fe^{2+} and only little affinity for Ag^+, which is, however, reduced to colloidal silver metal. On the other hand, the tetrahydropteridine complexes with Cu^{2+} and Fe^{3+}. The spectrum of the cupric complex of tetrahydropteridine is similar to that of the cuprous complex of dihydropteridine.

Table 2. Polarographic half-wave potentials of the model pteridines.

Compound	Half-wave potential in 0·1M phosphate pH 7·0 (V)
6,8-Dimethyl- 7,8-dihydropteridine	−1·35 ± 0·03 −1·73 (shoulder)
+ Cu$^+$-ion (1 equivalent)	−1·36 −1·68) (after 2 min)
+ Ag$^+$-ion (1 equivalent)	−1·36 −1·60
6,8-Dimethyl- 5,6,7,8-tetrahydropteridine	−0·09 ± 0·01 +0·33 ± 0·04 (shoulder)
+ K$_3$[Fe(CN)$_6$] (1 equivalent)	−0·1 (34%) +0·35 (230%) −1·36 (weak, after 6 min)

    With ferric ion a fast oxido-reduction takes place, leading anaerobically within 20 min to the dihydropteridine in quantitative yield. In the presence of oxygen, however, this is converted to a dihydroxy-compound, probably with the second hydroxy group at C-7.

    These observations are expressed in the following reaction scheme:

Formation of Trihydropteridine Metal Complexes

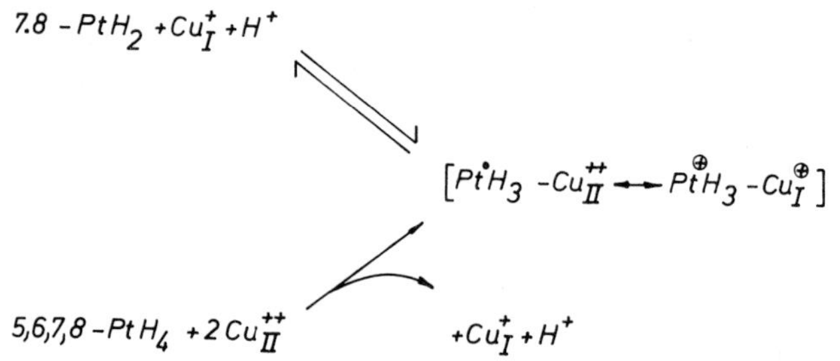

$$7,8 - PtH_2 \; +Cu_I^+ \;+H^+$$

$$[Pt\overset{\bullet}{H}_3 \; -Cu_{II}^{++} \longleftrightarrow Pt\overset{\bullet}{H}_3 \; -Cu_I^{\oplus}\,]$$

$$5,6,7,8 - PtH_4 \; +2\,Cu_{II}^{++} \qquad\qquad +Cu_I^+ +H^+$$

    The metal complexes are charge-transfer complexes. The pteridine is partially present as the trihydro-radical. Due to the poor solubility of the pteridines, however, it has not yet been possible to investigate the structure of the metal complexes further.

The evidence presented here not only describes the redox system, tetra-hydropteridine to dihydropteridine, but also allows us to speculate about the mechanism of the oxygen activation.

The potentiometric and polarographic titrations show that both reduction and oxidation proceed by two one-electron transfers. Both forms have affinity only to transitional elements, easily giving off or taking up electrons. With the

Table 3. Ultraviolet spectra of metal complexes of the model pteridines.

Compound	nm	log E
6,8-Dimethyl		
5,6,7,8-tetrahydropteridine (pH 6)	228	4·16
	273	3·96
	309	4·09
+ Cu^{2+} (1:20)	286	3·81
	350	3·64
+ Ag^+ (1:1)	(250)	(3·97)
	290	3·88
	306	3·86
	332	3·78
6,8-Dimethyl-		
7,8-dihydropteridine (pH 7)	234	4·35
	284	3·99
	331	3·71
+ Cu^+ (1:20)	231	4·20
	(287)	(3·57)
	356	3·55
+ Ag^+ (1:20)	230	4·05
	(295)	(3·53)
	350	3·53

tetrahydropteridine, the initial step is the reduction of the metal. The inter-mediate radical binds to the metal in its next higher oxidation level as a charge-transfer complex. In a similar fashion, dihydropteridines form complexes only with oxidizable metal ions.

In enzymatic hydroxylations three features are of relevance: (i) the tetra-hydropteridine is oxidized to the dihydropteridine in two one-electron steps, yielding at first a trihydropteridine radical, which has also been described by Ehrenberg and by Viscontini [6-8]; (ii) biochemically, an "oxidized tetra-hydropteridine" is the only substrate for pteridine reductase [15]; its spectrum is similar to that of our trihydropteridine radical; (iii) a transition metal ion may serve as the electron transfer catalyst to oxygen, but only if the higher oxidation state of the metal ion has affinity for the trihydropteridine radical. As shown, the pairs Fe^{3+}/Fe^{2+} or Cu^{2+}/Cu^+ meet these requirements.

Our attempt to apply our experimental findings to the phenylalanine hydroxylase reaction is depicted in Fig. 9. The function of the pteridine cofactor is merely to reduce the central metal of the postulated pteridine-enzyme-metal complex. The resulting trihydropteridine radical has no affinity for the reduced metal. The complex decays, and the trihydropteridine is reduced back to

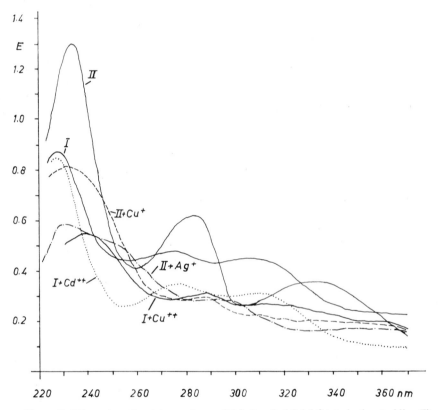

Figure 8. UV-spectra of metal-complexes of 6,8-dimethyl-5,6,7,8-tetrahydropteridine (I) and 6,8-dimethyl-7,8-dihydropteridine (II) at pH 6·0; c = 0·046 mM. The spectra were taken 2 to 3 min after mixing with the metal-ion indicated.

tetrahydropteridine by TPNH and the specific, possibly a flavin-containing, reductase system so that it can serve again as a specific electron donor for the still enzyme-bound metal ion. Subsequently, oxygen is reduced to peroxy anion by means of the pteridine-free Fe^{2+}-ion. The resulting enzyme-bound $[Fe^{3+}(O_2)^{2-}]^+$-species may react either with free Fe^{2+}-ion, yielding $OH^•$-radical and OH^--anion, completely analogous to Fenton's reagent, or it may be split heterolytically leading to an electrophilic OH^+-cation and OH^--anion.

In the first case, the OH•-radical may attack the mesomerized phenyl ring of phenylalanine. The intermediate so formed is oxidized by ferric ion to tyrosine and ferrous ion is regenerated.

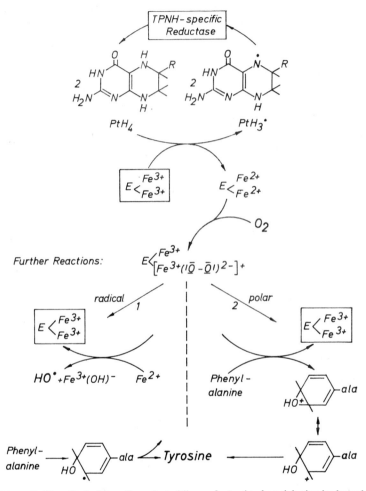

Figure 9. Hypothetical function of pteridine cofactor in phenylalanine hydroxylation.

In the second case, the OH^+-cation may add to the aromatic ring. The stabilization of the resulting oxepinium cation leads to tyrosine. Either hydroxylation mechanism receives support from experimental data recently published [4, 16, 17]. The suggested scheme does not try to distinguish between them.

In this reaction sequence, however, no hydroxylation of the pteridine cofactor [8] is postulated and the "quinonoid" dihydropteridine does not occur. The experimental evidence supporting such a structure, namely the tritium exchange experiments of Kaufman [3], can also be reconciled with the trihydropteridine radical. In this radical the hydrogen atoms at C-6 and C-7 are completely unaffected, and thus can neither become labelled by means of tritiated pyridine nucleotide and pteridine reductase in the recycling transformation to tetrahydropteridine, nor can the 7-H be lost by oxidation to the 7,8-tetrahydropteridine.

REFERENCES

1. Kaufman, S., *J. biol. Chem.* **237** (1962) PC 2712.
2. Kaufman, S., *Proc. natn. Acad. Sci. U.S.A.* **50** (1963) 1085.
3. Kaufman, S., *J. biol. Chem.* **239** (1964) 332.
4. Bobst, A. and Viscontini, M., *Helv. chim. Acta* **49** (1966) 884.
5. Viscontini, M., Leidner, H., Mattern, G. and Okada, T., *Helv. chim. Acta* **49** (1966) 1911.
6. Viscontini, M., *Fortschr. chem. Forsch.* **9** (1968) 605.
7. Viscontini, M., *Angew. Chem.* **80** (1968) 492.
8. Ehrenberg, A., Hemmerich, P., Müller, F., Okada, T. and Viscontini, M., *Helv. chim. Acta* **50** (1967) 411.
9. Wahlefeld, A. W., Jaenicke, L. and Hein, G., *Justus Liebigs Annln Chem.* **715** (1968).
10. Wahlefeld, A. W., Dissertation, Köln, 1966.
11. Boon, W. R. and Leigh, T., *J. chem. Soc.* (1951) 1497.
12. Michaelis, L., *in* "Physical Methods of Organic Chemistry", Vol. 2 (edited by A. Weisberger), Interscience Publishers, New York, 1963, p. 712.
13. Clark, J. M., "Oxidation-Reduction Potentials of Organic Systems", Williams & Wilkins, Baltimore, 1960, p. 163ff.
14. Hemmerich, P., *Angew. Chem.* **77** (1965) 711.
15. Kaufman, S., *J. biol. Chem.* **236** (1961) 804.
16. Guroff, G. and Daly, T., *Fedn Proc. Fedn Am. Socs exp. Biol.* **27** (1968) 587 Ref. 2087.
17. Guroff, G. and Daly, T., *Archs Biochem. Biophys.* **122** (1967) 212.

FEBS Symposium, Volume 16, 1969, pp. 261-265

Hydroxylation and Substrate Binding of Cyclohexane by Liver Microsomes

V. ULLRICH, J. SCHÄDELIN and Hj. STAUDINGER

Physiologisch-Chemisches Institut, The Justus Liebig-Universität, Giessen, Germany

Cytochrome P-450 of liver microsomes has been shown to participate as the oxygen-activating component in the mixed function oxygenation of a variety of drugs and other foreign compounds.

A special feature of this cytochrome is that most substrates are able to convert the oxidized form of the cytochrome with its Soret band at 420 nm to a new species absorbing at 390 nm [1, 2]. The mechanism of this substrate binding is not known, but has been interpreted as the formation of an enzyme-substrate complex by Schenkman and co-workers [3].

Looking at various compounds for their ability to bind to cytochrome P-450, we observed that aliphatic compounds like hexane, heptane, cyclopentane or cyclohexane gave a very high degree of binding, though little was known as to whether these compounds were hydroxylated or not by the microsomal system.

Gas chromatographic investigations of assay mixtures containing these hydrocarbons, together with rat or rabbit liver microsomes, NADPH and oxygen, revealed that they are hydroxylated to the corresponding alcohols. Cyclohexane proved to be a very good substrate because only cyclohexanol can be formed as a primary hydroxylation product, in contrast to all other substrates of microsomal mixed function oxygenases. A trace amount of cyclohexanone was formed as a secondary oxidation product and was accounted for as cyclohexanol.

We first looked at the effect of pretreatment of rats with phenobarbital and benzpyrene. For comparison we also determined the hydroxylation of acetanilide under these conditions (Table 1).

It is well known that benzpyrene treatment of rats greatly stimulates the hydroxylation of acetanilide, but the hydroxylation of cyclohexane was slightly inhibited. Phenobarbital injections had the opposite effect; an increase in cyclohexane hydroxylation and only a small increase in acetanilide hydroxylation.

The content of protein, cytochrome b_5, and cytochrome P-450 changed in agreement with other reports. A two-fold increase of the P-450 content is

Table 1. Hydroxylation and substrate binding of cyclohexane and acetanilide in rat liver microsomes. Effect of pretreatment with benzpyrene and phenobarbital.

	Control	Benzpyrene 1 x 20 mg/kg	Phenobarbital 3 x 100 mg/kg
mg Micros. protein x g liver^{-1}	16·9	19·2	25·5
nmoles Cytochrome b_5 x mg protein^{-1}	0·42	0·47	0·46
nmoles Cytochrome P-450 x mg protein^{-1}	0·66	0·97	1·20
nmoles Cyclohexanol x mg protein^{-1} x min^{-1}	4·2	3·1	22·2
nmoles 4-Hydroxyacetanilide x mg protein^{-1} x min^{-1}	0·8	4·5	1·3
Δ O.D. (390-420) nm x mg protein^{-1} Cyclohexane, 10^{-2} M	0·010	0·017	0·048
Δ O.D. (420-490) nm x mg protein^{-1} Acetanilide, 10^{-2} M	0·007	0·010	0·011

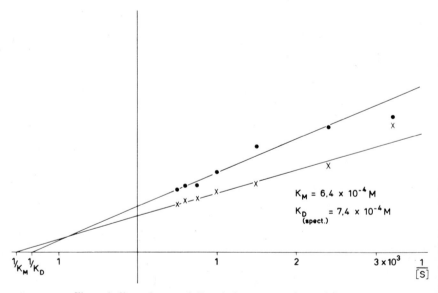

Figure 1. K_m and spectral dissociation constant for cyclohexane.

accompanied by a nearly five-fold increase in specific activity for cyclohexane hydroxylation.

However, when we compare the amount of substrate binding, there is a 4,8-fold increase closely matching the observed increase in hydroxylation activity. No correlation, however, is found for acetanilide, which is a type II substrate.

In all our induction experiments with phenobarbital the hydroxylating activity for cyclohexane proved to be proportional to the extent of substrate binding as measured by the difference spectrum.

A similar result was reported by Schenkman and co-workers [4] for the sex differences in hexobarbital oxidation. These authors also found identical values for the K_m of the reaction and the spectral dissociation constant of the substrate binding. We were able to confirm this for cyclohexane (Fig. 1).

It should be emphasized again that the correlation of substrate binding and hydroxylation activity is valid only for phenobarbital-inducible mixed-function oxygenations and for substrates without basic nitrogen atoms which may cause the type II spectral change. The mere fact that aliphatic or alicyclic hydrocarbons having no functional groups will bind to cytochrome P-450 gives evidence that only lipid solubility is a sufficient criterion for the mechanism of substrate binding.

Obviously cytochrome P-450 represents a necessary, but not the limiting, factor of the hydroxylation reaction. This is further supported by solubilization experiments with Triton N 101 in the presence of glycerol (Fig. 2).

Under these conditions rat liver microsomes form clear solutions and cytochrome P-450 stays fairly constant with increasing detergent concentrations. The hydroxylation activity, as well as the substrate binding and the light scattering, however, decrease in parallel.

Cytochrome P-450 of rabbit liver microsomes is completely stable under these conditions but the hydroxylation activity disappears even more rapidly than the substrate binding, indicating the destruction by the detergent of another essential step in the reaction sequence, probably electron transport (Fig. 3).

It is interesting to note that in triton-clarified preparations the spectral dissociation constant increases by a factor of 10 and the affinity for cyclohexane hydroxylation is also decreased; this would indicate that K_m values for microsomal hydroxylations really are "apparent" K_m values.

The high specific activity towards cyclohexane and the formation of only one product suggested cyclohexane as a suitable substrate for studying the stoichiometry of the hydroxylation. In order to determine the ratio of oxygen consumption to product formation, which should be 1, we followed the oxygen uptake polarographically before and after addition of cyclohexane and measured cyclohexanol in the electrode vessel (Table 2).

V. ULLRICH *et al.*

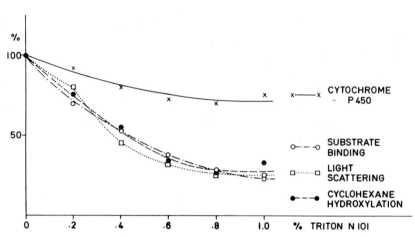

Figure 2. Effect of Triton N 101 on rat liver microsomes in the presence of glycerol.

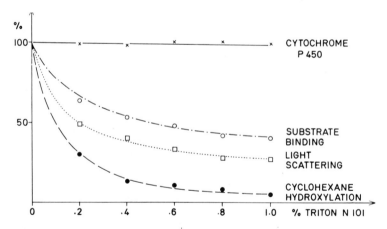

Figure 3. Effect of Triton N 101 on rabbit liver microsomes in the presence of glycerol.

We observed a rather high oxygen uptake of the microsomal suspension in the presence of NADPH but without substrate, which even increased after prolonged standing. Addition of cyclohexane then leads only to a slightly further increase of oxygen uptake, as shown in the first two experiments. With fresher preparations the increase was more distinct but the difference of the two oxygen traces, which usually is taken as the amount of oxygen due to substrate hydroxylation, never reached the amount of product found.

It is evident from these experiments that NADPH oxidation without substrate must involve in part cytochrome P-450. This is supported by the results of Staudinger and Zubrzycki [5] who described two oxygen reducing systems in NADPH-oxidation: one has a high affinity towards oxygen with a K_m the same as that determined for cyctochrome P-450 and with a sensitivity for carbon

Table 2. Oxygen consumption and product formation during the hydroxylation of cyclohexane.

Expt. No.	O_2-Consumption nmoles/10 min + NADPH	+ NADPH + C_6H_{12}	ΔO_2-Consumption nmoles/10 min	Cyclohexanol formed nmoles/10 min
1	920	1140	220	980
2	1050	1280	230	980
3	640	1500	860	1190

monoxide. A partial inhibition of NADPH oxidation by CO was also described very recently by Das et al. [6]. We do not know if this is due to a hydroxylation of endogenous substrate or an uncoupled hydroxylation where, in the absence of substrate, the active oxygen is formed yielding H_2O_2. Cyclohexane also proved to be a suitable substrate for the investigation of an isotope effect during mixed function oxygenations. The ratio of hydroxylation activity of cyclohexane: dodecadeuterocyclohexane was found to be 1:1. This lack of an isotope effect indicates that the breaking of the carbon-hydrogen bond does not occur as the rate-limiting step of the overall hydroxylation reaction.

REFERENCES

1. Remmer, H., Schenkman, J. B., Estabrook, R. W., Sasame, H. A., Gillette, J. R., Cooper, D. Y., Narasimhulu, S. and Rosenthal, O., Molec. Pharmac. 2 (1966) 187.
2. Imai, Y. and Sato, R., Biochem. biophys. Res. Commun. 22 (1966) 620.
3. Schenkman, J. B., Remmer, H. and Estabrook, R. W., Molec. Pharmac. 3 (1967) 113.
4. Schenkman, J. B., Frey, I., Remmer, H. and Estabrook, R. W., Molec. Pharmac. 3 (1967) 516.
5. Staudinger, Hj. and Zubrzycki, Z., Hoppe-Seyler's Z. physiol. Chem. 340 (1965) 191.
6. Das, M. L., Orrenius, S. and Ernster, L., Eur. J. Biochem. 4 (1968) 519.

FEBS Symposium, Volume 16, 1969, pp. 267-272

Direct Hydrogen Transfer from Substrate to Enzyme in Hydroxylations Catalysed by Xanthine Oxidase

R. C. BRAY, P. F. KNOWLES* and F. M. PICK

*Chester Beatty Research Institute,
Institute of Cancer Research, Royal Cancer Hospital,
London, England*

Milk xanthine oxidase (EC 1.2.3.2) is an enzyme which has been widely studied [1] and whose mechanism of action is becoming comparatively well understood. It catalyses the hydroxylation of a considerable range of substrates (see Fig. 1 for examples), the oxygen atom which is introduced into the molecule being derived from the medium rather than from oxygen [2]. In the

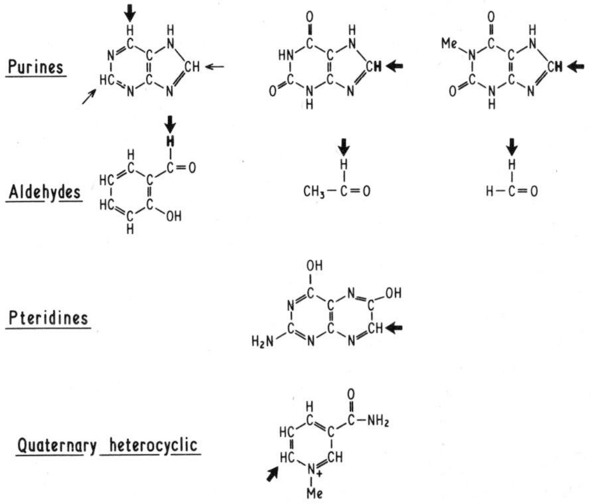

Figure 1. Examples of substrates of xanthine oxidase. The arrows denote the position in which hydroxylation takes place. Hydrogen atoms in heavy type are those whose transfer to the enzyme has been demonstrated (Fig. 4).

Abbreviations: ESR—electron spin resonance; SH (or AH)—substrate; SD—substrate deuterated specifically in the position at which hydroxylation takes place.

* Present address: Department of Biophysics, University of Leeds, Leeds.

case of aldehydes, the non-hydrated molecule is the true substrate [3], so that the overall process is properly regarded as one of hydroxylation.

Data on the mechanism of action of the enzyme has been provided mainly by electron spin resonance studies using the rapid-freezing technique [4-8]. On the basis of these and of more recent results, we wish to put forward tentatively the scheme shown in Fig. 2, involving direct transfer of hydrogen from substrate to

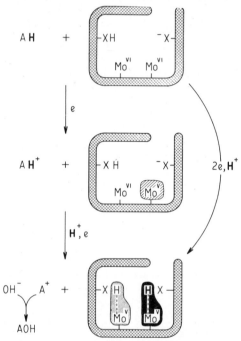

Figure 2. Tentative scheme of the interaction of a reducing substrate, AH, with the active centre of xanthine oxidase. The three species giving ESR signals are denoted by different types of shading. The dotted lines between Mo and H denote an interaction demonstrated by ESR. These hydrogens are exchangeable at a measurable rate with protons in the medium. The initial form for the active centre, (at the top of the diagram), is shown in its high pH form. At lower pH values the group X⁻ is supposed to be protonated.

enzyme, as one possible mechanism for the process of interaction between the enzyme and reducing substrates. The main features of the scheme are as follows. The enzyme, which contains two molybdenum atoms per molecule [9], is depicted with both of these in a single active centre. The reaction is shown as involving the transfer of two electrons and a proton from substrate to enzyme. The hydroxylation of the former is then completed by the uptake of a hydroxyl ion from the medium. The two electrons are received by the two molybdenums, which are reduced from Mo(VI) to Mo(V), while the proton is received by a negatively-charged site from which it interacts, in a manner not yet fully understood, with only one of the two molybdenum atoms. The other molybdenum also interacts with a proton but in this case it is not a proton which has been derived from the substrate. With a substrate like xanthine, the primary step is the transfer of the first electron and this step can be distinguished from the subsequent electron-plus-proton step. With other substrates the steps cannot be separated from one another.

The experimental data will be discussed in the light of the above scheme. During the turnover processes two types of molybdenum ESR signals are seen [4, 5]. One represents a simple Mo(V) species while the other represents Mo(V) interacting with a proton [6]. The simple Mo(V) signal is almost exclusive to xanthine as substrate [7], while kinetically this signal seems to be a precursor of the Mo(V)-H signal (Fig. 3), as required in Fig. 2.*

Figure 4 shows Mo(V)-H signals in the early stages of reaction of the enzyme with three substrates, salicylaldehyde, xanthine and 1-methylxanthine. These are compared with their corresponding specifically-deuterated analogues and in each case there is definite evidence for partial replacement of the hydrogen doublet of the signal by a single deuterium line. Since under these conditions the three substrates give spectra very similar to one another, it is reasonable to assume that they represent reduced enzyme, rather than complexes of enzyme and substrate. Hence we conclude that the substrate hydrogen is transferred directly to the enzyme. At longer reaction times the signals from the deuterated substrates become progressively more like those from the normal substrates, indicating that the deuterium introduced into the enzyme is exchanging out again into the medium.

1-Methylxanthine was selected for more detailed study, with the aim of identifying the proton-accepting group in the enzyme. Figure 5 (bottom) illustrates signals obtained with the deuterated substrate in H_2O and shows the gradual decrease with time in the proportion of deuterium in the signal. The reverse experiment, giving a comparable result, is also shown (top), in which ordinary substrate was employed in D_2O. It is noteworthy that, with the two systems, the signals initially detected are distinctly alike. They do in fact resemble those obtained at long reaction times from the substrate in 1:1 $D_2O:H_2O$ (centre). The explanation proposed for this (Fig. 2) is that the two Mo atoms in the enzyme give almost identical superimposed spectra, but that only one Mo is interacting with hydrogen which is derived from the substrate. Thus, the total signal would be expected to be much the same, whether the first Mo is interacting with H and the second with D, or whether the reverse situation holds. And it would also be the same in the mixed solvent, when both Mo atoms have, statistically, an equal chance of interacting with H or with D. (In support of this scheme, a more highly resolved spectrum from 1-Me-xanthine obtained on

---

* According to the scheme a substrate radical, AH^+, should be formed at the same time as the simple Mo(V) species. We have not as yet detected this, possibly owing to instability.

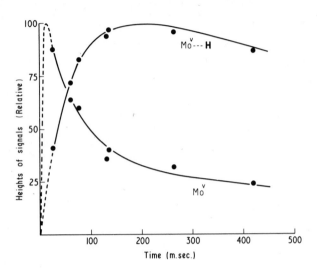

Figure 3. Relative intensities of Mo(V) and Mo(V)-H ESR signals from xanthine oxidase during the approach to steady-state conditions in the oxidation of xanthine. (Data replotted from [5]).

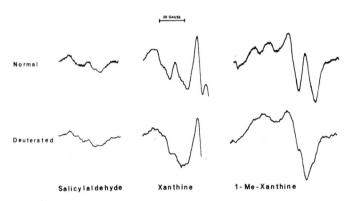

Figure 4. ESR signals in the early stages of reaction at pH 8·2 between xanthine oxidase and salicylaldehyde, xanthine and 1-methylxanthine, compared with the corresponding specifically-deuterated analogues. Reaction times were the shortest ones at which an acceptable signal/noise ratio was obtainable on the traces. With salicylaldehyde, dimethylsulphoxide (20% final concentration) was added to increase substrate solubility.

a Q-band apparatus by T. Vänngård did in fact appear to be made up from two very similar, though not quite identical, spectra present in roughly equal amounts.)

Attempts have been made to determine the rates of the processes illustrated in Fig. 5, by measuring signal intensities and the proportions of their H and D forms, as a function of time, employing an analogue computer to analyse the data. Provisional values of the rate constants are presented in Table 1. The rate of signal development, k_1, paralleled the overall rate of product appearance, as measured in conventional spectrophotometric assays, indicating that signal development may represent the rate-limiting step of the complete enzyme

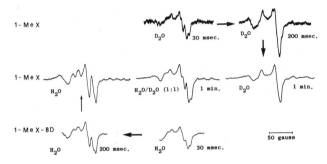

Figure 5. ESR signals from treatment of xanthine oxidase with 1-methylxanthine and 1-methylxanthine-8D in H_2O and D_2O at various reaction times.

turnover process. The constants in the table appear to be consistent with Fig. 2, if it is assumed that the group X^- is largely unionized at pH 8·4, but fully ionized at pH 10. This would mean that at the lower pH, where an XH or an XD bond has to be broken to make way for the substrate, it is the relatively greater strength of the XD bond which causes the overall reaction to proceed more slowly in system SH/D_2O than it does in system SH/H_2O. At pH 10, however, since the group in the enzyme is fully ionized, no D_2O effect on the rate is observed. At either pH, in H_2O, the overall rate is slower for the deuterated than for the normal substrate, as expected from the fact that an SD rather than an SH bond has to be broken. Finally, it is noteworthy that after D has been introduced into the enzyme from the deuterated substrate, its exchange rate out of the enzyme, k_e, is greatly increased at the higher pH. This would not be predicted from the scheme and may reflect changes in the ionization of other groups in the vicinity.

In conclusion it must be emphasized that the mechanism put forward is very provisional and that further work is required. Nevertheless it is interesting that, though the proposed proton-accepting group in the enzyme has not been

272   R. C. BRAY, P. F. KNOWLES AND F. M. PICK

Table 1. Provisional velocity constants (sec^{-1} at 10°C).

System	pH (or pD) 8·4		pH (or pD) 10·0	
	k_1	ke	k_1	ke
SH/H$_2$O	3·0	–	1	–
SH/D$_2$O	1·7	10	1	–
SD/H$_2$O	1·4	10	0·3	⩾ 50

SH = 1-Methylxanthine.
SD = 1-Methylxanthine-8D.
k_1 = velocity constant for formation of Mo signals.
k_e = velocity constant for exchange of H or D in signal.

identified, no particularly abnormal properties* have to be postulated for it, other than the slow exchangeability of protons bound to it, which might of course be related to their interaction with molybdenum.

ACKNOWLEDGEMENTS

We thank Dr. J. F. Gibson of Imperial College for help with the ESR work and Mr. B. Hammond of the National Institute for Medical Research for help with analogue computing. The work was supported by grants to the Chester Beatty Research Institute (Institute of Cancer Research: Royal Cancer Hospital) from the Medical Research Council and the British Empire Cancer Campaign for Research, and by the Public Health Service Research Grant No. CA-03188-10 from the National Cancer Institute, U.S. Public Health Service.

REFERENCES

1. Bray, R. C., in "The Enzymes", Vol. 7 (edited by P. D. Boyer, H. Lardy and K. Myrbäck), Academic Press, New York, 1963, p. 533.
2. Mason, H. S., Science, N.Y. 125 (1957) 1185.
3. Fridovich, I., J. biol. Chem. 241 (1966) 3126.
4. Palmer, G., Bray, R. C. and Beinert, H., J. biol. Chem. 239 (1964) 2657.
5. Bray, R. C., Palmer, G. and Beinert, H., J. biol. Chem. 239 (1964) 2667.
6. Bray, R. C. and Meriwether, L. S., Nature, Lond. 212 (1966) 467.
7. Bray, R. C., Knowles, P. F. and Meriwether, L. S., in "Magnetic Resonance in Biological Systems" (edited by A. Ehrenberg, B. G. Malmström and T. Vänngård), Pergamon Press, Oxford, 1967, p. 249
8. Bray, R. C. and Knowles, P. F., Proc. R. Soc. (A) 302 (1968) 351.
9. Hart, L. I. and Bray, R. C., Biochim. biophys. Acta 146 (1967) 611.

* The conclusion given in the abstract, that access of protons to the group is rate-limiting in the exchange process, has not been substantiated.

FEBS Symposium, Volume 16, 1969, pp. 273-278

Lipid Peroxide Formation and Drug Hydroxylation by Microsomes

E. D. WILLS

Biochemistry Department, The Medical College of St. Bartholomew's Hospital, London, England

INTRODUCTION

During our studies on lipid peroxide formation in separated sub-cellular components of liver we observed [1] that the microsome fraction after

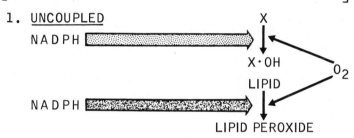

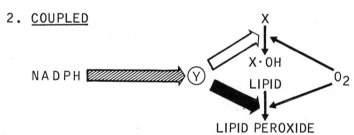

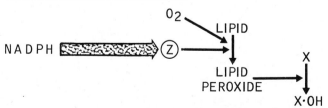

Figure 1. Possible mechanisms of lipid peroxide formation in microsomes.

273

incubation formed much more lipid peroxide than the other fractions. The rate of lipid peroxide formation in the microsome fraction can be increased greatly by addition of ascorbate or NADPH, but not NADH [2].

It has been known for several years that many steroids, drugs and related compounds are hydroxylated by microsomes in the presence of NADPH and oxygen and that an electron transport chain is involved in the process [3]. It is therefore possible that the processes of peroxide formation and hydroxylation both depend on the same electron transport chain. Possible formulations of the mechanisms of, and relationships between, lipid peroxide formation and hydroxylation are shown in Fig. 1.

EXPERIMENTAL

Suspensions of microsomes prepared from a 0·25M sucrose homogenate of liver and containing 2·5 mg protein/ml were incubated at 37°C in a medium containing phosphate buffer (0·02M), pH 6·0-7·4, NADPH (40 μM), nicotinamide (50 mM) or ascorbate (0·5 mM) and potassium chloride (125 mM).

The rate of lipid peroxide formation was measured by the thiobarbituric acid method [4] and the rate of oxygen uptake by the oxygen electrode. Oxidative demethylation of aminopyrine (10 mM) was followed by estimating the formaldehyde produced [5] and the hydroxylation of aniline by measuring the p-aminophenol formed.

RESULTS

Lipid peroxide formation and oxygen uptake were rapid when microsomes were incubated in the presence of NADPH or ascorbate, but very little oxidation of aminopyrine occurred when NADPH was replaced by ascorbate.

Addition of aminopyrine to microsome suspensions depressed the rate of lipid peroxide formation and the rate of oxygen uptake, whether the peroxide formation was induced by ascorbate or by NADPH (Fig. 2). The rate of lipid peroxide formation was reduced to zero by 10 mM aminopyrine in presence of NADPH, but oxygen uptake was maintained at a reduced rate.

Addition of chelating agents such as EDTA or o-phenanthroline (mM) to microsomes before incubation with NADPH or ascorbate completely abolishes lipid peroxide formation [7], and, if the initial homogenization of the liver was carried out in 0·25M sucrose containing EDTA (mM) instead of in pure sucrose, no lipid peroxide was formed when the microsomes prepared were incubated with NADPH or ascorbate. Lipid peroxide formation was, however, restored to that of microsomes prepared from untreated homogenate, and increased beyond that rate, if Fe^{2+} in a low concentration (25 μM) was added.

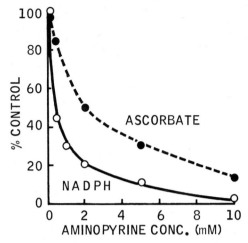

Figure 2. Effect of aminopyrine on lipid peroxide formation in microsomes.

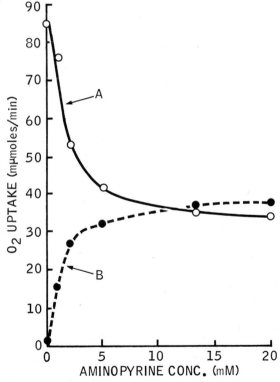

Figure 3. Effect of aminopyrine on oxygen uptake of microsomes prepared from a sucrose homogenate (Curve A) and from sucrose-EDTA homogenate (Curve B).

The addition of aminopyrine to microsomes prepared from sucrose-EDTA now increased the rate of oxygen uptake and when the concentration of aminopyrine was 10 mM the rate of oxygen uptake was nearly the same whether the microsomes had been prepared from sucrose or from a sucrose-EDTA mixture (Fig. 3).

Sulphydryl reagents such as p-chlormercuribenzoate (0·5 mM) strongly inhibited aminopyrine oxidation and lipid peroxide formation if induced by NADPH but had no effect on lipid peroxide formation induced by ascorbate.

Sodium desoxycholate in concentrations greater than 0·2% (w/v) strongly inhibited aminopyrine oxidation and lipid peroxide formation in the presence of NADPH although aminopyrine oxidation was somewhat more sensitive than lipid peroxide formation. This indicates that membrane integrity is essential for both processes.

Treatment of microsomes with 0·1% desoxycholate followed by centrifugation at 100,000 g for 30 min produces three components, a sediment consisting mainly of ribosomes, a fluffy layer above consisting of membranes and vesicles, and a supernatant [6]. When each fraction was incubated with NADPH, aminopyrine oxidation and lipid peroxide were associated mainly with the same fraction, the membrane fraction.

Other drugs oxidized by microsomes, such as codeine, caffeine and phenobarbitone were much less effective than aminopyrine in reducing lipid peroxide formation in microsomes incubated with NADPH. Thus phenobarbitone (10 mM) did not alter the rate which was reduced to zero by aminopyrine in the same concentration.

A study of a large number of aliphatic and aromatic compounds has demonstrated that the majority of aliphatic hydrocarbons, alcohols and ketones do not effect the rate of lipid peroxide formation, even when added in very high concentrations (1M). Halogenated compounds such as chloroform or carbon tetrachloride did, however, block lipid peroxide formation.

Many aromatic compounds tested strongly inhibited peroxide formation. Benzene and other aromatic hydrocarbons reduce lipid peroxide formation, but phenols such as p-cresol or catechol were much more effective in low concentrations (5 mM), as were amino compounds such as aniline. Aromatic acids such as benzoic or salicyclic were ineffective. Many of these aromatic compounds which reduce the rate of lipid peroxide formation are known to be hydroxylated by microsomes, but the most effective, e.g. polyhydric phenols, are well established as antioxidants.

The effect of lipid peroxide formation on the capacity of the microsomes to carry out hydroxylation was studied by incubating microsome suspensions with NADPH, or ascorbate, or by treating them with ionizing radiation. The rate of oxidation of aminopyrine or hydroxylation of aniline was measured after peroxide formation, As the extent of lipid peroxidation in the microsome suspension increases, the capacity of microsomes to hydroxylate decreases (Fig. 4). Oxidized microsomes were not inhibitory when added to fresh microsomes, thus demonstrating that products formed during peroxidation were not responsible for the inhibition of hydroxylation.

It may therefore be concluded that lipid peroxide formation occurs rapidly in microsomes incubated with NADPH or ascorbate, provided low concentrations of loosely complexed inorganic iron are present. Iron in this form is not necessary for oxidation of aminopyrine. Many aromatic compounds, especially

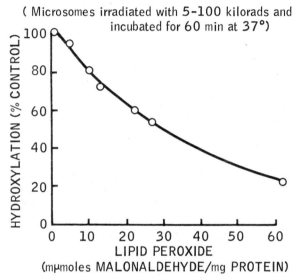

Figure 4. Relation between lipid peroxide formation and the rate of aniline hydroxylation by irradiated microsomes.

established antioxidants, and a few aliphatic compounds block lipid peroxide formation, but all compounds which undergo hydroxylation do not inhibit lipid peroxide formation.

Evidence at present available is in agreement with the coupled scheme [2] (Fig. 1). It is considered likely that lipid peroxide formation leads to membrane disintegration and that it may be part of the process of metabolic turnover and remodelling of the microsomal membranes when suitable substrates for hydroxylation are unavailable.

REFERENCES

1. Wills, E. D. and Wilkinson, A. E., *Radiat. Res.* **31** (1967) 732.
2. Orrenius, S., Dallner, G. and Ernster, L., *Biochem. biophys. Res. Commun.* **14** (1964) 329.

3. Omura, T., Sato, R., Cooper, D. Y., Rosenthal, O. and Estabrook, R. W., *Fedn Proc. Fedn Am. Socs exp. Biol.* **24** (1965) 1181.
4. Wills, E. D., *Biochem. J.* **99** (1966) 667.
5. Ernster, L. and Orrenius, S., *Fedn Proc. Fedn Am. Socs exp. Biol.* **24** (1965) 1190.
6. Dallner, G., *Acta path. microbiol. scand.* Suppl. 166, (1963).
7. Wills, E. D., 7th International Congress of Biochemistry, (1967) Abstract E-35.

FEBS Symposium, Volume 16, 1969, pp. 279-281

Concluding Remarks

S. ORRENIUS

Department of Biochemistry, University of Stockholm,
Stockholm, Sweden

I have been asked to present a brief summary of this symposium on the Hydroxylation of Drugs and Chemical Action of Their Metabolic Products within the Organism. In doing so I am not going to take your time by repeating again the experimental findings and conclusions of the almost forty papers presented during the past two days. Instead I will select only a few aspects to illustrate our present view of the hydroxylation process and how it has been enriched by this symposium.

We have heard that the hydroxylation reaction is the most common metabolic pathway to making foreign lipid-soluble compounds more polar and thereby possible for the organism to excrete, mostly after previous conjugation to various acids. The metabolites are generally less toxic than the parent compound. Sometimes, however, the hydroxylated products are pharmacologically more active, and sometimes even deleterious to the organism, e.g. the hydroxylated carcinogenes which, by way of interaction with nucleic acids or proteins, or both, may cause tumour development.

Now, let us for a moment consider which of the known enzymes present in the liver microsomes participate in the hydroxylation reaction. I think that we all agree about the central role of cytochrome P-450 as the terminal oxidase, and as the binding-site, for the various substrates capable of undergoing hydroxylation. Both these functions have been further elucidated in several papers during the symposium. The N-oxygenation reaction, however, seems to be one important exception.

How then is cytochrome P-450 reduced? It has been suggested that the substrate forms a complex with the oxidized cytochrome and that this complex is subsequently reduced by a NADPH-dependent reductase, presumably the NADPH-cytochrome c reductase. There is now substantial evidence for the involvement of the latter enzyme in the reduction of cytochrome P-450. However, the purification and reconstruction of the hydroxylating enzyme system has still not been reported. Furthermore, there are certain indications that the isolated NADPH-cytochrome c reductase may differ considerably from the native, membrane-bound enzyme. More work is needed to elucidate this part of the hydroxylation process.

The involvement of additional catalysts, like a non-heme iron protein, in the electron transfer to cytochrome P-450 in the liver microsomes has still not been excluded. Although no direct biochemical evidence supporting this hypothesis has been presented, one must bear in mind that a non-heme iron protein has been shown to participate in the reduction of cytochrome P-450, both in the adrenal cortex and testis systems.

Another important question which certainly will be answered by future work is whether cytochrome P-450 is one single enzyme or a family of enzymes. We do not have enough evidence to decide this question now. However, several findings regarding, for example, the stereospecificity of certain hydroxylations, sex and species differences, and a varying inducibility of the hydroxylation activity as measured with various substrates, would certainly be more easy to explain if cytochrome P-450 turns out to be a family of closely related enzymes. The hydroxylation of the carcinogenic polycyclic hydrocarbons shows many similarities with drug hydroxylation but also exhibits some obvious differences from the latter which, at the present time, makes it difficult to visualize both these processes as functions of exactly the same enzyme system.

The concentration of cytochrome P-450 in the liver microsomes is indeed very high, whereas most substrates are hydroxylated at a slow, or very slow, rate. At this symposium the enzymic reduction of cytochrome P-450 has been suggested as the rate-limiting step in the hydroxylation process. At least the initial rate of this reduction, when studied in the liver microsomes, however, appears to be quite fast. It cannot yet be decided whether the rate-limiting step in the hydroxylation process is the concentration of the cytochrome, the rate at which it is reduced or the formation or splitting of the enzyme-substrate complex. Further studies are needed to solve this problem.

The elucidation of the mechanism of microsomal hydroxylation has been made difficult not only by the low activities but also by the existence of the endogenous NADPH oxidase. Due to these difficulties the stoichiometry involved in the hydroxylation of most substrates has not yet been reported. These difficulties have now been partly overcome by using liver microsomes from "induced" animals exhibiting a several-fold enhanced rate of over all hydroxylation due to repeated drug administration in vivo. Whereas induction studies have rendered valuable information about several aspects of the hydroxylation process, little is known about the actual molecular mechanism by which the inducing drug causes the enhanced enzyme levels and membrane proliferation.

The hydroxylation of steroid hormones and the ω-oxidation of fatty acids have been shown to be functions of the microsomal hydroxylating enzyme system. However, it seems probable that future work will add several more physiologically occurring compounds to the list of substrates for this enzyme system, which sometimes seems to be so highly non-specific in its action and sometimes reveals the most striking specificity.

Finally, let me just mention one of the more neglected aspects in this research field, which concerns the role of membrane lipids. Although I am convinced that studies of the organization of this enzyme system within the membrane, and especially the role of the lipids, will contribute considerably to our knowledge about these problems, up to now little has been done in this respect and even less is known.

This symposium has, however, not only elucidated the complexity of this field, but also illustrated how important it is to study these reactions in order to increase our knowledge about these so obviously vital phenomena in the organism. The symposium has also clearly revealed that there is still plenty of work to be done when we return to our laboratories, which is, indeed, a very good thing to know. I now ask the audience to join me in my sincere thanks to the organizers—Dr. Wagner and Professor Williams—for all the work and effort they have devoted to make this symposium as successful and fruitful as it has turned out.

Author Index

Numbers in parentheses are reference numbers and are included to assist in locating references. Numbers followed by an asterisk refer to the page on which the reference is listed.

A

Åberg, B., 222(81), 225*
Acheson, R. M., 85(10), 94*
Acros, J. C., 130(62), 141*
Adams, D. A., 1(7), 9*
Adamson, R. H., 38(12), 47*, 110(6), 123*
Adler, F. L., 7(48, 49), 10*
Afzelius, B. A., 211(37), 224*
Allen, D. W., 162(11), 176(11), 177(11), 178(11), 180*
Allen, M. J., 196(44), 202(44), 204*
Al-Nahas, A., 44(23), 47*
Alvares, A. P., 110(24), 123*
Anderson, J. H., Jr., 2(14), 9*
Angier, R. B., 51(19), 63*
Arias, J. M., 138(29), 140*
Arrhenius, E., 110(14), 123*, 162(17, 19), 180*, 211(31, 32, 33, 34, 35, 36, 37, 38), 212(40, 43), 213(33, 34, 35, 40), 214(33, 34, 38, 40), 215(40, 43), 216(32, 35, 38, 40, 43, 66), 217(66), 218(66), 219(40), 220(43), 221(40, 43, 66, 79), 222(32, 43, 79), 224*, 225*
Asahina, Y., 90(32), 94*
Atkinson, J., 1(2), 8*
Axelrod, J., 110(4), 123*, 143(3, 4, 7), 158*, 239(4), 247*

B

Baer, H., 231(9), 232*
Bahr, C., von, 156(51), 157(53), 160*
Baker, B. R., 66(2, 3), 79*
Ball, J. A., 120(47), 124*
Bamberger, E., 216(68), 225*
Barnes, B. A., 1(2), 8*
Barnes, J. K., 167(38), 181*

Barnes, J. M., 205(2), 207*
Battye, R., 199(55), 204*
Baucum, R., 129(49), 141*
Baxi, A. J., 167(37), 181*
Beinert, H., 268(4, 5), 269(4, 5), 270(5), 272*
Ben, T., 138(24), 140*
Benacerraf, B., 229(4), 232*
Benedict, J. D., 16(22), 21*
Benke, P. J., 18(30), 21*
Bennett, L. L., 2(15), 9*
Berenbaum, M. C., 3(22), 9*
Bergamini, A., 233(7), 238*
Berger, F. M., 89(28), 94*
Berlin, M., 222(80), 225*
Berliner, D. L., 214(57), 225*
Bertino, J. R., 37(11), 38(11), 42(17), 47*, 49(3, 6), 63*
Bertolani, F., 233(7), 238*
Betts, J. J., 85(11), 94*
Bhatia, H. M., 167(37), 181*
Bieber, S., 2(17), 4(30), 9*, 13(14), 18(26), 21*
Bien, E. J., 16(22), 21*
Blair, A. E., 16(23), 18(23), 21*
Blake, D. F., 114(39), 124*
Blakley, R. L., 49(9), 50(16), 63*
Blum, S., 190(24), 203*
Bobst, A., 250(4), 259(4), 260*
Bodanski, O., 97(29), 104(29), 107*
Bolland, J. L., 213(47), 224*
Bonser, G. M., 197(46), 204*
Boon, W. R., 251(11), 260*
Booth, J., 130(55), 141*, 162(4), 180*, 200(57), 204*
Boothe, J. H., 51(19), 63*
Borel, Y., 5(35), 10*
Bottiger, L.-E., 148(36), 159*
Bousquet, W. F., 110(7), 114(39), 123*, 124*, 129(45), 141*

Bowser, R. T., 231(9), 232*
Boyland, E., 92(36, 37), 95*, 102(21),
107*, 162(4), 180*, 184(2, 3),
186(12, 13, 14, 15, 16), 188(19),
190(26), 191(27), 193(2, 29, 30),
195(27), 196(41, 44), 197(46),
199(56), 200(57, 58), 202(44,
56), 203(62), 203*, 204*,
214(50), 224*
Boyse, E. A., 209(9), 223*
Bray, H. G., 85(11), 94*, 233(8),
238*
Bray, R. C., 267(1), 268(4, 5-6, 7, 8,
9), 269(4, 5, 6, 7), 270(5), 272*
Brazda, F. G., 129(49), 141*
Bresnick, E., 139(33), 140*
Brettschneider, L., 1(1), 8*
Breuer, H., 143(9), 158*
Brill, E., 101(22), 102(22, 23), 107*
Brockman, R. W., 2(15), 9*
Brodie, B. B., 109(1), 110(1, 4, 5),
123*, 125(2), 128(11), 139*,
140*, 143(1, 3, 4, 7, 8), 145(27),
154(27), 158*, 159*, 190(21),
203*, 210(15), 211(15), 216(15),
223*
Brooke, M. S., 4(32), 10*
Brookes, P., 184(4), 194(31), 195(31),
203*, 204*, 205(6), 207(13),
207*
Brown, R. R., 202(59), 204*
Bryan, G. T., 202(59), 204*
Bui-Duy Tam, Jenny, E., 49(5), 63*
Bunyan, J., 213(49), 224*
Burchall, J., 38(14), 42(14), 47*
Burchall, J. J., 49(10, 11), 63*, 66(1),
79*
Burger, A., 104(39), 107*, 162(9),
166(31), 167(32, 33), 168(31),
169(32), 170(32, 33), 171(9, 31,
32, 33), 172(9, 42), 173(9, 42),
174(42), 179(9), 180*, 181*
Burnet, M., 6(40), 10*
Burns, J. J., 110(5), 123*, 125(1, 2),
129(1, 47, 48), 130(1), 138(1),
139*, 141*, 143(11), 159*
Busby, E. R., 197(46), 204*
Bush, M. T., 128(10), 140*
Butenandt, A., 192(28), 204*
Butler, T. C., 128(10), 140*
Buu-Hoi, Ne, Ph., 130(62), 141*

C

Caldwell, I. C., 2(16), 9*, 19(37), 22*
Callahan, S., 2(17), 9*, 13(14, 15),
21*
Callahan, S. W., 2(18), 9*
Calne, R. Y., 1(4), 9*
Caputto, R., 213(48), 224*
Carpenter, D. G., 18(33), 22*
Carpenter, M. P., 213(48), 224*
Carswell, E. A., 209(9), 223*
Carter, C. H., 18(33), 22*
Case, R. A. M., 196(36), 204*
Castro, J. A., 110(15), 111(33),
112(34), 123*, 124*
Cefis, F., 203(61), 204*
Chandra, P., 138(25), 140*
Chenau, V. A., 213(48), 224*
Chenkin, T., 239(4), 247*
Chiesara, E., 129(41, 44, 46), 130(46),
141*
Chumley, S., 2(15), 9*
Ciotti, M. M., 176(48), 181*
Clark, J. M., 252(13), 260*
Clark, W. G., 233(3), 238*
Clarke, D. A., 209(9), 223*
Clayson, D. B., 197(46), 204*, 209(4),
211(4), 223*
Cleland, W. W., 69(11), 80*
Cleveland, R. J., 1(3), 8*
Colas, A., 143(6), 158*
Condie, R. M., 4(29), 9*
Conney, A. H., 85(7), 94*, 101(16),
107*, 110(10, 11, 20), 111(20),
123*, 125(1, 7), 129(1, 47, 48),
130(1), 130(60, 61, 62), 138(1),
139*, 141*, 143(10, 11, 13),
149(37), 150(43), 152(13),
155(10, 49), 158*, 159*, 160*
Cook, J. W., 184(7, 10), 203*
Cooper, D. Y., 110(27, 28), 119(28),
123*, 150(41, 43), 159*, 160*,
261(1), 265*, 274(3), 278*
Cooper, J. R., 143(4), 158*
Cornier, M. J., 163(26), 180*
Cox, A. J., 196(38), 204*
Craddock, V. M., 205(6), 206(10, 11),
207*
Cramer, J. W., 97(5), 106*, 190(20),
196(43), 197(47), 203*, 204*,
210(12), 212(12, 39), 213(39),

215(39), 219(39), 220(39),
222(39), 223*, 224*
Crawford, E. J., 44(23), 47*, 66(4, 5),
79*
Culp, H. W., 90(24), 94*
Curtis, M. R., 196(40, 42), 204*

Druckrey, H., 205(3), 206(3), 207*
Dukes, C. E., 196(44), 202(44), 204*
Dulmadge, E. A., 2(15), 9*
Duncan, I. W., 166(46), 175(46), 181*
Dunnine, W. F., 196(40, 42), 204*
Dutton, R. W., 7(50, 51), 10*

D

Dallner, G., 114(38), 116(38), 124*,
144(22), 150(40), 159*, 274(2),
276(6), 277*, 278*
Daly, J. W., 85(13), 86(13), 94*,
235(12), 238*, 245(5), 246(5),
247*
Daly, T., 259(16, 17), 260*
Dameshek, W., 4(26, 27, 28, 31),
8(31), 9*, 10*
Dannenberg, H., 162(21), 163(28),
180*, 192(28), 195(33), 204*
Das, M. L., 114(40), 124*, 143(16),
144(16, 20), 152(44), 154(20),
157(16), 159*, 160*, 265(6),
265*
Daudel, R., 185(11), 203*
Davies, D., 112(35), 124*
Davies, G. E., 227(3), 232*
Davies, G. H., 4(33), 10*
Davison, C., 125(1), 129(1), 130(1),
138(1), 139*
Debackere, M., 99(13), 100(13), 107*
De Eds, F., 196(38), 204*
De Graw, J., 44(23), 47*
Deichmann, W. B., 102(23), 107*
Dennelle, R., 231(8), 232*
Desforges, J., 167(35), 181*
Dickison, H. L., 128(10), 140*
Diner, S., 83(2), 93*
Dingell, J. V., 110(16), 123*, 129(50),
141*
Diplock, A. T., 213(49), 224*
Dixon, G. J., 2(15), 9*
Dixon, R. L., 110(13, 17, 18), 123*
Dohrn, M., 239(2), 247*
Donati, G. J., 49(7), 63*
Donovan, E. F., 44(23), 47*
Dougherty, T. F., 214(57), 225*
Douglas, J. F., 89(28), 94*
Drell, W., 12(8), 21*, 233(3), 238*

E

Eagle, H., 32(3), 33(3), 35(3), 37(3),
38(3), 46*
Edwin, E. E., 213(49), 224*
Ehrenberg, A., 218(76), 225*, 250(8),
257(8), 259(8), 260*
Eisner, A., 4(28), 9*
Ekman, L., 222(81), 225*
Ekstrand, V., 166(46), 175(46), 181*
Elion, G. B., 2(9, 11, 12, 13, 17, 18,
19), 3(20, 21), 4(30), 9*, 11(1,
2), 13(12, 13, 14, 15, 17, 18, 19),
14(17, 20), 16(24a), 18(24a, 27),
19(39), 20*, 21*, 22*
El Khatib, S., 213(48), 224*
Ellederova, D., 163(27), 180*
Elliott, T. H., 88(19, 20, 21, 22), 94*
El Masri, A. M., 89(29), 94*
Engelman, K., 12(10, 11), 21*
Enomoto, M., 197(48), 204*,
210(21), 216(21), 219(21), 224*
Ericsson, J. L. E., 138(23), 140*,
156(50), 160*
Ernster, L., 102(25), 107*, 114(38,
40), 116(38), 124*, 137(22),
138(23), 140*, 143(14, 16),
144(16, 20, 21, 42), 150(40, 42),
152(44), 154(20), 156(50),
157(16), 159*, 160*, 265(6),
265*, 274(2, 5), 277*, 278*
Essner, E., 211(29), 224*
Estabrook, R. W., 104(28), 107*,
110(25, 26, 27, 28, 30), 111(25,
26), 116(26), 119(28, 30),
120(47), 122(30), 123*, 124*,
131(12, 13, 14), 134(14), 137(15),
138(15), 140*, 145(26), 150(41,
43), 159*, 160*, 261(1, 3), 263(4),
265*, 274(3), 278*
Evans, D. F., 218(73), 225*
Eyestone, W. H., 196(39), 204*
Eyring, H., 213(46), 224*

F

Falco, E. A., 2(9), 9*, 11(1, 2, 4), 20*, 21*
Farber, E., 162(15), 180*, 197(49), 204*, 205(5), 207*
Farr, A. L., 144(24), 159*
Fauconnet, M., 5(35), 10*
Felton, L. D., 3(24), 9*
Ferone, R., 49(11), 63*
Ferré, J., 1(3), 8*
Fifth International Symposium on Immunopathology, 1(6), 9*
Finch, L. R., 6(43), 10*
Finkelstein, M. S., 5(37), 10*
Fischer, G. A., 37(9), 38(9), 46*
Fishman, M., 7(47, 48, 49), 10*
Fouts, J. F., 110(6, 12, 13, 17, 18, 21, 22), 111(21, 22), 123*, 125(5), 130(53, 56, 58), 139*, 141*, 153(45), 160*
Frazier, P. D., 18(25), 21*
Freedland, R. A., 167(38), 181*
Frey, I., 137(15), 138(15), 140*, 263(4), 265*
Fridovich, I., 268(3), 272*
Friedkin, M., 44(23), 46(25), 47*, 49(15), 63*, 66(4, 5), 68(10), 79*, 80*
Friedman, R., 18(26), 21*
Frisch, A. W., 4(33), 10*
Fueno, T., 213(46), 224*
Fujimoto, J. M., 129(39), 130(52), 140*, 141*
Fukuyama, T., 91(35), 94*
Futterman, S., 49(13), 63*

G

Gardiner, R. C., 49(4), 63*
Garren, L., 110(11), 123*
Garrod, A. B., 12(7), 21*
Gastel, R., 125(1), 129(1), 130(1), 138(1), 139*
Gazzola, A. L., 51(19), 63*
Geipert, F., 102(23), 107*
Gelboin, H. V., 138(24), 139(32), 140*
Gell, P. G. H., 229(4, 5), 232*
Gey, K. F., 233(4, 5), 234(11), 237(13), 238*

Ghazal, A., 130(57), 141*
Gibb, J. W., 235(12), 238*
Gibbard, S., 85(10), 94*
Gibson, Q. H., 143(17), 159*
Gigon, P., 111(32, 33), 112(35), 114(41), 123*, 124*
Gigon, P. L., 114(41), 124*
Gillette, J. R., 83(1), 93*, 109(1, 2, 3), 110(1, 2, 3, 9, 15, 19, 28), 111(9, 32, 33), 112(34, 35), 114(36, 41), 116(3), 117(3), 118(3, 43, 44), 119(28), 121(44), 123*, 124*, 125(3), 128(11), 129(50), 130(55), 139*, 140*, 141*, 143(1), 145(27), 154(27), 158*, 159*, 175(44), 181*, 210(15), 211(15), 216(15), 223*, 261(1), 265*
Gnosspelius, Y., 143(16), 144(16), 152(44), 157(16), 159*, 160*
Goldberg, I. H., 24(3), 29*
Goldfinger, S. E., 15(21), 21*
Goldfischer, S., 211(29), 224*
Goldschmidt, S., 89(26), 94*
Good, R. A., 4(29), 9*
Goodall, C. M., 210(17), 214(17, 55), 215(17), 223*, 224*
Goodman, L., 44(23), 47*
Goodwin, S., 125(2), 139*
Gordon, A., 1(7), 9*
Gorini, L., 6(44), 10*
Goshman, L. M., 194(32), 195(32), 204*
Götz. E., 104(39), 107*, 162(9), 171(9), 172(9), 173(9), 179(9), 180*
Gram, T. E., 110(22), 111(22, 32), 114(41), 123*, 124*
Grantham, P. H., 216(65), 225*
Grayzel, A. I., 12(9), 21*
Green, B., 191(27), 195(27), 203*
Green, J., 213(49), 224*
Greenberg, D. M., 49(2, 5), 63*
Greene, F. E., 111(33), 114(36), 124*
Greim, H., 101(20), 104(20), 107*, 110(25), 111(25), 123*, 131(12, 14), 134(14), 137(19), 138(25, 26), 140*
Greitz, U., 222(81), 225*
Groth, C. G., 1(1), 8*
Grover, P. L., 197(46), 204*

Grünberger, D., 29(10), 30*
Grunberg-Manago, M., 29(7, 8), 29*
Guroff, G., 85(13), 86(13), 94*, 245(5), 246(5), 247*, 259(16, 17), 260*
Gustafsson, J.-Å., 146(31, 32, 34, 35), 148(34), 159*
Gustafsson, R. G., 211(37), 224*
Gutman, A. B., 14(20), 16(22), 21*
Gutteridge, W. E., 49(12), 63*

H

Haddow, A., 214(51), 224*
Hakala, M. T., 32(1, 2, 4, 5), 33(2), 34(5, 7), 35(5, 7), 36(7), 37(5), 38(4), 40(15), 41(4, 5, 7, 16, 26, 27), 42(16), 43(16, 21), 44(21, 22), 45(5, 22, 28, 29), 46*, 47*, 49(1), 51(1), 63*
Hamilton, L., 13(12), 21*
Hanam, J., 88(22), 94*
Harris, J., 196(41), 204*
Hart, L. G., 110(13), 123*, 130(56, 58), 141*
Hart, L. I., 268(9), 272*
Hartwell, J. L., 209(5, 6), 223*
Haslewood, G. A. D., 184(10), 203*
Hawtrey, A. O., 162(18), 180*
Hayaishi, O., 86(15, 16), 94*, 211(25), 224*
Heidelberger, C., 194(32), 195(32), 204*
Heiger, I., 184(7), 203*
Heimberg, M., 110(16), 123*
Hein, G., 250(9), 260*
Hemmerich, P., 250(8), 254(14), 257(8), 259(8), 260*
Henderson, J. F., 2(16), 9*, 18(32), 19(32, 36, 37), 22*
Hermanová, E., 66(8), 67(8), 74(8), 80*
Heubner, W., 97(1, 30), 106*, 107*, 162(20), 180*
Hewett, C. L., 184(7, 8), 203*
Hildebrandt, A., 110(26), 111(26), 116(26), 123*
Hillcoat, B. L., 49(6, 9), 63*
Hitchings, G. H., 2(9, 10, 11, 12, 17, 18), 3(21), 4(30), 9*, 11(1, 2, 3, 4, 5, 6), 12(7a), 13(7a, 13, 14, 15, 16, 18, 19), 14(20), 16(7a), 18(26, 27), 19(39), 20*, 21*, 22*, 49(10, 11), 63*, 66(1), 79*
Ho, T. B., 66(3), 79*
Hoagland, D. R., 129(45), 141*
Hoefnagel, D., 18(33), 22*
Hoffmann, K., 90(31), 94*
Hollmann, S., 137(18), 140*
Holtzman, J. L., 111(32), 123*
Holy, A., 24(5), 26(5), 29(10), 29*, 30*
Horii, Z., 229(6), 232*
Horn, F., 215(61), 219(61), 225*
Hornef, W., 137(20), 140*
Horner, L., 218(75), 219(75), 220(75), 225*
Horning, E. C., 125(2), 139*
Horning, E. S., 196(41, 44), 202(44), 204*
Huennekens, F. M., 42(20), 47*
Hueper, W. C., 203(60), 204*
Huggins, C., 193(30), 204*
Hultin, T., 110(14), 123*, 162(16, 17, 19), 180*, 211(26, 27, 28, 31, 32, 33, 34, 35, 36), 213(33, 34, 35), 214(33, 34), 216(32, 35), 222(32), 224*
Hume, D. M., 1(3), 8*
Hutchison, D. J., 37(10), 46*, 49(7), 63*
Hykes, P., 162(6, 7), 173(7), 174(7), 176(7), 180*

I

Iannotti, A. T., 37(11), 38(11), 47*
Iball, J., 195(34), 204*
Ichikawa, K., 209(2), 223*
Ide, H., 88(23), 94*
Ikeda, M., 150(43), 160*
Ikehara, M., 29(9), 30*
Imai, Y., 110(29), 123*, 261(2), 265*
Inamori, K., 233(6), 238*
Irving, C. C., 198(53), 201(53), 204*
Ischinara, K., 233(6), 238*
Ishidate, M., 90(32), 94*
Ishihara, T., 32(5), 34(5), 35(5), 37(5), 41(5), 45(5), 46*

Ivankovic, S., 205(3), 206(3), 207*
Iwasaki, Y., 1(5), 9*

J

Jacobson, M., 143(13), 152(13), 159*
Jaenicke, L., 250(9), 260*
Jaffe, J. J., 49(12), 63*
James, S. P., 85(11), 92(38), 94*, 95*
Janata, V., 162(6, 7, 10), 173(7), 174(7), 176(7, 10, 47, 49), 177(10, 147), 180*, 181*
Jandl, J. H., 162(11), 176(11), 177(11), 178(11), 180*
Jařosková, L., 6(45), 10*
Jeffrey, D. J., 92(38), 95*
Jerina, D. M., 85(13), 86(13), 94*, 245(5), 246(5), 247*
Jick, H., 138(27), 140*
Jindra, A., 239(3), 247*
Johns, D. G., 37(11), 38(11), 47*, 49(3), 63*
Jondorf, W. R., 138(24), 140*
Jual, U., 197(50, 52), 204*, 216(63), 220(63), 225*
Juchau, M. R., 130(53), 141*, 153(45), 160*
Jull, J. W., 197(46), 204*

K

Kacl, K., 162(6, 7), 173(7), 174(7), 176(7, 47), 177(47), 180*, 181*
Kahrie, C., 176(50), 181*
Kaighen, M., 85(5), 93(5), 94*
Kamin, H., 143(17), 150(39), 159*
Kamm, J. J., 175(44), 181*
Kampffmeyer, H., 98(11), 106*, 214(53), 216(53), 217(70), 219(53, 70), 224*, 225*
Kaneko, J. J., 167(38), 181*
Kaplan, N. O., 176(48), 181*
Kara, J., 24(2), 29*
Karlson, P., 231(7), 232*
Karrer, E., 213(45), 224*
Kashiwagi, N., 1(5), 9*
Katagiri, M., 86(15, 16), 94*
Kato, R., 110(9, 19), 111(9), 123*, 125(4), 129(4), 129(38, 41, 42, 43, 44, 46), 130(46), 138(24), 139*, 140*, 141*

Kauffman, H. M., Jr., 1(3), 8*
Kaufman, B. T., 42(18, 19), 47*, 49(4), 63*
Kaufman, S., 249(1, 2, 3), 253(3), 255(3), 257(15), 260(3), 260*
Keberle, H., 90(31), 94*
Kelley, W. N., 18(31, 32, 34), 19(32, 34, 35, 36, 37), 21*, 22*
Kennaway, E. L., 184(6), 203*
Kessel, D., 49(8), 63*
Khanolkar, V. R., 167(37), 181*
Kiese, H., 162(22), 180*
Kiese, M., 97(2, 4, 32), 98(4, 11, 38), 99(4), 102(4), 104(32), 106*, 107*, 162(1, 5, 21, 23, 24, 25), 163(5, 24, 25, 28, 29), 164(5), 165(24), 166(5, 24, 29), 173(25), 180*, 210(20), 214(53), 215(20), 216(20), 216(53), 217(70), 219(53, 70), 222(20), 223*, 224*, 225*
Kilpatrick, S. J., 1(3), 8*
King, C. M., 198(54), 204*
King, L. J., 85(4), 94*
Kisliuk, R. L., 44(23), 47*
Klein, E., 209(8), 223*
Klein, G., 209(8), 223*
Klempau, I., 130(57, 59), 141*
Klinenberg, J. R., 12(10, 11), 15(21), 21*
Klutch, A., 143(10), 155(10), 158*
Knowles, P. F., 268(7, 8), 269(7), 272*
Kolman, Z., 66(7), 80*
Komiyama, Y., 229(6), 232*
Koransky, W., 130(57, 59), 138(31), 140*, 141*
Kovensky, A., 13(18), 21*
Krause, W., 129(37), 130(37), 140*
Krenitsky, T. A., 13(19), 19(38), 21*, 22*
Kriek, E., 197(51, 52), 204*
Külz, E., 91(34), 94*
Kummerow, F. A., 210(18), 213(18), 213(44), 215(18), 223*, 224*
Kuntzman, R., 110(24), 123*, 143(13), 149(37), 152(13), 159*
Kunz, J., 175(43), 181*
Kunz, W., 137(16a), 140*
Kuratsune, M., 184(5), 203*
Kurita, S., 37(10), 46*

Kuriyama, Y., 138(30), 140*
Kwok, G., 44(23), 47*

L

La Du, B. N., 109(1), 110(1), 123*, 128(11), 140*, 143(1), 145(27), 154(27), 158*, 159*, 210(15), 211(15), 216(15), 223*
Landsteiner, K., 227(1), 232*
La Plante, E. S., 4(29), 9*
Laster, L., 16(23), 18(23), 21*
Lawley, P. D., 184(4), 194(31), 195(31), 203*, 204*, 205(6), 207(13), 207*
Lawrence, D., 149(37), 159*
Lederberg, J., 6(42), 10*
Lee, H. M., 1(3), 8*
Lee, K. Y., 206(7, 12), 207*
Leidner, H., 250(5), 260*
Leigh, T., 251(11), 260*
Lesch, M., 18(28), 21*
Levi, A. A., 186(16), 203*
Levin, M. H., 12(8), 21*
Levin, S., 110(27), 123*, 150(41), 159*
Levin, W., 110(24), 123*, 150(43), 160*
Levine, B. B., 227(2), 228(2), 232*
Levitt, M., 233(1), 235(1, 12), 237(1), 238*
Leybold, K., 143(5), 146(33), 158*, 159*
Lijinsky, W., 205(4), 206(7), 207*
Lipton, M., 235(12), 238*
Lisboa, B. P., 145(28, 29, 30), 146(31, 32, 34, 35), 148(34, 36), 156(51), 159*, 160*
Lisy, V., 24(5), 26(5), 28(6), 29*, 30*
Loeb, L. A., 138(24), 140*
Löhr, G. W., 167(36), 168(36), 178(51), 181*
Loo, J., 205(4), 207*
Lorz, D. C., 11(5, 6), 21*
Lotlikar, P. D., 198(53), 201(53), 204*, 210(21, 22), 213(22), 216(21, 22, 62), 219(21, 22), 220(62), 224*, 225*
Love, E., 12(9), 21*
Löw, H., 144(23), 159*, 211(36), 224*

Lowry, O. H., 144(24), 159*
Ludwig, B. J., 89(28), 94*

M

McCormack, J. J., Jr., 49(12), 63*
MacDonald, S. G. G., 195(34), 204*
McDougall, B. M., 50(16), 63*
McHale, D., 213(49), 224*
Machinist, J. M., 216(67), 225*
Mackay, I. R., 1(8), 9*
McKechnie, D., 216(64), 225*
McLean, A. E. M., 215(58), 225*
McLean, E. K., 215(58), 225*
McMahon, R. E., 90(24), 94*, 211(24), 214(52), 216(24), 217(71), 224*, 225*
Maeno, H., 86(15, 16), 94*
Magee, P. N., 205(1, 2, 5, 6), 206(7, 8, 9, 10, 11, 12), 207*, 211(36), 224*
Magi, A., 222(81), 225*
Magour, S., 138(31), 140*
Maickel, R. P., 143(8), 158*, 190(21), 203*
Maitra, P. K., 145(26), 159*
Makela, O., 7(32), 10*
Mannering, G. J., 110(23), 111(23, 31), 123*, 153(46), 157(52), 160*
Manova, I., 176(47, 49), 177(47), 181*
Manson, D., 102(21), 107*, 200(58), 203(62), 204*, 214(50), 224*
Marchioro, T. L., 1(1, 5), 8*, 9*
Margreth, A., 210(22), 213(22), 216(22), 219(22), 224*
Marroqin, F., 162(15), 180*, 197(49), 204*
Marshall, E. K., 91(33), 92(33), 94*
Marshall, F. J., 90(24), 94*
Mason, H. S., 246(6), 247*, 267(2), 272*
Masters, B. S. S., 143(17), 159*
Masuda, Y., 184(5), 203*
Maté, C., 85(12), 94*
Mattern, G., 250(5), 260*
Matthew, 183(1), 203*
Maun, M. E., 196(40), 204*
Maxwell, M. H., 1(7), 9*

Mayer, R. L., 162(12), 180*
Maynert, E. W., 89(30), 94*
Medawar, P. B., 3(23), 9*
Mehler, A. H., 86(14), 94*
Meier, R., 162(20), 180*
Meissner, L., 29(10), 30*
Meister, A., 233(10), 238*
Meriwether, L. S., 268(6, 7), 269(6, 7), 272*
Merker, H. J., 137(16, 17), 140*
Messiha, F., 237(13), 238*
Méstecký, J., 6(45), 10*
Metz, E., 13(18), 21*
Meyer, M., 89(28), 94*
Michaelis, L., 252(12), 260*
Michaelson, I. A., 129(48), 141*
Michelson, A. M., 29(7, 8), 30*
Miech, R. P., 2(14), 9*
Miescher, P. A., 5(35, 38), 10*
Miller, E. C., 85(7), 94*, 97(5), 100(14), 106*, 107*, 100(10), 123*, 125(7), 130(60, 61), 139*, 141*, 190(20, 25), 196(43), 197(47, 48, 50, 52), 198(53), 201(53), 203*, 204*, 209(7, 10), 210(11, 12, 13, 21, 22), 211(11), 212(11, 12, 13, 39), 213(22, 39), 214(11), 215(13, 39), 216(21, 22, 62, 63, 64), 219(21, 22, 39), 220(39, 62, 63, 78), 222(13, 39), 223*, 224*, 225*
Miller, G. A., 125(7), 139*
Miller, J. A., 85(7), 94*, 97(5), 100(14), 106*, 107*, 110(10), 123*, 130(60, 61), 141*, 190(20, 25), 196(43), 197(47, 48, 50, 52), 198(53), 201(53), 203*, 204*, 209(7, 10), 210(11, 12, 13, 21, 22, 23), 211(11), 212(11, 12, 13, 39), 213(22, 39), 214(11), 215(13, 39), 216(21, 22, 62, 63, 64), 219(21, 22, 39), 220(39, 62, 63, 78), 222(13, 39), 223*, 224*, 225*
Miller, J. M., 18(31, 32), 19(32, 35), 21*, 22*
Mills, J., 90(24), 94*
Mishell, R. I., 7(50, 51), 10*
Mitchison, N. A., 3(25), 9*
Miya, T. S., 114(39), 124*, 129(45), 141*

Montesano, R., 203(61), 204*
Montgomery, J. A., 2(15), 9*
Morales, D. R., 49(2), 63*
Mori, K., 184(5), 203*, 215(59), 225*
Morningstar, J. F., Jr., 44(23), 47*
Morris, H. P., 196(39), 204*, 215(60), 225*
Motyčka, K., 66(8), 67(8), 74(8), 80*
Mowat, J. H., 51(19), 63*
Mueller, G. C., 210(23), 224*
Mueller, S., 13(13), 21*
Mukherjee, T., 211(37), 225*
Müller, F., 250(8), 257(8), 259(8), 260*
Mulliken, R. S., 218(74), 225*
Murphy, J. R., 173(41), 181*
Murray, J. E., 1(2), 8*

N

Nagatsu, T., 233(1), 235(1), 237(1), 238*
Nahas, A., 46(25), 47*
Naik, S. N., 167(37), 181*
Narasimhulu, S., 110(27, 28), 119(28), 123*, 150(41), 159*, 261(1), 265*
Nash, T., 145(25), 159*
Nasu, H., 233(6), 238*
Nathan, H. C., 4(30), 9*, 13(14), 21*
Nelson, N., 190(23), 203*
Nery, R., 200(58), 204*, 214(50), 224*
Nestel, K., 101(19), 107*
Newman, M. S., 190(24), 203*
Nichol, C. A., 32(4, 6), 38(4, 13), 41(4, 27), 45(29), 46*, 47*, 49(1), 51(1), 63*
Noronha, J. M., 49(14), 63*
North, J. C., 246(6), 247*
Nossal, G. J. V., 7(52), 10*
Nováková, E., 66(8), 67(8), 74(8), 80*
Novick, W. J., 130(54), 141*
Novikoff, A. B., 211(29), 224*
Nyhan, W. L., 18(28, 29, 33), 21*, 22*

O

O'Brien, J., 1(3), 8*
Ockel, E., 176(50), 181*
Ohtsuka, E., 29(9), 30*

Okada, T., 250(5, 8), 257(8), 259(8), 260*
Old, L. J., 209(9), 223*
Omura, T., 138(28, 30), 140*, 143(18, 19), 159*, 274(3), 278*
Orme-Johnson, W. H., 216(67), 225*
Orrenius, S., 114(38, 40), 116(38), 124*, 125(6), 137(22), 138(23), 139*, 140*, 143(14, 15, 16), 144(15, 16, 20, 42), 150(15, 38, 40, 42), 152(44), 154(20, 38), 156(50, 51), 157(16, 53), 159*, 160*, 265(6), 265*, 274(2, 5), 277*, 278*
Orris, L., 190(23), 203*
Otsuka, S., 175(45), 181*
Otsuki, K., 229(6), 232*
Owens, A. H., 91(33), 92(33), 94*
Ozon, R., 143(9), 158*

P

Pages, B., 49(5), 63*
Palade, G. E., 138(28), 140*, 144(21), 159*
Palmer, E. D., 190(23), 203*
Palmer, G., 268(4, 5), 269(4, 5), 270(5), 272*
Pannacciulli, L., 167(39), 181*
Parke, D. V., 85(4), 85(8, 9), 88(19, 22), 94*
Parks, R. E., Jr., 2(14), 9*
Pastore, E. J., 44(23), 47*, 49(15), 50(18), 63*
Paterson, A. R. P., 2(16), 9*
Pauling, L., 6(41), 10*
Perkins, J. P., 49(3, 6), 63*
Pettit, F. H., 212(41, 42), 213(42), 214(42), 215(41, 42), 216(41, 42, 69), 219(42), 224*, 225*
Phillips, B., 198(54), 204*
Pineda, O., 137(18), 140*
Plaa, F. L., 129(39), 140*
Plante, L. T., 44(23), 47*, 66(4, 5), 79*
Pletscher, A., 234(11), 238*
Pogrund, R. S., 233(3), 238*
Poirier, M. M., 216(64), 225*
Pomales, R., 18(26, 27), 21*
Portig, J., 130(57, 59), 141*
Pott, P., 209(1), 223*
Powell, L. S., 89(28), 94*

Prankerd, T. A. J., 173(40), 181*
Preussmann, R., 205(3), 206(3), 207*
Price, J. M., 202(59), 204*
Prout, G. R., Jr., 1(3), 8*
Pullman, A., 185(11), 187(17, 18), 203*, 218(77), 225*
Pullman, B., 187(17, 18), 203*, 218(77), 225*
Putnam, C. W., 1(1), 8*

Q

Quinn, G. P., 110(4), 123*, 143(7), 158*

R

Rabinowitz, M., 24(3), 29*
Radomski, J. L., 102(23), 107*
Radzialowski, F. M., 110(7), 123*
Ramarastri, B. V., 50(16), 63*
Randall, R. J., 144(24), 159*
Rapoport, S. M., 176(50), 181*
Ratzan, J., 44(23), 47*
Raunio, R., 41(26), 44(22), 45(22), 47*
Ree, T., 213(46), 224*
Rehn, L., 195(35), 204*
Reichenthal, J., 125(2), 139*, 143(3), 158*
Reinwein, D., 162(23, 24), 163(24), 165(24), 166(24), 180*
Reiss, W., 90(31), 94*
Remmer, H., 101(15), 102(24), 104(28), 107*, 110(8, 25, 26, 28, 30), 111(8, 25, 26), 116(26), 119(28, 30), 122(30), 123*, 125(8, 9), 129(9, 34, 35, 36, 40), 130(36), 131(12, 13, 14), 134(14), 137(15, 16, 17, 20, 21), 138(15), 139*, 140*, 141*, 143(12), 159*, 261(1, 3), 263(4), 265*
Renner, G., 210(20), 215(20), 216(20), 222(20), 223*
Renson, J., 85(13), 86(13), 94*, 245(5), 246(5), 247*
Reyes, P., 42(20), 47*
Rhode, H., 162(20), 180*
Richert, D. A., 92(40), 95*
Roberts, D., 49(8), 63*
Robertson, J. S., 88(21), 94*
Robinson, R., 184(9), 203*

Roche, M., 16(22), 21*
Roe, F. J. C., 190(22), 203*
Rogers, L. A., 110(22), 111(22), 123*
Rose, K., 125(2), 139*
Rosenbloom, F. M., 18(31, 32, 34), 19(32, 34, 35, 36, 37), 21*, 22*
Rosenthal, O., 110(27, 28), 119(28), 123*, 150(41, 43), 159*, 160*, 261(1), 265*, 274(3), 278*
Ross, A. E., 205(4), 207*
Ross, J., 167(35), 181*
Rostorfer, H. H., 163(26), 180*
Rousebrough, N. J., 144(24), 159*
Rowson, K. E. K., 190(22), 203*
Ruckteschell, A., von, 162(22), 180*
Rundles, R. W., 2(17, 18), 9*, 13(14, 15, 18), 21*
Russell, P. B., 2(9), 9*, 11(1, 2), 20*
Ryan, A. J., 85(12), 94*
Rychlik, I., 24(5), 26(5), 29*
Ryman, B. E., 233(8), 238*

S

Saffiotti, U., 203(61), 204*
Sahiar, K., 5(34), 10*
Sakamoto, Y., 233(6), 238*
Salaman, M. H., 190(22), 203*
Salvidio, E., 167(39), 181*
Sansone, A., 51(20), 63*
Sartorelli, A. C., 2(14), 9*, 37(11), 38(11), 47*
Sasame, H. A., 110(15, 28), 111(33), 116(42), 117(42), 118(43, 44), 119(28), 120(42, 45), 121(44, 45), 122(42, 45), 123*, 124*, 261(1), 265*
Sato, R., 110(29), 123*, 143(18, 19), 159*, 261(2), 265*, 274(3), 278*
Sato, T., 91(35), 94*
Schabel, F. M., 2(15), 9*
Schadelin, J., 122(46), 124*
Schaude, G., 137(16a), 140*
Schellhas, H., 137(20), 140*
Schenkman, J. B., 104(28), 107*, 110(25, 28, 30), 111(25), 119(28, 30), 120(47), 122(30), 123*, 124*, 131(12, 13, 14), 137(15), 138(15), 140*, 261(1, 3), 263(4), 265*

Scheuch, D., 176(50), 181*
Schilling, G., 110(24), 123*
Schimassek, H., 137(16a), 140*
Schimke, R. T., 138(29), 140*
Schirren, V., 162(18), 180*
Schlicht, I., 138(31), 140*
Schmähl, D., 205(3), 206(3), 207*
Schmid, W., 137(16a), 140*
Schmidt, K., 90(31), 94*
Schmidt-Volkmar, W., 129(35), 140*
Schmitt, F. L., 190(23), 203*
Schnebli, H. P., 2(15), 9*
Schneider, C., 163(29), 166(29), 167(34), 180*
Schneidman, K., 143(13), 152(13), 159*
Schnitger, F., 102(23), 107*
Schoental, R., 205(1), 207*
Schulte-Hermann, R., 138(31), 140*
Schulz, H., 162(13), 180*
Schwartz, R. S., 4(26, 27, 28, 31), 5(34), 8(31), 9*, 10*
Schwarz-Speck, K. 162(14), 180*
Schwarz-Speck, M., 162(14), 180*
Scott, E., 166(46), 175(46), 181*
Scribner, J. D., 216(62), 220(62, 78), 225*
Seegmiller, J. E., 12(9, 10, 11), 15(21), 16(23), 18(23, 25, 31, 32, 34), 19(32, 34, 35, 36, 37), 21*, 22*
Seifert, J., 138(25), 140*
Sellakumar, A. R., 203(61), 204*
Semb, J., 51(19), 63*
Serrone, D. M., 130(52), 141*
Sherwood, M. B., 2(9), 9*, 11(1, 2), 20*
Shubik, P., 209(6), 223*
Shultice, R. W., 110(17, 18), 123*, 130(56), 141*
Shumaker, S., 137(18), 140*
Shuster, L., 138(27), 140*
Siekevitz, P., 138(28), 140*, 144(21), 159*
Siess, M., 137(16a), 140*
Silverman, D. A., 214(54), 224*
Silverman, M., 49(14), 63*
Silverstein, A. M., 229(5), 232*
Sims, P., 92(37), 95*, 186(13, 14, 15), 190(26), 193(29, 30), 203*, 204*
Šípal, Z., 239(3), 247*

Sirotnak, F. M., 37(10), 46*, 49(7), 63*
Sjoerdsma, A., 12(10, 11), 21*
Sjöqvist, F., 157(53), 160*
Sjövall, J., 146(32, 34, 35), 148(34), 159*
Skipper, H. E., 2(15), 9*
Skoda, J., 24(1, 2, 4, 5), 26(5), 28(6), 29*, 30*
Skorczewski, W., 239(1), 247*
Sladek, N. E., 110(23), 111(23), 123*
Slapak, M., 1(3), 8*
Slavík, K., 44(24), 45(28), 47*, 66(6, 7, 8), 67(6, 8, 9), 74(8), 77(6), 79*, 80*
Slaviková, V., 66(7, 8), 67(8), 74(8), 80*
Sloane, N. H., 86(17, 18), 94*
Smart, J., 24(5), 26(5), 28(6), 29*, 30*
Smidová, J., 67(9), 80*
Smith, J., 167(38), 181*
Smith, J. N., 85(6), 89(27, 29), 94*, 233(9), 238*
Smithies, R. H., 89(27), 94*
Smuckler, E., 110(14), 123*
Snihs, J.-O., 222(81), 225*
Sohn, I., 239(1), 247*
Sorensen, L. B., 18(30), 21*
Sorm, F., 24(2, 4, 5), 26(5), 29(10), 29*, 30*
Sormova, Z., 24(2), 29*
Souček, J., 66(8), 67(8), 74(8), 80*
Spiegelberg, H. L., 5(38), 10*
Spirtes, M. A., 114(37), 116(37), 124*
Špundová, M., 66(8), 67(8, 9), 74(8), 80*
Stack, J., 4(26), 9*
Starzl, T. E., 1(1, 5), 8*, 9*
Staudinger, Hj., 122(46), 124*, 143(5), 146(33), 154(47, 48), 158*, 159*, 160*, 265(5), 265*
Sterzl, J., 6(45, 46), 7(46, 53), 10*
Stetten, D., 16(22), 21*
Stitzel, R. E., 157(52), 160*
Stock, K., 130(51), 141*
Stöffler, G., 105(33), 107*, 164(30), 166(30, 31), 168(31), 171(31), 180*
Stohler, C. M., 130(54), 141*
Strelitz, R. A., 13(19), 21*

Stripp, B., 114(36), 124*
Stuckey, B. N., 218(72), 225*
Sugai, M., 210(18), 213(18), 215(18), 223*
Sullivan, H. R., 214(52), 217(71), 224*, 225*
Suolinna, E. M., 41(16), 42(16), 45(28), 47*
Sussman, H., 110(15), 123*
Suzuki, T., 91(35), 94*
Swagzdis, J., 130(54), 141*
Swann, P. F., 205(6), 206(8), 207*
Sweetman, L., 18(33), 22*

T

Talalay, P., 143(2), 158*, 214(54), 224*
Tao, R. C. C., 88(20), 94*
Taylor, E., 32(2), 33(2), 46*
Tchirner, F., 216(68), 225*
ten Have, P., 213(47), 224*
Tephly, T. R., 153(46), 157(52), 160*
Terasaki, P. I., 1(1), 8*
Thauer, R. K., 105(33), 107*, 164(30), 166(30), 180*
Thomas, H. J., 2(15), 9*
Thorpe, W. V., 85(11), 94*, 233(8), 238*
Ti Li Loo, 38(12), 47*
Tizianello, A., 167(39), 181*
Tomsová, Z., 66(8), 67(8, 9), 74(8), 80*
Touster, O., 137(18), 140*
Trivus, R. H., 114(37), 116(37), 124*
Trucco, R. E., 213(48), 224*
Tsubomura, H., 218(74), 225*
Tsuchiyama, H., 210(18), 213(18), 215(18), 223*
Tsugi, H., 90(25), 94*
Tsukamoto, H., 88(23), 90(25), 94*
Tsutsui, H., 209(3), 223*

U

Udenfriend, S., 85(13), 86(13), 94*, 233(1, 2), 235(1, 12), 237(1), 238*, 245(5), 246(5), 247*
Uehleke, H., 97(3, 4, 31), 98(4, 6, 7, 8, 9, 10, 37, 38), 99(4, 10, 12, 13, 37), 100(13), 101(17, 18, 19, 20,

22), 102(4, 22, 23, 27), 103(27), 104(20, 26, 27, 31, 39), 105(33, 34), 106(35, 36), 106*, 107*, 162(2, 3, 8, 9), 164(30), 166(30, 31), 167(33), 168(31), 170(33), 171(9, 31, 33), 172(9), 173(9), 174(8), 175(8), 179(9), 180*, 210(16), 211(16), 216(16), 223*
Uhr, J. W., 5(36, 37), 10*
Ullrich, V., 122(46), 124*

V

Vallin, I., 144(23), 159*
Vandekar, M., 206(9), 207*
Vander Werff, H., 2(9), 9*, 11(1, 2), 20*
Van Duuren, B. L., 190(23), 203*
Vanneste, M., 246(6), 247*
Vasanelli, P., 129(38, 41, 43, 44, 46), 130(46), 140*, 141*
Vernikos-Danellis, J., 214(56), 224*
Viscontini, M., 250(4, 5, 6, 7, 8), 257(6, 7, 8), 259(8), 260*
Vohland, H. W., 130(57, 59), 141*
Von der Decken, A., 162(16), 180*

W

Wagenknecht, C., 176(50), 181*
Wagner, H. H., 167(34), 180*
Wagner, J., 104(39), 107*, 162(6, 7, 8, 9, 10), 163(27), 166(31), 167(32, 33), 168(31), 169(32), 170(32, 33), 171(9, 31, 32, 33), 172(9, 42), 173(7, 9, 42), 174(7, 8, 42), 175(8), 176(7, 10, 47, 49), 177(10, 47), 179(9), 180*, 181*
Wahba, A. J., 68(10), 80*
Wahlefeld, A. W., 250(9), 251(10), 260*
Waller, C. W., 51(19), 63*
Waller, H.-D., 162(24, 25), 163(24, 25, 29), 165(24), 166(24, 29), 167(36), 168(36), 173(25), 178(51), 180*, 181*
Walpole, A. L., 196(37), 204*
Wang, D. H., 35(8), 38(8), 46*
Watkins, R. C., 231(9), 232*
Watson, J. G., 196(44), 202(44), 204*
Watson, M. L., 211(30), 224*

Watts, R. W. E., 12(10, 11), 21*
Wehr, R., 89(26), 94*
Weiner, M., 110(5), 123*
Weisburger, E. K., 196(45), 204*, 210(14, 19), 212(14), 214(19), 215(14, 19, 60), 216(65), 222(14), 223*, 225*
Weisburger, J. H., 196(45), 204*, 210(14, 19), 212(14), 214(19), 215(14, 19, 60), 216(65), 222(40), 223*, 225*
Werkheiser, W. C., 35(8), 38(8), 46*
Westermann, E., 130(51), 141*
White, H. J., 1(3), 8*
Wiedemann, I., 210(20), 215(20), 216(20), 222(20), 223*
Wilkinson, A. E., 273(1), 277*
Williams, C. H., 143(17), 150(39), 159*
Williams, G. M., 1(3), 8*
Williams, J., 188(19), 203*
Williams, K., 92(36), 95*
Williams, M. H. C., 196(37), 204*
Williams, R. T., 85(3, 4, 5, 6, 8), 88(19, 20, 21, 22), 89(27, 29), 92(39), 93(5), 93*, 94*, 95*, 246(7), 247*
Williamson, K. L., 50(18), 63*
Wills, E. D., 273(1), 274(4, 7), 277*, 278*
Wilson, D. B., 5(39), 10*
Wilson, L., 44(23), 47*
Wilson, R. G., 139(32), 140*
Wilson, R. M., 196(38), 204*
Witkop, B., 85(13), 86(13), 94*, 245(5), 246(5), 247*
Witting, L. A., 210(18), 213(18), 215(18), 223*
Wolf, G., 186(12), 203*
Wolf, J. S., 1(3), 8*
Wortham, J. S., 139(32), 140*
Wright, S. E., 85(12), 94*
Wyngaarden, J. B., 16(23, 24), 18(23), 21*

XYZ

Yamada, H., 91(35), 94*
Yamagiwa, K., 209(2), 223*
Yamamoto, S., 86(15, 16), 94*

Yamamura, Y., 229(6), 232*
Yoshimura, H., 88(23), 90(25), 94*
Yü, T. F., 14(20), 16(22), 21*
Zakrzewski, S. F., 32(4, 6), 38(4),
41(4, 27), 44(24), 46*, 47*,
49(1), 50(17), 51(1, 20), 55(21),
57(17), 63*, 66(6), 67(6), 77(6),
79*

Ziegler, D. M., 212(41, 42), 213(42),
214(42), 215(41, 42), 216(41, 42,
67, 69), 219(42), 224*, 225*
Zubrzycki, Z., 154(47, 48), 160*,
265(5), 265*
Zuckerman, R., 12(8), 21*